Mathematics for Christian Living Series

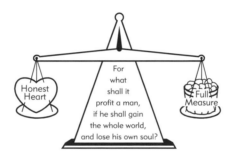

Honest Heart

For what shall it profit a man, if he shall gain the whole world, and lose his own soul?

Full Measure

Mathematics for Christian Living Series

Mastering Mathematics

Grade 7

Rod and Staff Publishers, Inc.
Hwy. 172, Crockett, Kentucky 41413
Telephone: (606) 522-4348

Acknowledgements

We are indebted to God for the vision of the need for a *Mathematics for Christian Living Series* and for His enabling grace. Charitable contributions from many churches have helped to cover the expenses for research and development.

This revision was written by Brother Glenn Auker. The brethren Marvin Eicher, Jerry Kreider, and Luke Sensenig served as editors. Brother Lester Miller and Sisters Barbara Schlabach and Amy Herr drew the illustrations. The work was evaluated by a panel of reviewers and tested by teachers in the classroom. Much effort was devoted to the production of the book. We are grateful for all who helped to make this book possible.

—*The Publishers*

ISBN 978-07399-0481-7

Catalog no. 13701.3

7   8   9   10   —   20   19   18   17   16   15   14   13   12

Table of Contents

Chapter 6   Working With Ratios, Proportions, and Percents

Chapter 7   More Work With Percents

Chapter 8   Money and Banking

Chapter 9   Geometry—Working With Lines and Planes

Chapter 10   Geometry—Working With Solid Figures

Chapter 11   Metric and Bible Measures

Chapter 12   Introduction to Algebra

Chapter 13   Year-End Reviews

Chapter 1

Adding and Subtracting Numbers

And the Lord said unto Noah, Come thou and all thy house into the ark;
for thee have I seen righteous before me in this generation.
Of every clean beast thou shalt take to thee by sevens. . . .
Of fowls also of the air by sevens . . .
For yet seven days, and I will cause it to rain upon the earth. . . .
And Noah did according unto all that the Lord commanded him.

(Genesis 7:1–5)

1. Large Numbers in Everyday Life

Trillions	Billions	Millions	Thousands	Units
H T O	H T O	H T O	H T O	H T O
4 2 7,	5 5 0,	0 1 5,	5 8 5,	4 0 3

Each group set off by commas is a period. The number above contains five periods. Each period except the period farthest to the left must contain three digits.

The number is read, "Four hundred twenty-seven trillion, five hundred fifty billion, fifteen million, five hundred eighty-five thousand, four hundred three."

Numbers are not hard to read if you remember a few simple rules.

1. Large numbers need commas after every third digit, beginning at the right. Each of these three-digit sets is called a period.

2. Each period has a name. To read a number, simply read the number within a period and then say the name of the period. For example, in the number above, the period farthest to the left is read, "Four hundred twenty-seven trillion."

3. Never say *and* when reading a number unless the number contains a fraction or a decimal point. Say, "Four hundred twenty-seven," not "Four hundred and twenty-seven."

CLASS PRACTICE

Use words to write these numbers.

a. 475,600   b. 34,771,322   c. 5,650,000,000   d. 7,678,000,000,000

Use digits to write these numbers.

e. Four hundred seventy-one million, four hundred thousand, six

f. Six million, one hundred fifty-six thousand, seven hundred ninety

g. Eleven billion, seven hundred thousand

h. Seventeen trillion, sixty billion

WRITTEN EXERCISES

A. *Following are the populations of some towns, cities, and countries. Write these numbers with words, using commas just as when writing the numbers with digits.*

1. Metter, Georgia 3,707   2. Poplar Bluff, Missouri 16,996

3. Worcester, Mass. 169,759   4. Chicago, Illinois 2,783,726

5. Ontario 10,084,885   6. United Kingdom 58,135,000

7. Philippines 69,809,000   8. Nigeria 98,091,000

9. Asia (1950) 1,368,000,000   10. Asia (1994) 3,344,000,000

11. 2,527,400,000,000   12. 5,500,400,000,400

B. *Use digits to write the following numbers.*

13. Fourteen thousand, five hundred sixty-seven

14. Two hundred seventy-five thousand, seventy-four

15. Four hundred seven thousand, five

16. Nine million, six hundred four thousand, fifty-seven

17. Two hundred twenty million, four hundred sixty thousand, thirty

18. Five billion, seven hundred fifty million

19. Seventy-five billion, six hundred million

20. Four trillion, four hundred sixty billion

C. *Solve these reading problems.*

21. Bellingham, Massachusetts, had a population of 14,877 in 1990. Write this number, using words.

22. The 1990 population of Morgan County, Kentucky, was 11,648. Write this number, using words.

23. What is the name of the first period of a number, beginning at the right?

24. What is the name of the fourth period from the right of a number?

25. The greatest distance from the sun to the planet Pluto is four billion, five hundred seventy-one million, two hundred thousand miles. Write this number, using digits.

26. Revelation 9:16 mentions an army of horseman that numbered two hundred thousand thousand, or two hundred million. Write this number, using digits.

D. *Solve these problems. Write any remainders as whole numbers.*

27. $\begin{array}{r} 7,892 \\ + 4,812 \end{array}$
28. $\begin{array}{r} 8,371 \\ + 8,281 \end{array}$
29. $\begin{array}{r} 14,831 \\ + 41,921 \end{array}$
30. $\begin{array}{r} \$12,929.81 \\ + 15,125.95 \end{array}$

31. $\begin{array}{r} 4,781 \\ - 2,982 \end{array}$
32. $\begin{array}{r} 9,512 \\ - 5,835 \end{array}$
33. $\begin{array}{r} 81,192 \\ - 16,676 \end{array}$
34. $\begin{array}{r} \$11,292.41 \\ - 7,181.92 \end{array}$

35. $\begin{array}{r} 421 \\ \times 21 \end{array}$
36. $\begin{array}{r} 835 \\ \times 43 \end{array}$
37. $8\overline{)1,656}$
38. $9\overline{)15,918}$

2. Studying Place Value

The number system used throughout the world today is known as the Arabic system. This number system was probably developed by the Hindus of India. The Arabs learned the system and introduced it into Europe more than 1,000 years ago.

The Arabic number system uses only ten different symbols: 0, 1, 2, 3, 4, 5, 6, 7, 8, 9. These symbols are known as digits, and they are used to write numerals that represent every number possible. They can be used in this way because the value of each digit depends on its location in a number. A 3 in the first place from the right represents 3 ones, or three; a 3 in the second place from the right represents 3 tens, or thirty, and so on. The value of a digit becomes ten times larger each time it is moved one place to the left in a number.

units	(1)
tens	(10)
hundreds	($10 \times 10 = 100$)
thousands	($10 \times 10 \times 10 = 1,000$)
ten thousands	($10 \times 10 \times 10 \times 10 = 10,000$)
hundred thousands	($10 \times 10 \times 10 \times 10 \times 10 = 100,000$)
millions	($10 \times 10 \times 10 \times 10 \times 10 \times 10 = 1,000,000$)

We usually think of the zero as having no value. However, the zero is important in writing numbers because it gives place value to other digits. Take away the two zeroes in the number 300, and all you have left is 3. Leaving out the zero in 309 would change it to 39.

The example below shows the value of the digit 3 in each place in the number 3,333,333. Notice that moving the 3 one place to the left increases its value ten times. Moving the 3 one place to the right decreases it to one-tenth of its previous value.

$$
\begin{aligned}
3 \times 1,000,000 &= 3,000,000 = 3 \times 10 \times 10 \times 10 \times 10 \times 10 \times 10 \\
3 \times 100,000 &= 300,000 = 3 \times 10 \times 10 \times 10 \times 10 \times 10 \\
3 \times 10,000 &= 30,000 = 3 \times 10 \times 10 \times 10 \times 10 \\
3 \times 1,000 &= 3,000 = 3 \times 10 \times 10 \times 10 \\
3 \times 100 &= 300 = 3 \times 10 \times 10 \\
3 \times 10 &= 30 = 3 \times 10 \\
3 \times 1 &= 3 = 3 \times 1 \\
\hline
& 3,333,333
\end{aligned}
$$

CLASS PRACTICE

Give the value of each underlined digit.

a. 7,864

b. 57,182,000

c. 73,112,000,000

d. 34,000,000,000,000

e. 45,234,560,000,000

WRITTEN EXERCISES

A. Write the value of each underlined digit.

1. 435
2. 582
3. 8,192
4. 9,152
5. 55,813
6. 18,812
7. 912,182
8. 144,812
9. 3,129,138
10. 3,020,192
11. 114,150,000
12. 412,021,414
13. 45,090,000,000
14. 2,100,000,000,000

B. Show the value of each underlined digit below by multiplying the digit by the place value.

> *Examples:* 141,320
> *Answers:* 4 × 10,000 = 40,000
>
> 4,192,010
> 4 × 1,000,000 = 4,000,000

15. 250
16. 455
17. 5,182
18. 7,812
19. 457,919
20. 699,700
21. 19,121,000
22. 62,192,321
23. 44,100,000,000
24. 19,000,000,000,000

C. Solve these reading problems.

25. What is the value of a 6 in the third place from the right of a number?

26. What is the value of a 5 in the fourth place from the right of a number?

27. The digit 6 in the number 234,567 will have a value ten times more than it does now if it is placed in another place in the number. Write the digit that is presently in that place.

28. Suppose the digit 7 is in the third place from the right of a number. To which place must the 7 be moved to have only one-tenth of its present value?

29. Which has more value, the 1 in 45,125 or the 9 in 48,190?

30. In Numbers 26:2, God commanded Moses to number the men of Israel. The tribe of Gad had 40,500 men. What is the value of the digit 4 in the number 40,500?

REVIEW EXERCISES

D. Use words to write these numbers. *(Lesson 1)*

31. 45,182

32. 382,001,000

33. 5,500,000,000

34. 1,500,000,000,000

E. Use digits to write these numbers. *(Lesson 1)*

35. Four million, sixty thousand, forty-seven

36. Fifty-six billion, four hundred seventeen million, six

37. Seven trillion, fifty billion

38. Five billion, four thousand

F. Solve these problems.

39.
$$\begin{array}{r} 48,921 \\ + 53,912 \\ \hline \end{array}$$

40.
$$\begin{array}{r} \$1,212.89 \\ + 5,787.91 \\ \hline \end{array}$$

41.
$$\begin{array}{r} 80,213 \\ - 15,684 \\ \hline \end{array}$$

42.
$$\begin{array}{r} \$2,898.00 \\ - 1,975.12 \\ \hline \end{array}$$

43.
$$\begin{array}{r} 381 \\ \times 72 \\ \hline \end{array}$$

44.
$$\begin{array}{r} 857 \\ \times 26 \\ \hline \end{array}$$

45. $7\overline{)16,242}$

46. $15\overline{)65,121}$

3. Rounding Numbers

Many numbers that we use regularly are round numbers. You may say that you live 3 miles from school when the exact distance is $2\frac{8}{10}$ miles. You might say that it is 9:20 when the time is exactly 9:18:30.

Round numbers are used when a general statement is satisfactory. It is proper to say that you are about 60 inches tall when your height is $59\frac{3}{4}$ inches or $60\frac{1}{4}$ inches. However, cutting a board or a piece of fabric to the length of 60 inches is usually not satisfactory if you need a piece $59\frac{3}{4}$ inches long. Rounding to the nearest inch is not accurate enough for these purposes. Rather, you need to measure to the nearest $\frac{1}{8}$ inch or $\frac{1}{16}$ inch.

When rounding numbers, remember the following points.

Step 1:   Select the place value to which you will round the number. In the examples below, that place value is underlined.

Step 2:   Look at the digit one place to the right of the place to which you are rounding. If that digit is less than 5, round down as in Example A. If it is 5 or more, round up as in Example B.

Example A

$\underline{7}45$ rounded to the nearest hundred = 700

The 4 in the tens' place is less than 5, so 745 is nearer to 700 than to 800 and should be rounded to the next lower hundred. To do this, keep the 7 in the hundreds' place and change all digits to its right to zeroes.

Example B

$\underline{5},787,000,000$ rounded to the nearest billion = 6,000,000,000

Because the 7 in the hundred millions' place is 5 or more, 5,787,000,000 is nearer to 6,000,000,000 than to 5,000,000,000. Therefore, 5,787,000,000 should be rounded to the next higher billion. This is done by changing the 5 in the billions' place to 6 and changing all the digits to its right to zeroes.

Example C

$\$1\underline{5}.38$ rounded to the nearest dollar = $15.00

When rounding money to the nearest dollar, look at the cents. Round any amount less than 50 cents by dropping the cents, and round any amount 50 cents or more to the next higher dollar.

Example D

$\underline{}246$ rounded to the nearest thousand = 0

The thousand next lower than 246 is 0, and the thousand next higher is 1,000. The 2 in the hundreds' place is less than 5, so 246 is nearer to 0 than to 1,000. Therefore, it is rounded to the next lower thousand.

CLASS PRACTICE

Round these numbers as indicated.

a. 753 *(ten)*   b. 1,443 *(hundred)*   c. 2,178 *(ten thousand)*

d. 345,119,293 *(ten million)*   e. 476,122,843 *(hundred million)*

f. 34,870,000,000 *(billion)*   g. 7,260,000,000 *(billion)*

WRITTEN EXERCISES

A. Round the numbers in each set as indicated.

	157	31	348	901
Nearest ten	1. _____	2. _____	3. _____	4. _____
Nearest hundred	5. _____	6. _____	7. _____	8. _____

	11,557	1,915	25,220	74,761
Nearest thousand	9. _____	10. _____	11. _____	12. _____
Nearest ten thousand	13. _____	14. _____	15. _____	16. _____

	1,215,400	3,507,000	11,491,600
Nearest hundred thousand	17. _____	18. _____	19. _____
Nearest million	20. _____	21. _____	22. _____

	49,632,692	118,865,000	889,417,000
Nearest ten million	23. _____	24. _____	25. _____
Nearest hundred million	26. _____	27. _____	28. _____

	2,994,000,000	5,333,000,000
Nearest billion	29. _____	30. _____

B. Round these prices to the nearest dollar.

31. $5.75   32. $6.12   33. $9.50   34. $9.49

35. $29.95   36. $196.15   37. $435.52   38. $199.75

C. Solve these reading problems.

39. The airline distance between Boston and San Francisco is 2,345 miles. Round this distance to the nearest hundred miles.

40. Philadelphia, Pennsylvania, had a population of 1,585,577 in 1990. Round this number to the nearest hundred thousand.

41. The average distance between the planet Venus and the sun is 67,270,000 miles. Round this distance to the nearest million miles.

42. The average distance between the planet Jupiter and the sun is 483,900,000 miles. Round this distance to the nearest hundred million miles.

43. The distance between the planet Neptune and the sun is 2,796,700,000 miles. Round this distance to the nearest billion miles.

44. The average distance between the planet Pluto and the sun is 3,675,300,000 miles. Round this distance to the nearest billion miles.

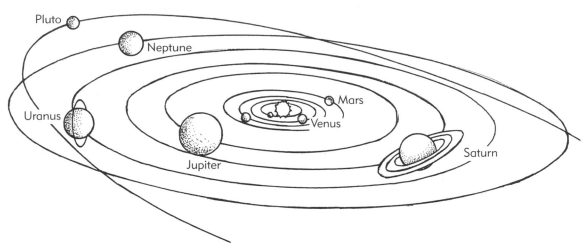

The heavens declare the glory of God; and the firmament sheweth his handiwork.
Psalm 19:1

REVIEW EXERCISES

D. Write the value of each underlined digit. *(Lesson 2)*

45. 89<u>2</u>   **46.** 1,<u>4</u>38   **47.** 7<u>8</u>3,919   **48.** 4,<u>3</u>00,000,000

E. Use digits to write these numbers. *(Lesson 1)*

49. Twenty-five million, sixteen thousand

50. Four billion, thirty-eight million, six hundred fifteen thousand, seventy-five

F. Use words to write these numbers. *(Lesson 1)*

51. 42,500   **52.** 37,980,000,000

4. Using Roman Numerals

I = 1	V = 5	X = 10	L = 50
C = 100	D = 500	M = 1,000	$\overline{V}$ = 5,000
$\overline{X}$ = 10,000	$\overline{L}$ = 50,000	$\overline{C}$ = 100,000	$\overline{M}$ = 1,000,000

The Arabic number system was not used in Europe until the 1500s. Before that, most Europeans used the Roman numeral system. This numbering system was developed by the Romans before the birth of Christ.

The Roman numeral system uses certain capital letters to express numbers. It is not a place-value system. Instead, its letters always represent the same values. For example, X always means ten, no matter where it is placed in a number. Because of this, Roman numerals are very cumbersome to use in multiplying and dividing.

We do use Roman numerals today in certain cases. They are often used in outlines and on date stones. Otherwise, they have been replaced by Arabic numerals.

Following are the rules for writing Roman numerals.

1. **When a numeral is repeated, add the values.** Never repeat V, L, or D.
   II = 1 + 1 = 2   MM = 1,000 + 1,000 = 2,000

2. **When a smaller numeral comes after a larger numeral, add the values.**
   XIII = 10 + 1 + 1 + 1 = 13   MCC = 1,000 + 100 + 100 = 1,200

3. **When a smaller numeral comes before a larger numeral, subtract the smaller from the larger.** Never subtract V, L, D, or M, and never use more than one smaller numeral before a larger one.   IV = 5 – 1 = 4   CM = 1,000 – 100 = 900

4. **A smaller numeral may precede only the next larger and second larger numerals.** Use only the following combinations.
   I — IV and IX   X — XL and XC   C — CD and CM

5. **Placing a line over a numeral increases its value 1,000 times.**
   $\overline{VI}$ = 6,000 $\overline{XX}$ = 20,000 $\overline{M}$ = 1,000,000
   $\overline{XL}$ = 40,000 $\overline{XX}$D = 20,500 $\overline{MMC}$ = 2,100,000

6. **It is neither proper nor necessary to use the same numeral more than three times.** Instead, use rule 3 to write the next number.
   90 = XC, not LXXXX   900 = CM, not DCCCC

CLASS PRACTICE

Express these numbers with Arabic numerals.

a. CCXXIV   b. DCCCXXXVIII   c. MMCDXLIV   d. $\overline{XX}$XCLV

Express these numbers with Roman numerals.

  e. 457   f. 789   g. 1,678   h. 50,500

WRITTEN EXERCISES

A. Express the following numbers with Arabic numerals.

  1. XX   **2.** XXXIV   **3.** XXXIX   **4.** LXXXVII   **5.** DCV   **6.** MI

B. Express the following numbers with Roman numerals.

  7. 45   **8.** 72   **9.** 99   **10.** 125   **11.** 1,300   **12.** 1,994

C. Express the following numbers with Arabic numerals. Remember that a line over a Roman numeral multiplies its value by 1,000.

  13. $\overline{\text{X}}$ **14.** $\overline{\text{L}}$ **15.** $\overline{\text{D}}$ **16.** $\overline{\text{MM}}$ **17.** $\overline{\text{MMMMM}}$ **18.** $\overline{\text{CL}}$

D. Express the following numbers with Roman numerals.

  19. 40,000   **20.** 600,000   **21.** 350,000

  22. 550,000   **23.** 1,200,000   **24.** 145,500

E. Solve these reading problems.

25. The *Martyrs Mirror* was first printed in the year MDCLX. Write that year with Arabic numerals.

26. The Hillside Mennonite Church was first built in MDCCCLI. Write that year with Arabic numerals.

27. The Hillside church was rebuilt in 1974. Write 1974 using Roman numerals.

28. The Union Station meetinghouse was originally built in 1878. An addition was built on in 1955. How old was the original structure when the addition was done? Write your answer with Roman numerals.

29. The average distance between the planet Saturn and the sun is 887,200,000 miles. Round this distance to the nearest hundred million miles.

30. The average distance between the planet Uranus and the sun is 1,784,800,000 miles. Write this number, using words.

REVIEW EXERCISES

F. Round these numbers as indicated. *(Lesson 3)*

Nearest hundred	**31.** 1,435	**32.** 3,166
Nearest million	**33.** 4,456,000	**34.** 7,701,000
Nearest billion	**35.** 12,345,000,000	**36.** 15,971,000,000
Nearest dollar	**37.** $3.75 **38.** $12.44	**39.** $8.24 **40.** $129.80

G. Write the value of each underlined digit. *(Lesson 2)*

41. 27,366,000   **42.** 17,500,000,000

5. Reviewing Addition

Example A	Example B
3,215 addend	
5,692 addend	$216.32
7,812 addend	771.74
3,771 addend	315.48
+6,818 addend	+211.06
27,308 sum	$1,514.60

Addition is the combining of two or more numbers. The numbers being added are **addends**. The answer to an addition problem is the **sum**.

Adding Vertically

The fastest way to add is to place the addends in columns. This way is fastest because in column addition, the digits with the same place value are directly in line with each other. The ones are all in the same column, the tens are all in the same column, and so forth. Keeping the columns straight is important for the sake of accuracy.

When adding money, use the following rules.
1. Copy and add as you would with any other addends.
2. Place the decimal point in the sum directly below the decimal points in the addends.
3. Remember to use the dollar sign in the sum.

Adding Horizontally

Horizontal addition is not used as often as column addition. It is used in many checkbook ledgers and in proving multicolumn ledgers. To add horizontally, first add the ones and then the tens, and continue in this way until you have finished the problem. Learn to add horizontally without copying the problems.

Example C
425 + 778 = 1,203
Think: 5 + 8 = 13.   Write 3 and carry the 1.   **3**
Think: 1 + 2 + 7 = 10.   Write 0 and carry the 1.   **03**
Think: 1 + 4 + 7 = 12.   Write 12.   **1,203**

CLASS PRACTICE

Solve these addition problems.

a.	b.	c.	d.
43,519	$45,678.90	425 + 3,192	43,567 + 38,116
22,182	+ 57,812.75		
45,602			
34,515			
+ 14,515			

WRITTEN EXERCISES

A. Copy and add. Check your work by adding upward and writing the check answer above the problem. In problems 1 and 2, write the proper addition term beside each part of the problems, including answers.

1.	2.	3.	4.
473 ____	822 ____	$123.81	$154.81
281 ____	162 ____	214.98	266.78
783 ____	399 ____	174.71	319.77
+ 181 ____	+ 717 ____	+ 673.18	+ 871.71

5.	6.	7.	8.
3,482	38,711	121,919	315,717
8,191	82,717	414,881	412,811
6,415	45,818	+ 881,771	335,818
7,171	66,899		+ 761,651
7,818	57,182		
+ 5,181	+ 14,444		

9.	10.
$3,717.89	$12,842.81
4,871.56	15,717.61
+ 5,817.78	22,171.73
	+ 18,332.17

B. Add horizontally, without copying the problems. Check by going over your work.

11. 4 + 3 + 5 + 7 + 9 + 2   12. 6 + 5 + 9 + 3 + 2 + 9 + 8

13. 9 + 7 + 4 + 9 + 3 + 6 + 8   14. 3 + 1 + 7 + 9 + 5 + 6 + 9 + 8

15. 45 + 23   16. 15 + 87

17. 21 + 86   18. 81 + 45 + 71

19. 71 + 25 + 71 + 23   20. 53 + 36 + 17 + 93 + 49

21. 427 + 534   22. 388 + 281

23. 484 + 382   24. 583 + 921

C. Solve these reading problems. Use horizontal addition for numbers 25 and 26.

25. When inspecting several dairy farms, Mr. Miller traveled these distances: 33 miles, 28 miles, 44 miles, and 39 miles. What was the total distance he traveled?

26. The reigns of the first five kings of Judah were of the following lengths: Rehoboam, 17 years; Abijah, 3 years; Asa, 41 years; Jehoshaphat, 25 years; and Jehoram, 8 years. How long in all did these five kings reign?

27. God told Moses and Aaron that the tribes of Judah, Issachar, and Zebulon were to camp on the east side of the tabernacle. Those that were numbered of Judah were 74,600; of Issachar, 54,400; and of Zebulon, 57,400. How many were numbered on the east side?

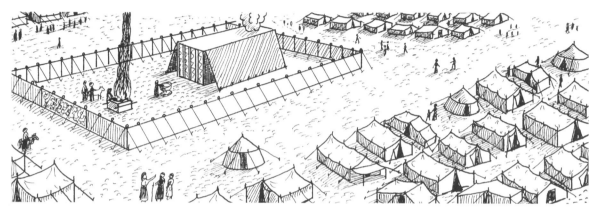

28. Those that were numbered of the tribe of Benjamin were 35,400 men. Write 35,400 as a Roman numeral.

29. King Josiah gave to the people for the Passover offerings 30,000 lambs and kids and 3,000 bullocks. The rulers of the house of God also gave 2,600 small cattle and 300 oxen. How many animals did they give?

30. Zerubbabel led the first group of Jews from Babylon back to Judah. They took along 736 horses, 245 mules, 435 camels, and 6,720 donkeys. What was the total number of these animals?

REVIEW EXERCISES

D. Write these numbers with Arabic numerals. *(Lesson 4)*

31. CC   32. MMMCC   33. CCCXC   34. $\overline{L}$CCC

E. Write the following numbers with Roman numerals. *(Lesson 4)*

35. 85   36. 119   37. 2,600   38. 75,000

F. Round these numbers as indicated. *(Lesson 3)*

39. 34,616,999 *(nearest million)*   40. 45,181,763 *(nearest ten million)*

G. Write these numbers, using words. *(Lesson 1)*

41. 875,400   42. 7,800,000,000,000

6. Adding Mentally

Mental math is important because it enables us to solve simple math problems when pencil and paper are not available. As your skill increases, so will your ability to calculate more difficult problems mentally.

The only way to become skilled at mental calculation is to practice it regularly. Try to do well with mental math, not just to solve problems in arithmetic lessons but to form a lifelong habit.

Adding Single-Digit Numbers Rapidly

One secret of adding numbers rapidly is to find addends that equal ten. With practice, you will start doing this almost automatically.

Example A	Example B
$4 + 6 + 7 + 3 + 5 + 5 + 7$	
$10 + 10 + 10 + 7 = 37$	$2 + 5 + 8 + 5 + 3 \qquad 10 + 10 + 3 = 23$
$(4 + 6) + (7 + 3) + (5 + 5) + 7$	

In Example A, all the pairs of addends equaling 10 are beside each other. In Example B, they are not. Do not spend much time searching for pairs of 10. Simply keep your eyes open for such pairs of addends that are close together.

Adding Larger Numbers Mentally

To mentally add numbers with more than one digit, add from left to right. It is easier to add from left to right because this is the normal way to read numbers.

Example C	Example D
To add $45 + 74$, think:	To add $450 + 360$, think:
$45 + 70 = 115 \qquad 115 + 4 = 119$	$450 + 300 = 750 \qquad 750 + 60 = 810$

CLASS PRACTICE

Solve these problems mentally.

a. $45 + 32$ b. $68 + 23$ c. $49 + 75$ d. $35 + 68$

e. $72 + 59$ f. $115 + 76$ g. $138 + 79$ h. $1,250 + 690$

WRITTEN EXERCISES

A. Add mentally and write only the answers. Look for opportunities to combine pairs that make 10.

1. $7 + 3 + 6 + 4 + 9$ 2. $5 + 5 + 8 + 2 + 4$

3. $5 + 6 + 5 + 7 + 3 + 8 + 2$ 4. $4 + 5 + 6 + 8 + 2 + 1 + 9$

5. $7 + 3 + 8 + 1 + 2 + 9 + 7$ 6. $8 + 6 + 2 + 4 + 9 + 2 + 1$

7. 8 + 7 + 2 + 3 + 4 + 6 + 4

8. 5 + 7 + 3 + 5 + 1 + 9 + 8

9. 4 + 8 + 6 + 2 + 7 + 3 + 5 + 7

10. 9 + 9 + 1 + 1 + 6 + 7 + 4 + 8

B. Add mentally. Do not copy the problems.

11. 35 + 22

12. 47 + 41

13. 27 + 64

14. 39 + 45

15. 59 + 38

16. 29 + 16

17. 42 + 63

18. 58 + 71

19. 105 + 42

20. 103 + 28

21. 110 + 77

22. 113 + 83

23. 1,400 + 700

24. 1,500 + 450

25. 1,825 + 500

26. 1,200 + 775

C. Solve these reading problems. See if you can solve problems 27–30 mentally.

27. Brother Paul was seating families for dinner at a Bible conference. There were 6 people in the first family, 7 in the second, 4 in the third, 8 in the fourth, and 3 in the fifth. How many places did Brother Paul need to find for them?

28. The Leesburg Christian School has the following numbers of students: first grade, 6; second grade, 4; third grade, 5; fourth grade, 5; fifth grade, 7; sixth grade, 6; seventh grade, 3; eighth grade, 4; ninth grade, 7; and tenth grade, 3. How many students attend the school?

29. Last week Sarah and her mother canned 48 quarts of fruit on Monday and 58 quarts on Wednesday. How many quarts did they can?

30. Carl picked 48 baskets of tomatoes, and his father picked 87 baskets. How many baskets of tomatoes did they pick together?

31. The Roman Empire divided into two parts in A.D. 395. The West Roman Empire, including much of western Europe, fell to the barbarian invaders in the year A.D. 476. Write 476 with Roman numerals.

32. The East Roman Empire, including Greece and Asia Minor, endured nearly 1,000 years longer than the western empire. The East Roman Empire fell to the Turks in MCDLIII. Write this date with Arabic numerals.

REVIEW EXERCISES

D. Copy and add. Check your work by adding upward and writing the check answer above the problem. In problems 33 and 34, write the proper addition term beside each part of the problem. (*Lesson 5*)

33.	$421.62	___	34.	$261.33	___	35.	3,131	36.	722,634
	342.61	___		812.51	___		4,156		456,757
	223.25	___		661.21	___		2,836		+ 242,856
	+ 414.13	___		+ 171.45	___		9,899		
							5,182		
							+ 6,444		

E. Change the Roman numerals to Arabic numerals and the Arabic numerals to Roman numerals. (*Lesson 4*)

37. CCCXCV

38. MCDXCII

39. 578

40. 1776

F. Write the value of each underlined digit. (*Lesson 2*)

41. 4<u>1</u>,456,000

42. <u>2</u>2,500,000

7. Reviewing Subtraction

Subtraction is the taking of one number from another. Subtraction shows how much larger one number is than another. The number from which another number is subtracted is the **minuend**. The number being subtracted is the **subtrahend**. The answer in a subtraction problem is the **difference** between the minuend and the subtrahend.

To check a subtraction problem, add the difference to the subtrahend. This sum should equal the minuend.

When you are subtracting money, the same rules apply in placing the decimal point as when you are adding money. Place the decimal point in the difference directly below the decimal points in the minuend and the subtrahend.

Example A		Check	**Example B**		Check
742	minuend	364	$425.00	minuend	$246.21
− 378	subtrahend	+ 378	− 178.79	subtrahend	+ 178.79
364	difference	742	$246.21	difference	$425.00

Horizontal subtraction is exactly like vertical subtraction but is a bit more difficult because the places in the minuend and the subtrahend are not in columns. Horizontal subtraction is used in many checkbook ledgers.

Example C	**Example D**
442 − 315 = 127	$22.45 − 17.78 = $4.67
Check: 127 + 315 = 442	Check: $4.67 + 17.78 = $22.45

CLASS PRACTICE

Solve these subtraction problems.

a. 45,761
    − 26,900

b. $45,678.22
    − 29,890.89

c. 567 − 387

d. 45,716 − 18,182

WRITTEN EXERCISES

A. *Copy and subtract. Check your work by adding the subtrahend to the difference. Label each part in problems 1 and 2, including answers.*

1. 3,421 _____
    − 1,821 _____

2. 7,612 _____
    − 4,822 _____

3. 9,233
    − 5,852

4. 12,874
    − 9,631

5.   38,747   6.   54,874   7. $3,832.56   8. $7,881.43
    – 18,793   – 22,952   – 1,828.83   – 3,821.91

9. 12,172,812   10.   38,912,573   11. $115,262.74   12. $289,876.14
   – 7,887,452   – 15,724,333   – 28,890.14   – 144,890.99

B. Subtract and check. Write only the answers and your check.

13. 455 – 321   14. 547 – 235

15. 721 – 496   16. 834 – 548

17. 2,215 – 1,146   18. 4,726 – 2,813

19. $26.54 – 14.65   20. $83.45 – 69.70

21. $456.32 – 189.65   22. $575.50 – 198.75

C. Solve these reading problems. Use horizontal subtraction for numbers 23 and 24.

23. In 1672, about 700 Mennonites fled persecution in Switzerland and settled in the Palatinate. Between 1717 and 1732, about 3,000 Mennonites emigrated from the Palatinate to Pennsylvania. How many more emigrated to Pennsylvania than had fled to the Palatinate in 1672?

24. In 1726, the rulers of the Palatinate passed a law called the "Right of Retraction." This law gave Catholics and Protestants the right to buy back at any time any real estate that they had sold to Mennonites. Although this law was later modified, parts of it were in force until 1801. How many years was it in force?

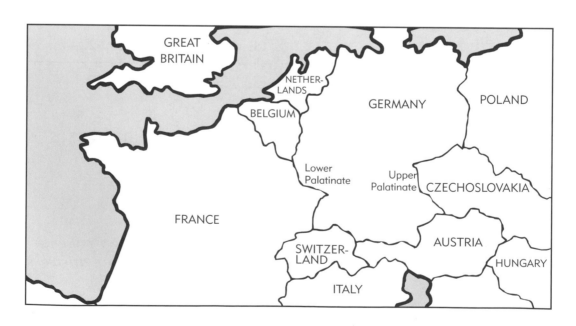

25. In 1671, the Mennonites in Holland gave at least 11,000 guilders for relief of the refugees in the Palatinate. About 40 years later the congregation in Hamburg, Germany, gave 1,470 guilders to help the Swiss refugees in Holland. What was the difference in the amounts contributed?

26. Beginning about 1690, the number of Mennonites in Holland began to decline steadily. The number of Mennonites believing in nonresistance in 1700 was about 160,000. By 1809, the number was less than 28,000. By how much did the number of nonresistant Mennonites decline from 1700 to 1809?

27. In 1994, the population of the Netherlands was estimated to be 15,368,000. Round this number to the nearest million.

28. In 1994, the population of Germany was estimated to be 81,088,000. Round this number to the nearest ten million.

REVIEW EXERCISES

D. Add mentally. Do not copy the problems. *(Lesson 6)*

29. 5 + 7 + 3 + 5 + 7 + 8 + 2

30. 4 + 1 + 6 + 9 + 3 + 8 + 3

31. 41 + 69

32. 52 + 79

33. 69 + 64

34. 78 + 65

E. Copy and add. Check your work by adding upward and writing the check answer above the problem. In problems 35 and 36, write the correct addition term beside each part of the problem, including answers. *(Lesson 5)*

35.
```
  $242.73  _____
   724.83  _____
   824.91  _____
 + 735.21  _____
```

36.
```
  $782.24  _____
   173.61  _____
   142.57  _____
 + 612.73  _____
```

37.
```
   3,192
   8,189
   1,653
   5,745
   3,813
 + 4,728
```

38.
```
   251,364
   745,745
 + 143,134
```

F. Round these numbers as indicated. *(Lesson 3)*

39. 975 *(nearest ten)*

40. 273,172,763 *(nearest hundred million)*

8. Subtracting Mentally

To subtract mentally, the best way is usually to first subtract those digits having the greatest place value. Then subtract the digits having the second greatest value, and proceed one place at a time to the ones' place.

Example A	Example B
72 – 38 Think: 72 – 30 = 42 42 – 8 = 34	354 – 146 Think: 354 – 100 = 254 254 – 40 = 214 214 – 6 = 208

CLASS PRACTICE

Subtract mentally. Check with mental addition.

a. 52 – 10   b. 83 – 50   c. 91 – 64   d. 82 – 34

e. 178 – 62   f. 154 – 38   g. 172 – 81   h. 152 – 87

WRITTEN EXERCISES

A. *Do these subtractions mentally. Check with mental addition.*

1. 48 – 20   2. 79 – 30   3. 74 – 60   4. 85 – 40

5. 72 – 16   6. 83 – 27   7. 92 – 58   8. 64 – 38

9. 71 – 49   10. 80 – 36   11. 172 – 41   12. 158 – 45

13. 145 – 23   14. 178 – 62   15. 174 – 58   16. 141 – 27

17. 125 – 72   18. 115 – 69   19. 142 – 55   20. 175 – 82

21. 250 – 120   22. 325 – 114   23. 245 – 150   24. 375 – 168

B. *Solve these reading problems. See if you can solve problems 25–28 mentally.*

25. Africa had 27 independent countries in 1960 and 52 in 1991. How many more independent countries were in Africa in 1991 than in 1960?

26. When the United States was founded in 1776, there were 13 states. Today there are 50 states. How many new states have been added to the nation since 1776?

27. When the United Nations was founded in 1945, 51 nations were members. In 1994 there were 184 member nations. How many more nations were members of the United Nations in 1994 than in 1945?

28. A school had 135 students one year and 157 the next year. What was the increase in enrollment?

29. The colony of Pennsylvania was established in MDCLXXXII. Write that number with Arabic numerals.

30. In North America, the oldest Mennonite church building still being used is in Germantown, Pennsylvania. This building was put up in the year MDCCLXX. Write that number with Arabic numerals.

REVIEW EXERCISES

C. Copy and subtract. Check your work by adding the subtrahend to the difference. Label each part in problems 31 and 32, including answers. (Lesson 7)

31.	27,351 _____	32.	485,154 _____	33.	$42,385.66	34.	82,176,123
	− 14,173 _____		− 277,894 _____		− 25,782.89		− 36,414,217

D. Add mentally. Do not copy the problems. (Lesson 6)

35. 8 + 6 + 2 + 7 + 1 + 3 + 9   36. 9 + 2 + 3 + 8 + 7 + 4 + 6

37. 75 + 46   38. 89 + 35

39. 450 + 85   40. 675 + 75

E. Change the Roman numerals to Arabic numerals and the Arabic numerals to Roman numerals. (Lesson 4)

41. DCCCXV   42. MVIII   43. 489   44. 1456

9. Reading Problems: Finding the Necessary Information

The math problems you face in everyday life do not come neatly arranged in columns and rows as in a math book. They rather come as a few facts among many. You need to decide which facts are necessary and use them to solve your problems.

Of all the problems in your math book, reading problems are most like the ones you face in life. They do not present facts in columns and rows. Rather, you need to analyze each problem to decide what facts are needed and how to use those facts.

In this lesson you will work with reading problems that do not have all the facts needed to solve them. Approach each one as you would if you faced that problem in real life.

1. Study the reading problem carefully. Think, "What question is being asked?"
2. Then think, "What information is needed to answer this question?"

Some of the needed information is missing in the following example.

> In 1992, Hurricane Andrew struck the southern part of Florida with winds reaching 165 miles per hour. This was just 3 years after Hurricane Hugo had caused severe damage along the coast of South Carolina. How much faster were the winds of Hurricane Andrew than those of Hurricane Hugo?
>
> Information needed: *The speed of Hurricane Hugo's wind*

CLASS PRACTICE

Tell what information is missing in each problem.

a. At what time should Dwight finish mowing the lawn if it usually takes him $2\frac{1}{2}$ hours?
b. The fastest airplane can travel how many times faster than the fastest passenger train?

WRITTEN EXERCISES

A. Read each problem carefully, and write what information is needed to solve it. Some problems have more than one answer.

1. Martha purchased 8 pounds of bananas. How much did she pay for them?

2. The price of a new textbook is $11.50. How much will it cost to purchase enough textbooks for each student to have one copy?

3. Brother Henry hired a man to paint his house. He paid the painter $14.00 per hour. What was the total cost of the labor to paint the house?

4. One day at the market, Brother Newton sold 160 heads of cauliflower, 3 bushels of lima beans, and 85 pounds of beets. How much money did he receive from the sale of these vegetables?

5. What is the cost of insulating an attic floor if insulation sells for 15.5 cents per square foot?

6. After a severe windstorm, Brother Mark needed to replace the roof of his barn, including some rafters. What was the cost of 8 rafters?

7. With the help of several brethren from church, Brother Mark had the roof replaced in 3 days. The brethren donated 48 hours of labor. If 20 hours of labor were donated on Monday, how many hours were donated on Wednesday?

8. Brother Paul mentioned that a neighbor had broken his leg and was unable to do his spring plowing. One brother volunteered to plow the 15-acre oats field. Another said he would plow the 8-acre squash field. Two brethren agreed together to plow the 45 acres for corn, while another said he would plow the 17-acre soybean field. How many acres of plowing were left for the neighbor to do?

9. A young family had a large hospital bill. The family was able to pay $5,500, and the local congregation paid $10,500. Other nearby congregations gave $18,250. How much was still needed to pay the bill?

10. The sisters from several churches volunteered to sew clothes for families whose homes were destroyed in an earthquake. One congregation planned to sew and donate 36 girl's dresses. How much will the material cost for the dresses?

11. When a river flooded, numerous brethren worked together to help clear away the debris. From one congregation, 47 brethren worked for 3 days. Some distant congregations joined together and sent 2 busloads of help. How many men worked on the cleanup project in all?

12. Several of the brethren scooped water and mud out of basements and dumped it into tractor loaders to be carried away. If the men scooped 840 bucketfuls of water and mud out of 3 houses, how many loader scoops did they fill?

Bear ye one another's burdens.   *Galatians 6:2*

B. Solve these reading problems.

13. In the contiguous United States, the states of Washington, Oregon, and California border the Pacific Ocean. The 1993 population of these states was as follows: Washington, 5,255,276; Oregon, 3,031,867; and California, 31,210,750. How many people lived in states bordering the Pacific Ocean?

14. The two states that raise the most potatoes are Idaho and Washington. In one recent year, Idaho produced 112,340,000 hundredweight of potatoes and Washington produced 67,980,000 hundredweight. How many hundredweight of potatoes did they produce together?

15. In 1993, how many more people lived in California than in Washington and Oregon together? (See problem 13.)

16. The area of Canada is 3,849,674 square miles. The area of the United States is 3,787,318 square miles. The area of Canada is how much larger than that of the United States?

REVIEW EXERCISES

C. Do these subtractions mentally. Check with mental addition. *(Lesson 8)*

17. 45 – 28   18. 73 – 48   19. 161 – 28   20. 134 – 65

D. Copy and subtract. Check your work by adding the subtrahend to the difference. Label each part in problems 21 and 22, including answers. *(Lesson 7)*

21.   41,351 _____   22.   515,626 _____   23. $71,836.78   24.   67,444,300
     – 24,624 _____   – 329,849 _____   – 35,611.42   – 24,717,278

E. Copy and add. Check your work by adding upward and writing the check answer above the problem. Label each part in problems 25 and 26, including answers. *(Lesson 5)*

25.   242,181 _____   26.   216,812 _____   27.   5,824   28. $16,883.24
       145,834 _____   352,712 _____   3,411   + 23,818.81
       491,433 _____   223,911 _____   8,412
     + 115,522 _____   + 116,743 _____   8,333
                                                           6,735
                                                         + 1,261

F. Use digits to write the following numbers. *(Lesson 1)*

29. Fourteen million, one hundred seventy thousand, ninety-four

30. Seven trillion, seven hundred billion

G. Use words to write these numbers. *(Lesson 1)*

31. 77,450,000   32. 15,500,000,000

10. Chapter 1 Review

A. Use words to write these numbers. Use commas just as with the digits. *(Lesson 1)*

1. 45,800,000

2. 3,750,000,000

3. 4,650,000,000,000

4. 7,000,700,000

B. Use digits to write the following numbers. *(Lesson 1)*

5. Seven million, thirty-two thousand, one hundred five

6. One hundred one billion, seven

C. Write the value of each underlined digit. *(Lesson 2)*

7. 7<u>2</u>,811   8. <u>5</u>68,940   9. <u>4</u>1,200,000   10. 2<u>7</u>7,912,000,000

D. Round these numbers as indicated. *(Lesson 3)*

11. 246 *(ten)*

12. 577 *(hundred)*

13. 45,289 *(thousand)*

14. 2,553,800 *(hundred thousand)*

15. 45,600,000 *(ten million)*

16. 14,700,000,000 *(billion)*

E. Express the following numbers with Arabic numerals. *(Lesson 4)*

17. CCCLXXV   18. CDXLVIII   19. $\overline{XXX}$ 20. $\overline{XII}CCC$

F. Express the following numbers with Roman numerals. *(Lesson 4)*

21. 83   22. 378   23. 17,000   24. 25,200

G. Copy and add. Check your work by adding upward and writing the check answer above the problem. Label each part in problems 25 and 26, including answers. *(Lesson 5)*

25.		26.		27.		28.	
5,371	____	27,380	____	165,235		278,289	
7,422	____	42,481	____	823,131		847,274	
3,166	____	79,492	____	+ 711,782		284,293	
6,729	____	11,811	____			+ 249,203	
1,616	____	26,711	____				
+ 9,341	____	+ 71,222	____				

H. Copy and subtract. Check your work by adding the subtrahend to the difference. Label each part in problems 29 and 30, including answers. *(Lesson 7)*

29.	28,391	_____	30.	3,005,211	_____	31.	86,919,233	32.	$45,382.09
	− 15,172	_____		− 1,683,539	_____		− 15,681,981		− 28,714.61

I. Solve these horizontal problems. Write the answers one digit at a time. *(Lessons 5, 7)*

33. 712 + 453   34. 587 + 678

35. 45,719 + 26,911   36. 12,516 + 39,946

37. 722 − 463   38. 547 − 235

39. 26,881 − 14,575   40. 48,717 − 29,102

J. Solve these problems mentally. Write only the answers. *(Lessons 6, 8)*

41. 2 + 6 + 8 + 4 + 5 + 9 + 1   42. 7 + 2 + 8 + 3 + 5 + 7 + 5

43. 1 + 2 + 8 + 9 + 7 + 3 + 9   44. 8 + 3 + 7 + 7 + 3 + 1 + 9

45. 48 + 38   46. 62 + 78

47. 157 + 48   48. 128 + 63

49. 82 − 28   50. 73 − 37

51. 81 − 18   52. 177 − 88

K. Read each problem carefully. Write what information is needed to solve it. *(Lesson 9)*

53. The Stauffers shipped 12 steers to market. What was their average weight? (You should remember that an average is found by division.)

54. How many steers did the Stauffers have left after they shipped 12 of them?

55. One steer weighed 350 pounds when they purchased it. On the average, how many pounds did it gain per day?

56. Father is planning to buy a truckload of steers. If the steers weigh an average of 500 pounds each, how much will all the steers weigh?

11. Chapter 1 Test

Chapter 2

Working With Multiplication and Division

And thou shalt number seven sabbaths of years unto thee, seven times seven years; and the space of the seven sabbaths of years shall be unto thee forty and nine years. Then shalt thou cause the trumpet of the jubilee to sound on the tenth day of the seventh month. . . . And ye shall hallow the fiftieth year, and proclaim liberty throughout all the land.

(Leviticus 25:8–10)

12. Solving Multiplication Problems

Suppose your father is selling a 95-pound calf for $1.25 per pound. Would he add $1.25 plus $1.25 plus $1.25 until he has added $1.25 ninety-five times? No, there is a much simpler operation for adding the same number again and again. That operation is multiplication.

Example A	Example B
$1.25 multiplicand $\underline{\times 95}$ multiplier 625 partial product $\underline{1125}$ partial product $118.75 product Multipliers and multiplicands are also known as factors.	3,215 $\underline{\times 9}$ 28,935

To multiply when the multiplier has more than one digit, use these steps.

1. Multiply the multiplicand by the digit in the ones' place of the multiplier.
2. Multiply the multiplicand by the next digit of the multiplier (in the tens' place). Place the first digit of this partial product directly under the digit by which you are multiplying.
3. If the multiplier has more than two digits, repeat step 2 until all the digits in the multiplier have been multiplied.
4. Add the partial products.
5. When multiplying money by a whole number, put the decimal point two places from the right in the product.

To multiply horizontally, multiply just as you do for vertical multiplication. Write the answer one digit at a time. Do not copy the problem.

CLASS PRACTICE

Solve these multiplication problems. Label each number in problem a, *including the answer.*

a. 58 _____
   $\times 9$ _____

b. 722
   $\times\ 7$

c. 7 × 48

d. 3 × 781

e. $48.12
   $\underline{\times\ \ 83}$

WRITTEN EXERCISES

A. *Solve these multiplication problems. In problems 1 and 2, label each number with the correct term, including answers. Do not copy the horizontal problems, but write the answers one digit at a time.*

1. 47 _____
   $\underline{\times 8}$ _____

2. 368 _____
   $\underline{\times 7}$ _____

3. 46
   $\underline{\times 6}$

4. 79
   $\underline{\times 4}$

5. 83
   $\underline{\times 9}$

6. 58
   $\underline{\times 9}$

7. 5 × 637   8. 3 × 391   9. 7 × 616   10. 9 × 561

11. 6 × 4,321   12. 9 × 6,793   13. 6 × 5,717   14. 8 × 3,919

15.	78	16.	73	17.	58	18.	91
	× 36		× 53		× 72		× 81

19.	$1.25	20.	$2.43	21.	$6.59	22.	$8.71	23.	5,482	24.	7,919
	× 15		× 23		× 54		× 36		× 30		× 70

B. Solve these reading problems.

25. The seventh and eighth grade students usually sing three songs each morning in devotions. At that rate, how many songs will they sing in a 180-day school year?

26. The class has a 30-minute devotional period at the beginning of each school day. How many minutes will they use for devotions in a 180-day school year?

27. One wild oats weed produces about 250 seeds. If a wheat field has 58 wild oats plants per acre, how many wild oats seeds will be produced in an acre of wheat?

28. Humus-rich farm soil can have over one million earthworms per acre. The Wenger farm, which has poorer soil, has only 450,000 earthworms per acre. How many earthworms may be on the farm if it has 75 acres?

29. Write 450,000 with Roman numerals.

30. Round 450,000 to the nearest hundred thousand.

REVIEW EXERCISES

C. Copy and subtract. Check your work by adding the subtrahend to the difference. Label each part in problems 31 and 32, including answers. (Lesson 7)

31.	46,111 _____	32.	476,121 _____	33.	$43,217.82	34.	48,182,010
	− 26,983 _____		− 284,555 _____		− 15,821.21		− 26,761,923

D. Change the Roman numerals to Arabic numerals and the Arabic numerals to Roman numerals. (Lesson 4)

35. MCCCXXXI   36. MDCCCIX   37. 115   38. 1,616

E. Round these numbers to the places indicated. (Lesson 3)

39. 409,501 *(thousand)*   40. 856 *(hundred)*

41. 3,456,999,000 *(hundred million)*   42. 5,499,000,000 *(billion)*

13. Checking Multiplication by Casting Out Nines

The best way to make certain that a multiplication problem is done properly is to solve it carefully. However, even with the best of care, mistakes can creep in. There are several ways to double check your answer. One way is to reverse the factors and multiply again.

Casting out nines is a quick way to check a multiplication problem. This method is a convenient check for homework problems as well as problems in everyday life.

$4,29\!\!\!/8 \longrightarrow 14 \longrightarrow 5$ $\underline{\times 40 8} \longrightarrow 12 \longrightarrow \underline{\times 3}$ $34384 15 \longrightarrow 6$ $\underline{171920}$ $1\,75\,3\!\!\!/5\,8\!\!\!/4 \longrightarrow 15 \longrightarrow 6$	Multiply the numbers obtained by adding the digits in the factors. The number obtained from this product should equal the number obtained from the product in the multiplication.

To cast out nines in multiplication problems, follow these steps.
1. Cross out all the nines in the factors. Also cross out any digits whose sum equals 9. (In casting out nines, 9 is equal to 0.)
2. In each factor, add the digits that were not crossed out. If a sum is greater than 9, add the digits of that sum. Continue doing this until you obtain a one-digit number. If this number is 9, change it to 0.
3. Repeat step 2 for the product. You should now have three check numbers: one for the multiplicand, one for the multiplier, and one for the product.
4. Multiply the check numbers obtained from the factors, and perform step 2 on that product. The resulting one-digit number must be equal to the check number obtained from the factors.

Casting out nines will never show that a right answer is wrong. However, there are times when it may indicate that a wrong answer is right. Casting out nines will not reveal the following three errors.
1. *Errors with zeroes.* Because a zero in a number has no effect on the sum of its digits, casting out nines will not show if there is a missing zero or an extra zero. For example, the digits in 44; 404; and 4,040 all add up to 8.
2. *Errors of transposition.* Two numbers with transposed digits will yield the same check number. For example, the check number obtained from both 754 and 745 is 7.
3. *Errors in copying.* There is only one way to discover the mistake of copying a problem wrong. That is to look back at the book and make certain that you copied the problem correctly.

CLASS PRACTICE

Solve these problems. Check your work by casting out nines. Show your check
numbers. Solve a horizontally.

a. 6 × 873	b. 489	c. 578	d. 3,415	e. 6,211
	× 32	× 324	× 145	× 1,215

WRITTEN EXERCISES

A. *Solve these problems, and check by casting out nines. Write your check*
numbers along with your answers. Solve problems 1–4 horizontally.
Label the parts of problems 5 and 6, including intermediate steps and
answers.

1. 5 × 525	2. 6 × 781	3. 8 × 276	4. 9 × 821

5. 475 _____	6. 581 _____	7. 697	8. 153
× 21 _____	× 36 _____	× 48	× 59

9. 426	10. 538	11. 1,787	12. 2,615
× 68	× 74	× 53	× 58

13. 478	14. 369	15. 715	16. 741
× 103	× 201	× 408	× 507

17. 2,234	18. 1,244	19. 5,798	20. 3,731
× 1,212	× 2,311	× 1,424	× 3,815

B. *Solve these reading problems.*

21. Brother James serves as a missionary in India. Every
Sunday he uses the mission van to bring people to
church and take them home again. He drives a total of
85 miles each Sunday. How far will he drive the van on
this route in a three-year term of mission service?
(Consider 1 year as 52 weeks.)

22. Every week, Brother James takes sick and injured people
to a hospital in a nearby city. He has set a goal of distributing 144 Gospel tracts in the city each week while he
waits for his passengers to receive treatment. At this
rate, how many tracts would he pass out in a three-year
term of service? (Consider 1 year as 52 weeks.)

23. The moon is 238,857 miles from the earth. If the sun is 389 times farther from the earth than the moon is, how far is the sun from the earth?

24. The earth is 7,926 miles in diameter. If the sun's diameter is 109 times as great, what is the diameter of the sun?

25. Father took the children to school one morning. Four people were in the van when it left home. Three school students got in the van at the Weavers, 4 at the Kaufmans, and 4 at the Reinfords. A total of 12 students got off the van at school. How many people remained in the van as it returned home?

26. Father had $45.00 in his wallet. He spent $7.85 at the hardware store and $18.50 at the service station. He placed $15.00 in the offering at winter Bible school. The next day Father went to the bank, withdrew $50.00, and put it into his wallet. How much money was in his wallet then?

REVIEW EXERCISES

C. Subtract mentally, and write only the answers. *(Lesson 8)*

27. 42 – 17   28. 83 – 46   29. 182 – 68   30. 141 – 58

D. Copy and add. Label each part of problems 31 and 32, including answers. *(Lesson 5)*

31.   488 _____   32.   5,715 _____   33.   4,823,172   34. $23,912.31
  + 616 _____   3,755 _____   + 8,181,182   + 31,218.77
                              7,182 _____
                              3,912 _____
                        + 5,684 _____

14. Estimating and Multiplying Mentally

Father and Uncle John were discussing the milk production of their herds. Uncle John said, "I am milking 48 cows, and they produce an average of 52 pounds of milk per day."

Father replied, "That means you're getting about 2,500 pounds of milk per day."

David got out a pencil and paper. He multiplied 52 × 48 and found that the answer is 2,496. He wondered, "How did Father get an answer that close?"

Father had estimated the answer by rounding both 52 and 48 to the nearest ten. Then he had multiplied mentally: 50 × 50 = 2,500.

Estimation is useful for two purposes. First, it can be used to obtain an approximate answer when an exact answer is not needed. Father did not need to know exactly how many pounds of milk Uncle John's cows were producing.

Second, estimation is useful to see if a multiplication answer is sensible. Since Father's estimate (2,500) is close to David's exact answer (2,496), it shows that David's answer is sensible.

To estimate the answer to a multiplication problem, use these steps.
1. Round each factor to the largest place in the number. Round a two-digit number to the nearest ten, a three-digit number to the nearest hundred, and so forth.
2. Mentally multiply the numbers that you rounded. This is easy because you need to multiply only the nonzero digits and annex the total number of zeroes in the factors. The answer is your estimate.

Example A		To estimate the product, think:
Calculation	Estimate	6 × 4 = 24. There is a total of 4 zeroes in the
567	600	factors, so 4 zeroes must be annexed to 24.
× 427	× 400	The estimated product is 240,000.
242,109	240,000	

As illustrated above, multiplying by tens, hundreds, and thousands is quick because it is simply a matter of annexing zeroes. In the examples below, notice that to multiply by 10, by 100, and by 1,000, annex one, two, or three zeroes to the other factor.

Example B	**Example C**	**Example D**
717	435	468
× 10	× 100	× 1,000
7,170	43,500	468,000

The same principle can be used to solve other multiplication problems. The problem 30 × 25 can be solved by thinking like this: 3 × 25 = 75; annexing one zero yields 750.

Example E: For 20 × 43, think: 2 × 43 = 86; annex 0; answer is 860.

Example F: For 200 × 43, think: 2 × 43 = 86; annex 00; answer is 8,600.

Example G: For 2,000 × 43, think: 2 × 43 = 86; annex 000; answer is 86,000.

CLASS PRACTICE

Estimate the products, and then find the exact answers.

a.	72	b.	356	c.	4,872	d.	3,232
	× 37		× 240		× 375		× 1,795

Solve these problems mentally.

e. 20 × 26   f. 200 × 35   g. 2,000 × 48   h. 200 × 61

i. 12 × 50   j. 12 × 500   k. 11 × 5,000   l. 9 × 5,000

WRITTEN EXERCISES

A. Estimate each product, and then find the exact answer. Show your work for both answers.

1.	91	2.	78	3.	390	4.	615	5.	478
	× 77		× 63		× 75		× 44		× 120

6.	832	7.	621	8.	781	9.	5,215	10.	6,799
	× 292		× 466		× 715		× 4,765		× 3,345

B. Do these multiplications mentally.

11. 10 × 34   12. 10 × 765

13. 10 × 878   14. 10 × 7,621

15. 100 × 23   16. 100 × 79

17. 100 × 871   18. 100 × 3,912

19. 1,000 × 32   20. 1,000 × 87

21. 1,000 × 391   22. 1,000 × 4,567

23. 38 × 20   24. 15 × 30

25. 12 × 70   26. 12 × 90

27. 7 × 600   28. 9 × 800

29. 11 × 900   30. 12 × 900

31. 7 × 7,000   32. 8 × 6,000

C. *Solve these reading problems mentally.*

33. Philip's teacher told him that a hurricane was moving toward the coast of the United States at a speed of 11 miles per hour. If it continues at that rate, how far will it travel in 20 hours?

34. The wind in the hurricane was traveling in a gigantic circle at a speed of 115 miles per hour. If it continues at that rate, how far will the wind swirl in 20 hours?

35. The Mosemann family is taking three youths from their home congregation to attend Millville Bible School. If they have traveled 14 hours at an average rate of 50 miles per hour, how far have they traveled?

36. The Mosemanns' car can travel 16 miles per gallon of gasoline. If they have 20 gallons in the tank, how far can they go on that fuel?

37. The Mosemanns traveled 124 miles from their home before they stopped to eat lunch. Then they traveled another 68 miles and stopped briefly at a scenic overlook. How far did they travel from their home to the scenic overlook?

38. Father estimated that the entire trip to Bible school would take 20 hours at an average speed of 50 miles per hour. Estimate how far the Mosemanns lived from the Bible school.

MILLVILLE
Bible School

REVIEW EXERCISES

D. *Solve these problems horizontally, and write only the answers.* (*Lesson 13*)

39. 9 × 471

40. 7 × 825

41. 8 × 949

42. 8 × 3,567

E. *Solve these addition problems mentally.* (*Lesson 6*)

43. 58 + 37

44. 68 + 79

45. 157 + 64

46. 1,250 + 650

15. More Mental Multiplication

Here are a few shortcuts for multiplying mentally. Practice them until you can use them readily.

Double-and-Divide Method

To use the double-and-divide method, double one factor and divide the other factor by 2. This works especially well when one factor ends with 5 and the other factor is an even number. Double the factor that ends with 5, and divide the other factor by 2.

Example A	**Example B**
For 16 × 15, think:	For 5 × 46, think:
15 × 2 = 30	46 ÷ 2 = 23
× 16 ÷ 2 = × 8	× 5 × 2 = × 10
240	230

Multiplying by 50. The double-and-divide method is useful for multiplying an even number by 50 because 50 × 2 = 100. To solve such a problem, divide the even number by 2 and multiply by 100 (annex two zeroes).

Example C: For 16 × 50, think: 16 ÷ 2 = 8; 8 × 100 = 800

Example D: For 42 × 50, think: 42 ÷ 2 = 21; 21 × 100 = 2,100

Multiplying by 25. A form of the double-and-divide method can be used to multiply mentally by 25. Multiplying 25 × 4 equals 100. If the other factor is divisible by 4, simply divide that factor by 4 and multiply by 100 (annex two zeroes).

Example E: For 16 × 25, think: 16 ÷ 4 = 4; 4 × 100 = 400

Example F: For 36 × 25, think: 36 ÷ 4 = 9; 9 × 100 = 900

Multiplying a Series of Factors

When multiplying a series of factors, first multiply those factors whose product is a multiple of 10. Any even number multiplied by a multiple of 5 equals a multiple of ten.

Example G: 8 × 9 × 5
Think: 8 × 5 = 40; 40 × 9 = 360

Example H: 4 × 3 × 50 × 7
Think: 4 × 50 = 200; 200 × 3 = 600; 600 × 7 = 4,200

CLASS PRACTICE

Use the double-and-divide method to solve these problems.

a. 8 × 45   b. 12 × 15   c. 6 × 55   d. 16 × 35

Multiply mentally by 50 and by 25.

e. 16 × 50   f. 18 × 50   g. 42 × 50   h. 66 × 50

i. 24 × 25   j. 44 × 25   k. 8 × 25   l. 60 × 25

Rearrange the factors to multiply mentally.

m. 3 × 4 × 9 × 5   n. 6 × 7 × 5 × 4   o. 50 × 7 × 6 × 3

WRITTEN EXERCISES

A. Use the double-and-divide method to solve these problems mentally.

1. 24 × 15   2. 12 × 35   3. 12 × 45

4. 18 × 15   5. 48 × 5   6. 66 × 5

B. Multiply mentally by 50 and by 25.

7. 88 × 50   8. 12 × 50   9. 32 × 50

10. 46 × 50   11. 62 × 50   12. 82 × 50

13. 12 × 25   14. 28 × 25   15. 36 × 25

16. 32 × 25   17. 25 × 48   18. 25 × 40

C. Solve these problems mentally by rearranging the factors. Remember to first multiply 5 or 50 by the even number.

19. 3 × 8 × 5   20. 5 × 7 × 8   21. 2 × 7 × 5 × 3

22. 5 × 9 × 4   23. 3 × 5 × 30   24. 6 × 3 × 50

D. Solve these reading problems mentally.

25. In the third week of July, Friesen Excavating operated 6 days. The average use of diesel fuel was 35 gallons per day. How many gallons of diesel fuel were used that week?

26. The Andersons bought a farm that included 25 acres of scrubby white pine trees. It will cost $88.00 per acre to have the trees removed so that those acres can be farmed. What will be the cost of having the land prepared?

27. The Hersheys have a peach orchard with 15 rows of trees and 18 trees in each row. How many peach trees are in the orchard?

28. Marvin spent half a Saturday picking 25 bushels of peaches. At an average weight of 48 pounds per bushel, how many pounds of peaches did he pick?

29. Judith read in the encyclopedia that there are nearly 10,000 different varieties of apples in the world, of which more than 7,000 are grown in the United States. About how many varieties of apples are *not* grown in the United States?

30. One day Marvin picked 34 bushels of apples, and Paul picked 29 bushels. How many bushels did they pick together?

REVIEW EXERCISES

E. Estimate the products. You do not need to find the exact answers. *(Lesson 14)*

31.
```
    48
  × 31
```
32.
```
    76
  × 83
```
33.
```
   462
  × 336
```
34.
```
   6,402
  × 4,579
```

F. Solve these problems horizontally, and write only the answers. *(Lesson 13)*

35. 7 × 48

36. 6 × 128

37. 8 × 486

38. 9 × 6,543

G. Solve these subtraction problems. Label the parts in problems 39 and 40, including answers. *(Lesson 7)*

39.
```
    8,921  _____
  − 3,698  _____
```

40.
```
   18,712  _____
 − 14,920  _____
```

41.
```
   $2,681.82
  − 1,732.12
```

42.
```
   $83,712.12
  − 17,821.88
```

16. Solving Division Problems

Division is the inverse operation from multiplication. In multiplication, one factor is multiplied a given number of times to find the product. In division, the dividend is divided by a given number to discover how many times the given number is contained in the dividend.

$$\begin{array}{r} 72 \\ \times\ 28 \\ \hline 2{,}016 \end{array} \qquad \text{divisor}\ \ 28\overline{)2{,}016}\ \ \begin{array}{l} \text{quotient} \\ \\ \text{dividend} \end{array}$$

The number being divided is the dividend, and the number by which it is divided is the divisor. The answer is the quotient. The remainder is an amount that is left over after the division.

There are three ways in which division is usually written. The expressions at the right all mean "240 divided by 6." $\qquad 6\overline{)240} \qquad 240 \div 6 \qquad \dfrac{240}{6}$

Division answers two kinds of questions. One question is, "How many groups of a given size can be made from the number?" The other question is, "What will be the size of each group if a given number of groups is made?" In the first problem below, $10 is divided into equal groups of $2, and the result is 5 groups of $2. In the second problem, $10.00 is divided into 5 equal groups, and the result is $2 in each group.

$$\begin{array}{l} \text{size of} \\ \text{groups} \end{array} \longrightarrow\ 2\overline{)\$10}^{\;5} \longleftarrow\ \begin{array}{l} \text{number} \\ \text{of groups} \end{array} \longrightarrow\ 5\overline{)\$10}^{\;\$2} \longleftarrow\ \begin{array}{l} \text{size} \\ \text{of groups} \end{array}$$

The steps for solving division problems are shown below.

1. **Estimate.** Round 18 to the nearest ten. The result is 20.
2. **Divide.** Think: $65 \div 20 = 3$. Write 3 above the 5 of the dividend because the partial dividend is 65, not 6.
3. **Multiply.** Multiply the divisor by the quotient figure you just wrote: $3 \times 18 = 54$. Write 54 below 65.
4. **Subtract.** Subtract $65 - 54 = 11$. If you cannot subtract because the subtrahend is more than the minuend, you will need to reduce the digit you wrote in the quotient.
5. **Compare.** Is 11 less than 18? Because it is less, go on to step 6. If the difference had been larger than the divisor, it would mean that the digit you wrote in the quotient was too small and would need to be increased.
6. **Bring down.** Bring down the next digit of the dividend (0), and write it beside the 11.
     Repeat these six steps for $110 \div 18$. Continue until the entire problem is solved. If there is a remainder, write it beside the quotient as shown in the example.

$$\begin{array}{r} \$3.61\ \text{R}\ 10\cent \\ 18\overline{)\$65.08} \\ 54 \\ \hline 110 \\ 108 \\ \hline 28 \\ 18 \\ \hline 10 \end{array}$$

To check a division problem, multiply the quotient by the divisor and add any remainder. If all your calculations are correct, the result will be equal to the original dividend.

CLASS PRACTICE

Answer the questions about the division problem below.

$$31\overline{)9,861}$$

a. What do you estimate will be the first quotient figure?

b. Will the first quotient figure be placed above the 9, the 8, or the 6?

c. Will the quotient have 2, 3, or 4 digits?

Solve these problems.

d. $31\overline{)9,861}$ e. $49\overline{)7,500}$ f. $23\overline{)\$93.51}$ g. $16\overline{)\$321.05}$

WRITTEN EXERCISES

A. **Copy and solve these problems. Check your work by multiplying the quotient by the divisor and adding any remainder.**

1. $7\overline{)5,361}$ 2. $6\overline{)4,671}$ 3. $8\overline{)15,843}$ 4. $9\overline{)42,912}$

5. $12\overline{)6,574}$ 6. $16\overline{)3,814}$ 7. $21\overline{)9,843}$ 8. $33\overline{)5,128}$

9. $53\overline{)\$14.82}$ 10. $38\overline{)\$64.21}$ 11. $44\overline{)\$219.54}$ 12. $71\overline{)\$921.66}$

13. $65\overline{)2,481}$ 14. $91\overline{)3,782}$ 15. $78\overline{)23,969}$ 16. $29\overline{)87,283}$

B. **Solve these reading problems.**

17. The Kulp family was called by their church to serve in mission work in Africa. The family decided that since they could not take their canned goods along, they would give them to the other families in their local congregation. If they distributed 288 quarts of canned fruit equally among 9 families, how many quarts did each family receive?

18. When the Kulps returned home from Africa after 3 years, the congregation replenished their canned goods. If 12 families together gave the Kulps 456 quarts and all gave equally, how many quarts did they each give?

19. Father agreed to build a porch for a neighbor. The wall around the porch has 88 ten-inch blocks, which weigh a total of 3,960 pounds. How much does one block weigh?

20. Father ordered 365 twelve-inch blocks for a basement addition. If the blocks weigh 55 pounds each, what is the total weight of the blocks?

21. The truck driver who delivered the blocks told Father that he may legally haul 30,000 pounds on his truck. How many twelve-inch blocks may the truck driver haul if they weigh 55 pounds each? Round your answer to the next lower whole number.

22. Two masons laid 1,556 blocks in two days. On the average, how many blocks did each man lay in one day?

REVIEW EXERCISES

C. Solve these problems mentally. *(Lesson 15)*

23. 26 × 50   **24.** 44 × 25

25. 3 × 9 × 4 × 5   **26.** 6 × 3 × 40

D. Estimate the products. You do not need to find the exact answers. *(Lesson 14)*

27.	92	**28.**	415	**29.**	581	**30.**	4,552
	× 17		× 287		× 714		× 2,311

E. Solve these subtraction problems mentally. *(Lesson 8)*

31. 62 − 28   **32.** 91 − 47   **33.** 165 − 38   **34.** 148 − 65

17. Working With Short and Long Division

Division problems that have one-digit divisors can usually be solved without writing out each step. That is, they can be solved by short division. To solve a problem by short division, work through the division steps mentally and write the quotient one digit at a time.

Example A

$$8\overline{)\$184.09} \quad \$23.01 \text{ R} 1¢$$

Check

$$
\begin{array}{r}
\$23.01 \\
\times \quad 8 \\
\hline
\$184.08 \\
+ \quad .01 \\
\hline
\$184.09
\end{array}
$$

Think: $1 \div 8$ is less than 1; use 18 as the first partial dividend.
$18 \div 8 = 2$ . . . . **Write 2.**

Think: $2 \times 8 = 16; 18 - 16 = 2$. Bring down the 4 beside the 2 (24).
$24 \div 8 = 3$ . . . . **Write 3.**

Think: $3 \times 8 = 24$; $24 - 24 = 0$. Bring down the 0 beside the 0 (00).
$0 \div 8 = 0$ . . . . **Write 0.**

Think: Bring down the 9 beside the 00 (009).
$9 \div 8 = 1$ . . . . **Write 1.**

Think: $1 \times 8 = 8$; $9 - 8 = 1$ . . . . **Write R 1¢.**

The answer is $23.01 R 1¢. Remember to place the decimal point directly above the decimal point in the dividend and to use the dollar and the cent signs. The check confirms that the answer is correct.

Division can be checked by casting out nines. To do this, first find the check numbers for the dividend, the divisor, the quotient, and the remainder. Multiply the check number of the quotient by that of the divisor, add on the check number of the remainder, and cast out nines from the result. The number you obtain must agree with the check number of the dividend.

Example B   (Numbers in parentheses are check numbers.)

$$
\begin{array}{r}
(5) \quad (3) \\
(4) \qquad 14 \text{ R} 93 \\
328\overline{)4,685} \quad (5) \\
\underline{328} \\
1405 \\
\underline{1312} \\
93
\end{array}
$$

Check number of quotient	5
Check number of divisor	× 4
	20
Check number of remainder	+ 3
	23 ⟶ **5**

The check numbers agree, indicating that the problem is solved correctly.

Remember that casting out nines is not a foolproof check. If you mistakenly add or omit zeroes, or transpose digits, casting out nines will indicate that a wrong answer is correct.

CLASS PRACTICE

Use short division to solve these problems. Check by multiplication.

a. $4\overline{)6,456}$ b. $6\overline{)8,781}$ c. $5\overline{)\$35.21}$ d. $6\overline{)26,151}$

Use long division to solve these problems. Check by casting out nines.

    e. 24)4,568   **f.** 58)34,812   **g.** 111)12,141   **h.** 397)$331.22

WRITTEN EXERCISES

A. ***Copy and solve by short division. Check your work, using multiplication. Your paper should show both your answer and your check.***

    1. 2)4,568   **2.** 3)6,831   **3.** 4)5,456   **4.** 5)8,772

    5. 6)$181.51   **6.** 7)$18.23   **7.** 8)$34.32   **8.** 9)$82.12

    9. 7)4,583   **10.** 8)8,312   **11.** 4)$145.14   **12.** 6)$421.21

B. ***Copy and solve by long division. Check your work by casting out nines. Show your check numbers.***

    13. 32)6,712   **14.** 51)8,314   **15.** 46)$78.12   **16.** 78)$91.21

    17. 121)8,583   **18.** 192)11,352   **19.** 211)$35.78   **20.** 415)$82.98

C. ***Solve these reading problems. Some of them can be done by short division.***

21. Seven bushels of barley weighs 336 pounds. How much does the barley weigh per bushel?

22. Nine bushels of wheat weighs 549 pounds. How much does the wheat weigh per bushel?

23. If Father bought 1 ton of shelled corn at 56 pounds per bushel, how many bushels of corn did he buy? Write the remainder as a fraction.

24. The weight of oats is 32 pounds per bushel. If Father bought 2 tons of oats, how many bushels did he buy?

25. How much does 2,000 bushels of shelled corn weigh at 56 pounds per bushel?

26. How much does 1,500 bushels of barley weigh at 48 pounds per bushel?

REVIEW EXERCISES

D. ***Solve these problems mentally.*** *(Lessons 14, 15)*

27. 4 × 3 × 50   **28.** 50 × 28   **29.** 25 × 48   **30.** 22 × 15

E. ***Solve these problems by horizontal multiplication.*** *(Lesson 13)*

31. 7 × 65   **32.** 6 × 342   **33.** 9 × 721   **34.** 4 × 4,523

F. ***Write these numbers with words as you would read them.*** *(Lesson 1)*

35. 245,006,000   **36.** 14,050,000,000,000

18. More Challenging Long Division

All long division problems are solved by using the same steps, no matter how many digits are in the dividend and the divisor. The steps shown in Lesson 16 will solve a problem with a four-digit divisor just as well as a problem with a two-digit divisor. However, longer dividends and divisors present more possibilities for errors. Accuracy is very important in long division, and checking by multiplying or by casting out nines should be a standard practice.

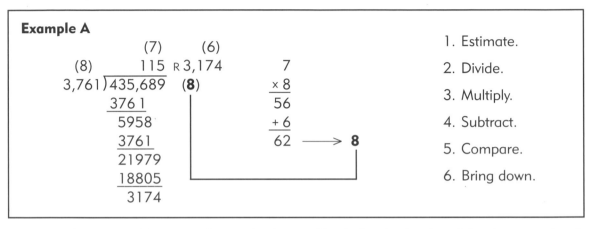

Long division problems can be made shorter if both the dividend and the divisor end with a zero or with several zeroes. In that case, cross out the same number of zeroes in both the dividend and the divisor. But if there is a remainder, you must annex as many zeroes to the remainder as you crossed out in the dividend.

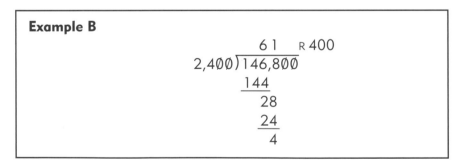

CLASS PRACTICE

Solve these problems. Simplify any that have ending zeroes.

a. 347)169,435   b. 2,147)457,182   c. 3,400)625,000

WRITTEN EXERCISES

A. *Copy and solve by long division. Check your work by casting out nines. Show your check numbers.*

1. 82)6,583
2. 93)8,215
3. 26)32,125
4. 38)54,912

5. 378)4,313
6. 721)18,812
7. 831)45,812
8. 641)85,215

9. 1,122)45,231
10. 2,314)42,812
11. 3,215)57,932

12. 4,101)$4,324.32
13. 4,200)3,100,000
14. 5,200)4,600,000

15. 6,000)4,500,000
16. 5,000)3,800,000

B. *Solve these reading problems.*

17. Brother Weaver and his wife drove to Guatemala to visit their son and the congregations there. Their small car went 7,464 miles on 311 gallons of gasoline. How many miles was this per gallon?

18. A building contractor is estimating the cost of the outdoor concrete work in a housing development. His estimates are $732 for each residence and a total of $41,724 for the entire development. How many houses are to be built?

19. The Burkhart family purchased 5 acres of land to build a house and plant a truck patch. They paid $65,000 for the land. How much did they pay per acre?

20. Before they purchased this land, the Burkharts had considered buying 4 acres priced at $62,200. What was the selling price per acre?

21. The Burkhart family is thinking of building a house with 1,600 square feet of floor space. A contractor quoted the price of the house at $70,000. What is the price per square foot?

22. Another contractor told the Burkharts that he could build a house with 1,800 square feet for $81,000. What is his price per square foot?

REVIEW EXERCISES

C. *Use short division to solve these problems.* (Lesson 17)

23. 4)6,151   **24.** 6)7,898   **25.** 8)13,141   **26.** 9)43,212

D. *Refer to this division problem to do exercises 27–30.* (Lesson 16)

$$\overset{8,892 \quad \text{R } 133}{389)\overline{3,459,121}}$$

27. Write the quotient.   **28.** Write the divisor.

29. Write the remainder.   **30.** Write the dividend.

E. *Estimate the products. You do not need to find exact answers.* (Lesson 14)

31.   345   **32.**   481   **33.**   1,154   **34.**   4,356
               × 312   × 223   × 2,812   × 2,811

F. *Write the place value of each underlined digit.* (Lesson 2)

35. 4,500,000,000   **36.** 425,000,000,000,000

19. Finding Averages

The average of a group of numbers is a summary of the numbers as a group. An average is calculated by adding the numbers together and then dividing the sum by the number of addends. Two other terms that mean the same as "average" are **arithmetic average** and **arithmetic mean**. (*Arithmetic* is pronounced /ăr´ith·met´ik/ in these terms.)

An average helps you to better understand a group of numbers. It shows what the numbers would be if they were all the same. For example, each grade on your report card shows what your grades in that subject would have been if they had all been the same throughout the marking period. This helps you and your parents to understand how well you are doing with your school work. Think of how hard it would be to compare all your grades for this marking period with all those for the previous period. It is much simpler to compare averages.

In finding averages, the division does not always come out even. The remainder is often expressed as a fraction, with the remainder as the numerator and the divisor as the denominator.

Find the average of these numbers. $85, 74, 79, 77, 83, 91$	$\begin{array}{r} 85 \\ 74 \\ 79 \\ 77 \\ 83 \\ +91 \\ \hline 489 \end{array}$ $\quad$ $81\frac{3}{6} = 81\frac{1}{2}$ $\quad$ $6\overline{)489}$

The remainder should be expressed as a fraction only when it is logical to do so. For example, if the numbers in the box refer to the high temperatures on six days, it would be logical to express the average as $81\frac{1}{2}°$. But if the numbers refer to people, it would not be logical to give the average as $81\frac{1}{2}$ people. Instead, the average should be rounded to the nearest whole number and stated as 82 people.

CLASS PRACTICE

Find the average of each set of numbers.

a. 8, 9, 11, 7, 4, 9

b. 18, 19, 14, 21, 18, 0

c. 58, 69, 55, 43, 71, 69

d. 98%, 88%, 84%, 92%, 83%, 99%

WRITTEN EXERCISES

A. *Find the average of each set of numbers. Express remainders as fractions.*

1. 89, 93, 75

2. 341, 415, 398

3. 93, 81, 95, 93

4. 125, 132, 120, 131

5. 165, 178, 161, 159, 175

6. 215, 205, 216, 209, 224

7. 89, 68, 43, 77, 55, 58

8. 88, 86, 91, 93, 96, 99, 76

9. 745, 658, 689, 777, 815

10. 834, 919, 991, 865, 685

11. 3,415; 4,563; 4,900; 5,113

12. 7,812; 7,325; 7,812; 8,192

B. *Solve these reading problems.*

13. During a cold week in January, the daily high temperatures were as follows: Sunday, 6°; Monday, 9°; Tuesday, 3°; Wednesday, 8°; Thursday, 12°; Friday, 14°; and Saturday, 17°. What was the average high temperature for the week? Round your answer to the nearest whole degree.

14. Church attendance for the month of October was as follows: 115, 121, 107, 111, and 139. What was the average attendance?

15. Over the last five years, the yield of corn per acre on the Witmer farm was 188 bushels, 176 bushels, 179 bushels, 94 bushels, and 144 bushels. What was the average yield per acre? Round your answer to the nearest whole bushel.

16. This year Father harvested 7,564 bushels of corn from a 65-acre field. What was the average yield per acre? Round your answer to the nearest whole bushel.

17. About 43 gallons of sap from sugar maple trees must be boiled off to make one gallon of maple syrup. Maple Hills Sugarbush collected 17,888 gallons of sap this spring. How many gallons of syrup could they make from it?

18. Maple Hills Sugarbush tapped large sugar maples that produced an average of 48 gallons of sap per tree. How many trees were tapped by Maple Hills Sugarbush? (See problem 17.) Round your answer to the nearest whole number.

REVIEW EXERCISES

C. *Solve these division problems, and check by casting out nines. Show your check numbers.* (Lesson 18)

19. $476\overline{)216,821}$

20. $1,011\overline{)454,812}$

D. *Use short division to solve these problems.* (Lesson 17)

21. $6\overline{)32,124}$ **22.** $5\overline{)13,812}$ **23.** $8\overline{)71,912}$ **24.** $9\overline{)14,123}$

E. *Solve these multiplication problems mentally.* (Lesson 15)

25. $3 \times 6 \times 40$ **26.** 15×22 **27.** 50×32 **28.** 25×32

F. *Round these numbers to the places indicated.* (Lesson 3)

29. 4,561,012 *(million)*

30. 35,001,100 *(ten million)*

20. Solving Division Problems Mentally

In Lesson 15 you used the double-and-divide method as a shortcut to solve multiplication problems mentally. For mental division, the divide-and-divide shortcut is a method somewhat like the double-and-divide method. But instead of dividing one number and multiplying the other, both the dividend and the divisor are divided by the same number. This means that the dividend and the divisor must have a common factor.

Example A	**Example B**
For 144 ÷ 16, think: 144 ÷ 2 = 72, and 16 ÷ 2 = 8 72 ÷ 8 = 9	For 120 ÷ 15, think: 120 ÷ 3 = 40, and 15 ÷ 3 = 5 40 ÷ 5 = 8

Some division problems can be simplified by doubling both numbers instead of dividing them. This double-and-double method works especially well for dividing by 5 and by 50. To divide mentally by 5 or by 50, double the dividend and the divisor. This simplifies the problem because you are then dividing by 10 (2 × 5) or by 100 (2 × 50).

Example C	**Example D**
For 95 ÷ 5, think: 95 × 2 = 190, and 5 × 2 = 10 190 ÷ 10 = 19	For 750 ÷ 50, think: 750 × 2 = 1,500, and 50 × 2 = 100 1,500 ÷ 100 = 15

A related approach can be used for dividing by 25. To divide mentally by 25, multiply both the dividend and the divisor by 4 because 25 × 4 = 100.

Example E
For   400 ÷ 25, think: 400 × 4 = 1,600, and 25 × 4 = 100 1,600 ÷ 100 = 16

Following are some rules that will help you quickly determine whether a number is divisible by 2, by 3, by 4, by 5, by 6, and by 9.

Divisor **Rule**	**Example**
2 A number is divisible by 2 if it is an even number.	478 is divisible by 2 because it is an even number.
3 A number is divisible by 3 if the sum of its digits is divisible by 3.	642 is divisible by 3 because the sum of its digits (12) is divisible by 3.

Divisor	Rule	Example
4	A number is divisible by 4 if the last two digits are divisible by 4 or are zeroes. Learn to recognize these multiples of 4: 52, 56, 60, 64, 68, 72, 76, 92, 96.	916 is divisible by 4 because the last two digits (16) are divisible by 4.
5	A number is divisible by 5 if it ends with 0 or 5.	835 is divisible by 5 because it ends with 5.
6	A number is divisible by 6 if it is even and the sum of its digits is divisible by 3.	726 is divisible by 6 because it is even and the sum of its digits (15) is divisible by 3.
9	A number is divisible by 9 if the sum of its digits is divisible by 9.	783 is divisible by 9 because the sum of its digits (18) is divisible by 9.

CLASS PRACTICE

Use the divide-and-divide method to solve these problems mentally.

   a. $112 \div 16$ b. $72 \div 18$ c. $132 \div 22$ d. $98 \div 14$

Use the best shortcut to solve each problem mentally.

   e. $125 \div 5$ f. $220 \div 5$ g. $400 \div 5$ h. $450 \div 50$

   i. $600 \div 50$ j. $950 \div 50$ k. $600 \div 25$ l. $700 \div 25$

Use the rules of divisibility to answer these questions.

   m. Is 724 divisible by 2?   by 3?   by 4?   by 5?

   n. Is 615 divisible by 2?   by 3?   by 6?   by 9?

   o. Is 342 divisible by 4?   by 5?   by 6?   by 9?

WRITTEN EXERCISES

A. Use the divide-and-divide method to solve these problems mentally.

   1. $108 \div 18$ **2.** $96 \div 16$ **3.** $120 \div 8$ **4.** $120 \div 24$

   5. $144 \div 18$ **6.** $180 \div 12$ **7.** $242 \div 22$ **8.** $168 \div 14$

B. Use the double-and-double method to solve these problems mentally.

   9. $85 \div 5$ **10.** $115 \div 5$ **11.** $145 \div 5$ **12.** $440 \div 5$

   13. $300 \div 5$ **14.** $325 \div 5$ **15.** $650 \div 5$ **16.** $850 \div 5$

   17. $450 \div 50$ **18.** $600 \div 50$ **19.** $650 \div 50$ **20.** $800 \div 50$

   21. $900 \div 50$ **22.** $850 \div 50$ **23.** $1,200 \div 50$ **24.** $1,600 \div 50$

C. Use the shortcut for dividing by 25 to solve these problems mentally.

   25. $500 \div 25$ **26.** $800 \div 25$ **27.** $1,000 \div 25$ **28.** $1,200 \div 25$

D. Write all the divisors from the group in parentheses by which each number is divisible. (2, 3, 4, 5, 6, 9, 10)

   Example: 532   *Answer:* 2, 4   *Example:* 540   *Answer:* 2, 3, 4, 5, 6, 9, 10

   29. 519   **30.** 320   **31.** 639   **32.** 588

E. Solve these reading problems. Do numbers 33–36 mentally.

33. Carolyn has washed and folded 128 towels. She must divide them equally among 16 rooms in the nursing home where she works. How many towels go to each room?

34. One Friday evening, Carolyn rode home with the Landises to visit her family for the weekend. The car traveled 320 miles and used 16 gallons of gasoline. What was the fuel consumption in miles per gallon?

35. The Nolts drove to their aunt's wedding in a distant state. They spent 50 hours traveling and drove 2,400 miles. What was their average speed in miles per hour?

36. Father calculated that the car used one gallon of gasoline for each 25 miles it traveled. How much fuel did it take to go 2,400 miles?

37. In Fairbanks, Alaska, the average temperatures during the summer months are 59°F in June, 62°F in July, and 57°F in August. In Miami, Florida, the average temperatures in the same months are 81°F in June, 83°F in July, and 83°F in August. On the average, how many degrees warmer is it in Miami than in Fairbanks during the summer months? Round both averages to the nearest degree for computing.

38. In Boston, Massachusetts, the average temperatures during the winter months are 34°F in December, 30°F in January, and 31°F in February. In Dallas, Texas, the average temperatures for the same months are 48°F in December, 44°F in January, and 49°F in February. On the average, how many degrees warmer is it in Dallas than in Boston during the winter months? Round both averages to the nearest degree for computing.

REVIEW EXERCISES

F. Find the average of each set of numbers. *(Lesson 19)*

39. 12, 16, 14, 13, 19   40. 51, 89, 66, 48, 38

G. Copy and solve by long division. Check by casting out nines, and show your check numbers. Label each part of the problems, including answers. *(Lessons 16, 17)*

41. _____   431)615,611 _____   42. _____   515)881,214 _____

H. Copy and multiply. Check by casting out nines, and show your check numbers. Label each part of the problems, including answers and intermediate steps. *(Lesson 12)*

43.   4,781 _____   44.   5,352 _____
    × 589 _____   × 682 _____

I. Write the Roman numerals as Arabic numerals and the Arabic numerals as Roman numerals. *(Lesson 4)*

45. CLXVIII   46. MCCLXXXIV   47. 479   48. 616

21. Working With Graphs: The Picture Graph

The Zimmerman Family
Major Household Expenses
January, 1992

Groceries	$ $ $ $ $ $ $ $ $ $ $ $ $
Housing	$ $ $ $ $ $ $ $ $ $
Automobile	$ $ $ $ $ $ $
Electricity	$ $ $ $
Clothing	$ $ $ $

$ = $25

Reading Picture Graphs

A picture graph uses pictures instead of words to portray facts. Each symbol on a picture graph represents a given quantity. The greater the number of symbols, the larger is the quantity represented.

A picture graph is beneficial because it shows how the facts are related to each other. In the graph above, it is easy to see that the Zimmermans are spending about twice as much for food as for automobile expenses, and about three times as much for food as for electricity or clothing. These conclusions can be drawn by comparing the number of symbols in each set.

Hymns Written by Several Hymn Writers

Fanny Crosby	𝄞 𝄞 𝄞 𝄞 𝄞 𝄞 𝄞 𝄞 𝄞 𝄞 𝄞 𝄞 𝄞 𝄞 𝄞
Charles Wesley	𝄞 𝄞 𝄞 𝄞 𝄞 𝄞 𝄞 𝄞 𝄞 𝄞 𝄞 𝄞 𝄞
Isaac Watts	𝄞 𝄞

𝄞 = 500 hymns

Source: *World Book Encyclopedia*

Drawing Picture Graphs

Making a picture graph requires neatness and accuracy. A neatly prepared graph has symbols that are all the same size and are in straight rows and in straight columns. Following are eight steps for making a picture graph.

1. Collect the information that you will show on your graph. Organize the information from the largest amount to the smallest.

2. Choose an appropriate symbol. Usually it is a simple picture or diagram that suggests the subject of the graph.

3. Decide how many things each symbol will represent. The number represented by each symbol should be large enough so that not too many symbols are needed, yet small enough so that the smallest number will have at least one symbol.

4. Decide how many symbols will be needed for each fact. A part of a symbol will sometimes be needed. (In the picture graph of the hymn writers, Isaac Watts wrote 761 songs and psalms. Because 761 is about halfway between 500 [1 symbol] and 1,000 [2 symbols], $1\frac{1}{2}$ symbols are used.)

5. Make your picture graph, taking enough time to draw it neatly and accurately.

6. Give your graph a title that explains clearly what information you are showing.

7. At the bottom of the graph, explain what the symbols represent.

8. If you obtained your information from an encyclopedia or another reference book, include the source at the bottom of the graph.

Number of Households in Some Latin American Countries

Puerto Rico

Paraguay

Costa Rica

Panama

Honduras

= 100,000 Households

Source: *Britannica Book of the Year, 1996*

CLASS PRACTICE

Refer to the last graph in the lesson to answer these questions.

a. What is the title of the graph?

b. How many households does Puerto Rico have?

c. How many households does Paraguay have?

d. How many households are in Costa Rica and Panama together?

e. How many more households does Costa Rica have than Honduras?

f. Which country has half as many households as Puerto Rico?

WRITTEN EXERCISES

A. *Refer to the following graph to answer the questions below.*

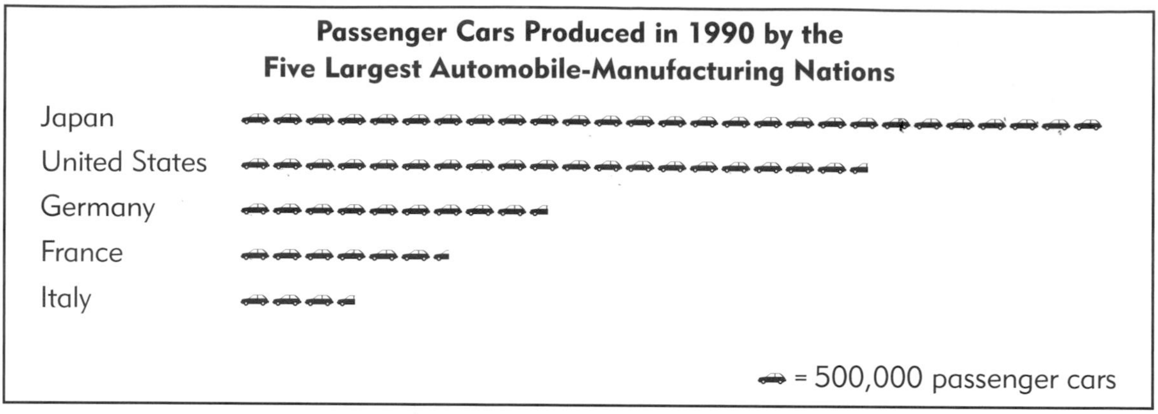

**Passenger Cars Produced in 1990 by the
Five Largest Automobile-Manufacturing Nations**

Japan

United States

Germany

France

Italy

🚗 = 500,000 passenger cars

Source: *World Almanac, 1992*

1. What is the title of the graph above?

2. Which country manufactured the most automobiles in 1990?

3. How many passenger cars did Italy produce in 1990?

4. How many more passenger cars did Japan produce in 1990 than the United States did?

5. How many passenger cars did Germany produce in 1990?

6. United States manufactured how many times as many passenger cars as France did?

B. *Construct picture graphs based on the following information. Use only whole and half symbols.*

7. The number of students in six schools. Use 1 symbol to represent 10 students.

> White Rock 62
> Pleasant Hill 59
> Indian Valley 42
> Narrow Valley 31
> Postville 20
> Mountainville 12

8. The number of books in five area libraries. Use 1 symbol of a book to represent 10,000 books. Use only whole and half symbols on the graph.

> Mount White 147,506
> Silver Branch 82,491
> Carterville 65,012
> Flemington 30,986
> Blue Point 23,603

C. Solve these reading problems.

9. What is the average number of students in the schools listed in exercise 7?

10. What is the average number of books in the libraries listed in exercise 8?

11. In the United States, 387,000 houses were built in 1910, 937,000 in 1925, and 221,000 in 1935. How many more houses were built in 1925 than in the average of the three years?

12. In 1945, 326,000 houses were built in the United States; in 1965, 1,510,000 houses were built; and in 1985, 1,745,000 houses were built. From 1945 to 1965, how much greater was the increase in houses built than the increase from 1965 to 1985?

13. Samuel and James would like to earn $69.50 to buy a bicycle. Samuel has already earned $23.60, and James has earned $32.15. How much more do they need?

14. The Ledville Mennonite School has the following numbers of students in each room: grades 1–3, 12 boys and 10 girls; grades 4 and 5, 10 boys and 11 girls; and grades 7–10, 9 boys and 6 girls. How many more boys than girls are in the school? Try to solve this problem mentally.

REVIEW EXERCISES

D. Use the rules of divisibility to answer these questions. *(Lesson 20)*

15. Is 466 divisible by 3? by 5? by 9?

16. Is 789 divisible by 2? by 3? by 6?

E. Use division shortcuts to solve these problems. *(Lesson 20)*

17. $800 \div 25$ **18.** $168 \div 24$

F. Find the average of each set. Express remainders as fractions. *(Lesson 19)*

19. 32, 35, 31, 37, 33 **20.** 178, 175, 192, 121

G. Solve these problems by short division. *(Lesson 17)*

21. $3\overline{)43,182}$ **22.** $5\overline{)17,821}$ **23.** $7\overline{)21,421}$ **24.** $9\overline{)17,281}$

H. Solve these problems by horizontal multiplication. *(Lesson 12)*

25. 8×64 **26.** 8×415 **27.** 7×526 **28.** $8 \times 2,712$

I. Copy and solve these addition problems. *(Lesson 5)*

29.
```
   23,182
   31,281
   16,822
 + 14,518
```

30.
```
  $14,182.31
 + 22,281.85
```

22. Reading Problems: Choosing the Correct Operation

Reading problems need to be evaluated carefully in order to solve them correctly. After you read the problem, ask yourself: "What question is being asked?" The next step is to choose the information that will be used to solve the problem. The third step is the one that is stressed in this lesson: "What operation or operations are needed to find the answer?"

To know which operation or operations to use, you must understand what each operation does. Reading problems often contain key words that hint at the operation required.

Addition is the combining of two or more amounts. Addition is usually indicated if the reading problem asks a question such as "How many were there in all?"

Multiplication is adding the same number repeatedly. Unlike addition, multiplication cannot be used to combine different numbers. If the same number is being added repeatedly, use multiplication. Reading problems that are solved by multiplication usually state the number of items and a number such as the price of each item. Then the question asks for the total.

Subtraction is finding how much larger one number is than another. Reading problems that are solved by subtraction often ask questions beginning with "How much larger," "How much more," or "What is the difference."

Division is finding how many times one number is contained in another. It is different from subtraction in that subtraction shows *how many more* one number is than another but division shows *how many times more* one number is than another. Reading problems that are solved by division often use a phrase such as "How many times larger," or they give a total that is to be broken into several equal groups.

CLASS PRACTICE

Solve these reading problems, being careful to use the correct operations.

a. What is the cost of 18 pounds of blueberries if the price is $0.44 per pound?

b. How many pounds of corn are on a pickup truck if the truck weighed 4,540 pounds when empty and 5,360 pounds when loaded?

c. How far did Brother Raymond travel in 5 hours if his average speed was 52 miles per hour?

d. Brother Raymond used 33 gallons of gasoline on the entire 726-mile trip. How many miles per gallon did his car travel?

WRITTEN EXERCISES

A. Solve these reading problems. Be careful to use the correct operation or operations.

1. Brother David paid $2,200 per acre for a 140-acre farm. How much did he pay for the entire farm?

2. Brother David harvested 4,825 bushels of corn in one cornfield, 3,678 bushels in the second field, 4,116 bushels in the third field, and 3,721 bushels in the fourth field. How many bushels of corn did he harvest in all?

3. In 1991, the population of Canada was estimated to be 27,296,859. What was the average population of the 12 provinces and territories?

4. Ontario, a large province of Canada, had an estimated population of 10,084,885 in 1991. Ranking second and third are the provinces Quebec and British Columbia, which had estimated populations of 6,895,963 and 3,282,061 respectively. How many more people lived in Quebec and British Columbia than in Ontario?

5. John worked in an orchard 6 hours on Monday, 7 hours on Tuesday, 7 hours on Wednesday, 6 hours on Thursday, and 5 hours on Friday. What was the total amount he earned if his wage was $4.75 per hour?

6. How much more will 5 pounds of butter cost at $1.89 per pound than 5 pounds of margarine at $0.52 per pound?

REVIEW EXERCISES

B. Construct picture graphs based on the following information. Use only whole and half symbols. *(Lesson 21)*

7. Quarts of food frozen by the Weaver family.

Corn 175   Lima beans 65
Beans 120   Kidney beans 40
Peas 105

Let one symbol represent 10 quarts. Use the outline of a freezer bag for your symbol.

8. Number of men of war in the five largest tribes of Israel (Numbers 1 and 2).

Judah 74,600   Zebulon 57,400
Dan 62,700   Issachar 54,400
Simeon 59,300

Let one symbol represent 10,000 men. Use a stick figure for your symbol.

C. Use the rules of divisibility to answer these questions. *(Lesson 20)*

9. Is 742 divisible by 2?   by3?   by 4?   10. Is 576 divisible by 5?   by 6?   by 9?

D. Do these divisions mentally. *(Lesson 20)*

11. $112 \div 14$ 12. $154 \div 22$ 13. $145 \div 5$
14. $650 \div 50$ 15. $1,400 \div 50$ 16. $600 \div 25$

E. Estimate the answers to these problems. You do not need to find the exact answers. *(Lesson 14)*

17.	18.	19.	20.
48	215	476	3,200
× 36	× 178	× 315	× 1,709

F. Solve these addition problems mentally. *(Lesson 6)*

21. $3 + 8 + 1 + 9 + 6 + 4$ 22. $3 + 8 + 7 + 1 + 8 + 9 + 2$
23. $47 + 38$ 24. $43 + 38$ 25. $68 + 49$ 26. $162 + 48$

23. Chapter 2 Review

A. Solve these problems. Check by casting out nines, and show your check numbers. Label the parts of problems 1 and 13, including the answers. *(Lessons 12, 13, 16, 17)*

1.	256 ____	2.	452	3.	729	4.	482
	× 8 ____		× 6		× 78		× 83

5.	52	6.	64	7.	$3.27	8.	$8.24
	× 14		× 17		× 48		× 62

9.	1,651	10.	2,381	11.	3,616	12.	4,271
	× 327		× 458		× 1,311		× 1,512

13. ____ 6)3,427 ____   14. 8)6,923   15. 31)17,721

16. 58)36,111   17. 41)$13.77   18. 48)$57.53

19. 400)72,300   20. 2,500)780,000   21. 301)2,371

22. 215)4,821   23. 1,132)21,643   24. 2,253)71,482

B. Solve by horizontal multiplication and short division. *(Lessons 12, 17)*

25. 7 × 46   26. 8 × 58   27. 6 × 436   28. 5 × 898

29. 3)2,632   30. 4)7,211   31. 5)6,723   32. 8)8,832

C. Solve these problems mentally. *(Lesson 14, 15, 20)*

33. 63 × 100   34. 49 × 1,000
35. 43 × 20   36. 11 × 60
37. 22 × 15   38. 82 × 5
39. 16 × 50   40. 24 × 25
41. 4 × 7 × 5   42. 126 ÷ 18

43. $264 \div 22$

44. $125 \div 5$

45. $850 \div 50$

46. $600 \div 25$

47. $1,100 \div 25$

48. $2 \times 70 \times 5 \times 3$

D. Estimate the products to these multiplication problems. *(Lesson 14)*

49.	**50.**	**51.**	**52.**
78	82	482	3,841
× 32	× 68	× 287	× 2,117

E. Find the average of each set of numbers. Express any remainders as fractions. *(Lesson 19)*

53. 38, 46, 52, 61, 48

54. 148, 165, 159, 135, 172

55. 472, 418, 466, 421, 489

56. 1,462; 1,683; 1,890; 2,126

F. Write all the divisors from the group in brackets by which each number is divisible. [2, 3, 4, 5, 6, 9, 10] *(Lesson 20)*

57. 432

58. 420

59. 631

60. 324

G. Refer to the graph to answer the questions below. *(Lesson 21)*

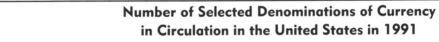

Number of Selected Denominations of Currency in Circulation in the United States in 1991

1-Dollar Bills

2-Dollar Bills

5-Dollar Bills

10-Dollar Bills

= 500,000,000 bills

Source: *World Almanac 1992*

61. About how many times more one-dollar bills than two-dollar bills were in circulation?

62. About how many one-dollar bills were in circulation?

63. About how many ten-dollar bills were in circulation?

64. About how many five-dollar bills were in circulation?

H. Solve these reading problems. Be careful to use the right operation or operations. *(Lesson 22)*

65. One Sunday the offering was $2,456.78 and the attendance was 115. What was the average amount given by each person? Round your answer to the nearest cent.

66. The Miller family has a large hospital expense. The church district decided to provide $25,500 to help them pay the bill. If the average contribution of 415 members in the church district is $70, how much will be collected for the need?

67. If the district-wide offering for the $25,500 need amounted to $28,700, how much money was remaining?

68. Harrison County, where David lives, became a county 168 years ago. If David is 14 years old, how many times older is his county than he is?

69. David's home state is 30 years older than his home county (problem 68). If David's home state is 11 times as old as David's brother is, how old is David's brother?

70. In 1990, the three most populous counties in Pennsylvania were Philadelphia County, with 1,585,577 people; Allegheny County, with 1,336,449; and Montgomery County, with 678,111. How many more people lived in Allegheny and Montgomery counties than in Philadelphia County?

---

24. **Chapter 2 Test**

Chapter 3

Using English Measures

And they did all eat, and were filled: and they took up of the broken meat
that was left seven baskets full.
(Matthew 15:37)

25. Units of Linear Measure

Linear measure is the measure of length or distance along a straight line. In Bible times, people made much use of the arms and hands for linear measure. The cubit was the distance from a man's elbow to the tip of his longest finger. This distance was used to measure larger objects such as buildings. The span was the distance on a man's outstretched hand from the tip of his thumb to the tip of his smallest finger. The handbreadth was the breadth of a man's hand at the base of the four fingers.

Using the arms and hands to measure short distances was quite convenient in that one always had his measuring tools with him! But such a system has a serious weakness, for the length of these units can vary widely from one person to another. To solve this problem, people developed standard units of measure.

A standard unit is a unit that is established at a specified amount. An inch is an exact unit. Its length never varies because it is established by a fixed standard. The same is true for the foot, the yard, the mile, and all other standard units.

Many countries of the world use the standard units in the metric system. In the United States, English units of measure are most commonly used. The units of English linear measure are listed below.

English Units of Linear Measure	
Common Units (Know these relationships.) 12 inches (in.) = 1 foot (ft.) 3 feet = 1 yard (yd.) 36 inches = 1 yard 5,280 feet = 1 mile (mi.) 1,760 yards = 1 mile	*Less Common Units* 1 rod = $16\frac{1}{2}$ feet 1 league = 3 miles

To change from a larger unit of measure to a smaller unit, multiply by the number of smaller units in the larger unit. To change from a smaller unit to a larger one, divide by the number of smaller units in the larger unit.

Example A	Example B
To change from larger to smaller units, multiply. 19 feet = _____ inches 19 × 12 inches in 1 foot = 228 inches	To change from smaller to larger units, divide. 240 inches = _____ feet 240 ÷ 12 inches in 1 foot = 20 feet

Example C	Example D
To change a compound measure to the smaller unit, change the larger unit to the smaller unit by multiplying. Add the smaller units to that product. 8 feet 4 inches = ___ inches $8 \times 12 = 96; \quad 96 + 4 = 100$ inches	To change a compound measure to the larger unit, change the smaller unit to the larger unit by writing a fraction. The numerator of the fraction is the number of units, and the denominator is the number of smaller units in one larger unit. Reduce the fraction to lowest terms. 8 feet 4 inches = $8\frac{4}{12}$ feet = $8\frac{1}{3}$ feet

CLASS PRACTICE

Change these measures as indicated.

a. 17 ft. = _____ in.

b. 16 yd. = _____ ft.

c. 156 in. = _____ ft.

d. 3 mi. = _____ ft.

e. 93 ft. = _____ yd.

f. 504 in. = _____ yd.

g. 4 ft. 7 in. = _____ ft.

h. 7 yd. 2 ft. = _____ ft.

WRITTEN EXERCISES

A. Write the measurement of each line in inches.

1. _____

2. _____

3. _____

4. _____

5. _____

6. _____

B. Write the abbreviation for each English unit of linear measure.

7. inch

8. foot

9. yard

10. mile

C. Change these measures as indicated.

11. 3 yd. = _____ ft.

12. 27 ft. = _____ yd.

13. 5 mi. = _____ ft.

14. 4 mi. = _____ yd.

15. 2 rods = _____ ft.

16. 5 leagues = _____ mi.

17. 576 in. = _____ ft.

18. 7 mi. = _____ ft.

19. 648 in. = _____ yd.

20. 126 ft. = _____ yd.

21. 444 in. = _____ ft.

22. 432 in. = _____ yd.

D. Change these compound measures as indicated.

23. 3 ft. 3 in. = _____ ft.

24. 3 ft. 3 in. = _____ in.

25. 4 ft. 10 in. = _____ in.

26. 7 ft. 2 in. = _____ ft.

27. 5 yd. 1 ft. = _____ yd.

28. 5 yd. 18 in. = _____ yd.

E. Solve these reading problems.

29. How many 9-inch boards can Dwight cut from a 3-foot piece of lumber?

30. The deepest parts of the ocean are over 6 miles deep. How many feet are in 6 miles?

31. The southern boundary of the Miller property is 325 yards from the kitchen door. If Marlin walks in a straight line from the kitchen door to this boundary and then returns to the kitchen door, how many feet does he walk?

32. David measured the living room of the Troyer home and found it to be 180 inches long. What is its length in yards?

33. How many inches longer is a board 5 yards long than a board 12 feet 9 inches long?

34. How many feet longer is a board 168 inches long than a board 2 yards long?

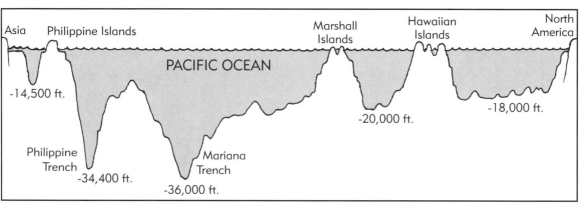

In his hand are the deep places of the earth: . . .The sea is his, and he made it.
Psalm 95:4, 5

REVIEW EXERCISES

F. Use the rules of divisibility to answer these questions. (Lesson 20)

35. Is 489 divisible by 2?   by 3?   by 4?

36. Is 555 divisible by 5?   by 6?   by 9?

G. Solve these division problems mentally. (Lesson 20)

37. $900 \div 25$ **38.** $1,200 \div 50$ **39.** $3,000 \div 50$

40. $168 \div 24$ **41.** $2,000 \div 25$ **42.** $128 \div 16$

H. Solve these subtraction problems mentally. (Lesson 8)

43. $73 - 47$ **44.** $65 - 38$ **45.** $91 - 67$ **46.** $84 - 27$

EXTRA CREDIT

47. The distance from the earth to the sun is approximately 93,000,000 miles. How many feet are in 93,000,000 miles?

26. Units of Weight

There are three common English units of weight: the ounce, the pound, and the ton.

English Units of Weight	
16 ounces (oz.) = 1 pound (lb.)	2,000 pounds (lb.) = 1 ton

There are several other English units of weight. The long ton is 2,240 pounds. Iron ore and coal are measured at mines by the long ton. The long ton is often used in shipping. However, when *ton* is used without *long* or *short,* it is assumed to mean the short ton, or 2,000 pounds.

The rules for changing larger measures to smaller measures and smaller measures to larger measures are the same as for changing linear measures.

> **To change from larger to smaller units, multiply.**
> **To change from smaller to larger units, divide.**

Example A	16 tons = _____ pounds
	16 × 2,000 pounds in 1 ton = 32,000 pounds
Example B	176 ounces = _____ pounds
	176 ÷ 16 ounces in 1 pound = 11 pounds
Example C	24 ounces = _____ pounds
	$\frac{24}{16}$ pounds = $\frac{3}{2}$ pounds = $1\frac{1}{2}$ pounds

The same rules also apply for changing compound English weights to the smaller unit and to the larger unit.

Example D	4 pounds 5 ounces = _____ ounces
	4 × 16 = 64; 64 + 5 = 69 ounces
Example E	4 pounds 5 ounces = _____ pounds = $4\frac{5}{16}$ pounds

CLASS PRACTICE

Change these measures.

a. 5 lb. = _____ oz.

b. 5 tons = _____ lb.

c. 12,000 lb. = _____ tons

d. 8 lb. 12 oz. = _____ oz.

e. 6 lb. 10 oz. = _____ oz.

f. 3 tons 800 lb. = _____ lb.

g. 40 oz. = _____ lb.

h. 7,000 lb. = _____ tons

WRITTEN EXERCISES

A. *Change these measures.*

1. 7 tons = _____ lb.
2. 19 lb. = _____ oz.
3. 256 oz. = _____ lb.
4. 11,000 lb. = _____ tons
5. 25 lb. = _____ oz.
6. 75 tons = _____ lb.
7. 102 oz. = _____ lb.
8. 35 lb. = _____ oz.
9. 9,000 lb. = _____ tons
10. 768 oz. = _____ lb.
11. 100 lb. = _____ oz.
12. 17,000 lb. = _____ tons

B. *Change these compound measures.*

13. 3 lb. 5 oz. = _____ oz.
14. 3 tons 700 lb. = _____ lb.
15. 7 lb. 9 oz. = _____ oz.
16. 12 tons 1,000 lb. = _____ lb.
17. 12 lb. 8 oz. = _____ oz.
18. 7 tons 955 lb. = _____ lb.
19. 2 lb. 8 oz. = _____ lb.
20. 5 lb. 12 oz. = _____ lb.
21. 4 tons 1,000 lb. = _____ tons
22. 6 tons 500 lb. = _____ tons
23. 6 lb. 7 oz. = _____ lb.
24. 12 lb. 4 oz. = _____ lb.

C. *Solve these reading problems.*

25. When Ann was born, she weighed 8 pounds 6 ounces. How many ounces did she weigh?

26. How many pounds did Ann weigh at birth? (See problem 25.)

27. Stephen works at the Muddy Run Feed Mill. One morning he mixed a batch of feed that weighed 3 tons 1,000 pounds. How many 50-pound bags should the batch of feed yield?

28. A truck was loaded with 350 bushels of wheat. If the wheat weighs 60 pounds per bushel, how many tons of wheat were on the truck?

29. A certain recipe calls for 4 ounces of butter. How many 4-ounce portions are in a 10-pound block of butter?

30. A 10-inch concrete block weighs about 45 pounds. At 45 pounds per block, how many tons would 1,000 blocks weigh?

REVIEW EXERCISES

D. *Change these measures as indicated.* (Lesson 25)

31. 19 ft. = _____ in.
32. 252 in. = _____ ft.
33. 900 yd. = _____ ft.
34. 7 mi. = _____ ft.

E. *Solve these division problems, and check by casting out nines. Show your check numbers.* (Lesson 16, 17)

35. $26\overline{)43,577}$

36. $552\overline{)73,412}$

27. Units of Capacity

Liquids and fresh fruits are usually sold by the amount of space they occupy. Units that measure according to space are known as units of capacity. In the English system, units of capacity are of two kinds: liquid measure and dry measure.

Liquid Measure

Liquid measure is used to measure liquids such as water, milk, and gasoline. The units of liquid measure in common use are the pint, the quart, and the gallon. For amounts less than a pint, the teaspoon, the tablespoon, and the cup are used. These units are known as household measures.

Household measures are used in recipes to measure both liquid and dry ingredients. For example, a recipe may call for $\frac{1}{2}$ cup sugar and 1 cup milk. The same unit is used to measure both. Household measures are related to the weight of water. One cup of water weighs 8 fluid ounces.

English Units of Liquid Measure		
3 teaspoons (tsp.)	=	1 tablespoon (tbsp.)
16 tablespoons	=	1 cup
8 fluid oz. (fl. oz.)	=	1 cup
2 cups	=	1 pint (pt.)
2 pints	=	1 quart (qt.)
4 quarts	=	1 gallon (gal.)

Dry Measure

Dry measure is used to measure fruits and vegetables such as strawberries, peaches, and pears.

English Units of Dry Measure		
2 pints	=	1 quart
8 quarts	=	1 peck (pk.)
4 pecks	=	1 bushel (bu.)

The pint and the quart are both liquid and dry measures, but they are not the same size. The dry pint and the dry quart are slightly larger than the liquid pint and the liquid quart.

Example A	4 gallons = _____ quarts
	4 × 4 quarts in 1 gallon = 16 quarts
Example B	30 pecks = _____ bushels
	30 ÷ 4 pecks in 1 bushel = $7\frac{1}{2}$ bushels

CLASS PRACTICE

Change these measures.

a. 4 gal. = _____ qt.

b. 3 bu. = _____ pk.

c. 8 cups = _____ pt.

d. 5 tsp. = _____ tbsp.

e. 12 tbsp. = _____ cup

f. 3 gal. 2 qt. = _____ qt.

g. 4 bu. 3 pk. = _____ bu.

WRITTEN EXERCISES

A. *Change these measures as indicated.*

1. 6 gal. = _____ qt.

2. 6 pt. = _____ qt.

3. 16 pk. = _____ bu.

4. 48 qt. = _____ pk.

5. 3 cups = _____ tbsp.

6. 9 tsp. = _____ tbsp.

7. 6 qt. = _____ gal.

8. 21 qt. = _____ pk.

9. 9 cups = _____ pt.

10. 6 bu. = _____ pk.

11. 5 pt. = _____ cups

12. 40 fl. oz. = _____ cups

13. 4 gal. 1 qt. = _____ qt.

14. 5 bu. 3 pk. = _____ pk.

15. 3 pt. 1 cup = _____ pt.

16. 3 pk. 5 qt. = _____ qt.

17. 5 gal. 1 qt. = _____ gal.

18. 4 bu. 2 pk. = _____ bu.

19. 2 pt. 1 cup = _____ pt.

20. 4 pk. 7 qt. = _____ pk.

B. *Solve these reading problems.*

21. The barrel is another English unit of liquid measure. A barrel of crude oil contains 42 gallons. In 1988, Canada was estimated to have produced 581,080,000 barrels of crude oil. How many gallons is that?

22. The barrel was also a unit of dry measure at one time, used for measuring things such as fruits and vegetables. If a dry barrel contained 105 dry quarts, how many pecks did it hold?

23. John 2:6, 7 states that at the wedding in Cana of Galilee, Jesus commanded the servants to fill six waterpots with water. These waterpots contained 2 or 3 firkins each. The firkin is a little-used English unit equal to about 11 gallons. If each waterpot could hold 2 firkins, how many gallons would the six waterpots have held?

24. Mother is mixing a fruit drink for the meal at a Bible conference. If 160 people each drink 1 cup, how many gallons should Mother make? First find the number of cups in 1 gallon.

25. There are 8 fluid ounces in 1 cup. How many tablespoons are in 1 fluid ounce?

26. A bottle of cough syrup holds 16 fluid ounces. The dosage for an adult is 1 tablespoonful. How many adult doses are in the bottle?

REVIEW EXERCISES

C. *Change these measures as indicated.* (Lessons 25, 26)

27. 18 ft. = _____ in.   28. 11 yd. = _____ in.

29. 120 ft. = _____ yd.   30. 15 lb. = _____ oz.

31. 68 oz. = _____ lb.   32. 4 tons = _____ lb.

33. 6 ft. 9 in. = _____ ft.   34. 7 lb. 8 oz. = _____ lb.

D. *Solve by short division. Express any remainders as fractions.* (Lesson 17)

35. $4\overline{)6,543}$ 36. $5\overline{)3,421}$ 37. $7\overline{)4,513}$ 38. $9\overline{)7,213}$

28. Units of Area

Square measure is used to measure area. Square measure has two dimensions: length and width. The figure to the right has an area of 1 square inch. A square inch is equal to the surface area in a square measuring 1 inch by 1 inch. Likewise, a square foot is equal to the surface area in a square measuring 1 foot by 1 foot.

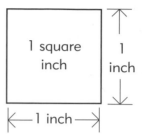

English Units of Area

144 square inches (sq. in.)	=	1 square foot (sq. ft.)
9 square feet	=	1 square yard (sq. yd.)
43,560 square feet	=	1 acre (a.)
640 acres	=	1 square mile (sq. mi.)

Except for the acre, the labels for all the units named above include the word *square*. The term *square* must be used because square units and linear units are different. An inch and a square inch are not the same at all. *Square* is not used with *acre* because an acre cannot be anything except a unit of area.

Remember the rule for changing measures from one unit to another.

To change from larger to smaller units, multiply.

To change from smaller to larger units, divide.

Example A	4 sq. yd. = _____ sq. ft.
	4 sq. yd. × 9 sq. ft. in 1 sq. yd. = 36 sq. ft.
Example B	720 sq. in. = _____ sq. ft.
	720 ÷ 144 sq. in. in 1 sq. ft. = 5 sq. ft.
Example C	30 sq. ft. = _____ sq. yd.
	30 ÷ 9 = $3\frac{3}{9}$ = $3\frac{1}{3}$ sq. yd.

CLASS PRACTICE

Change these measures as indicated.

a. 2 sq. ft. = _____ sq. in.

b. 7 sq. yd. = _____ sq. ft.

c. 3 sq. mi. = _____ a.

d. 1,280 a. = _____ sq. mi.

e. 20 sq. ft. = _____ sq. yd.

WRITTEN EXERCISES

A. *Change these measures as indicated.*

1. 4 sq. ft. = _____ sq. in.

2. 5 sq. yd. = _____ sq. ft.

3. 4 a. = _____ sq. ft.

4. 3,200 a. = _____ sq. mi.

5. 1,008 sq. in. = _____ sq. ft.

6. 12 sq. ft. = _____ sq. in.

7. 15 sq. yd. = _____ sq. ft.

8. 144 sq. ft. = _____ sq. yd.

9. 9 sq. ft. = _____ sq. in.

10. 9 a. = _____ sq. ft.

11. 5,120 a. = _____ sq. mi.

12. 35 sq. ft. = ___ sq. yd.

13. 22 sq. mi. = _____ a.

14. 15 sq. mi. = _____ a.

15. 1 sq. ft. 100 sq. in. = _____ sq. in.

16. 12 sq. mi. 400 a. = _____ a.

17. 14 sq. yd. 5 sq. ft. = _____ sq. yd.

18. 12 sq. yd. 7 sq. ft. = _____ sq. ft.

B. *Solve these reading problems.*

19. How many square inches are in a square yard?

20. One acre is equal to 160 square rods. How many square rods are in 1 square mile?

21. A church auditorium has an area of 2,610 square feet. If the price of carpet is $14 per square yard, what will be the cost of carpet for the auditorium?

22. At $14 per square yard, find the cost per square foot of carpet. Round your answer to the nearest cent.

23. In some areas, farmland sells for $4,500 per acre. At that rate, what is the price for 1 square mile of land?

24. A developer is dividing a 1-acre tract of land into 3 equal building lots. What is the area of each lot in square feet?

REVIEW EXERCISES

C. *Change these measures as indicated.* *(Lessons 25–27)*

25. 4 bu. = _____ pk.

26. 7 qt. = _____ gal.

27. 3 cups = _____ fl. oz.

28. 17 qt. = _____ pk.

29. 15 lb. = _____ oz.

30. 15,000 lb. = _____ tons

31. 200 oz. = _____ lb.

32. 150 in. = _____ ft.

33. 65 yd. = _____ ft.

34. 4 lb. 5 oz. = _____ oz.

35. 4 yd. 2 ft. = _____ ft.

36. 6 ft. 8 in. = _____ ft.

37. 3 lb. 8 oz. = _____ oz.

38. 5 bu. 3 pk. = _____ bu.

D. *Solve these division problems, and check by casting out nines. Show your check numbers.* *(Lesson 17)*

39. $421\overline{)36,141}$

40. $512\overline{)41,212}$

29. Units of Time

In the beginning of the world, God established the day and the week as the basic units of time. Genesis 1:14–19 records that God created the sun, the moon, and the stars both to give light and to mark time. The following units of time are based on the movement of these celestial bodies.

Day—The measurement of the day is based on the rotation of the earth once every 24 hours. This makes the sun appear to rise and set every day.

Month—The month is closely related to the phases of the moon. The time from one full moon to the next is about $29\frac{1}{2}$ days.

Year—A year is the time it takes for the earth to revolve around the sun. Because of this, the first day of each season comes on the same day every year. The positions of the stars are used to determine the exact length of the year, as mentioned in Genesis 1:14.

Most of the other units of time are fractions or multiples of the day and the year. But the week is not based on the motion of any heavenly body. This unit was established by God in memory of the week in which He created the heavens and the earth.

Memorize these relationships.

Units of Time		
60 seconds (sec.)	=	1 minute (min.)
60 minutes	=	1 hour (hr.)
24 hours	=	1 day
7 days	=	1 week (wk.)
12 months	=	1 year (yr.)
about 52 weeks	=	1 year
365 days	=	1 standard year
366 days	=	1 leap year
10 years	=	1 decade
100 years	=	1 century
1,000 years	=	1 millennium (*pl.* millennia)

Although these units of time are included in this chapter on English measures, they are not used only by those who use the English system. They are used throughout the world.

The same rules are used for changing measures of time from one unit to another as for changing other measures from one unit to another.

CLASS PRACTICE

Change these measures as indicated.

a. 7 wk. = _____ days

b. 4 days = _____ hr.

c. 3 centuries = _____ yr.

d. 84 mo. = _____ yr.

e. 18 mo. = _____ yr.

f. 30 yr. = _____ decades

g. 4 hr. 30 min. = _____ min. or _____ hr.

h. 6 wk. 3 days = _____ days or _____ wk.

WRITTEN EXERCISES

A. *Change these measures as indicated. Consider 1 year as 365 days.*

1. 108 mo. = _____ yr.   **2.** 8 yr. = _____ mo.   **3.** 5 days = _____ hr.

4. 15 yr. = _____ mo.   **5.** 3 hr. = _____ min.   **6.** 720 min. = _____ hr.

7. 18 wk. = _____ days   **8.** 288 hr. = _____ days   **9.** 6 hr. = _____ min.

10. 5 yr. = _____ days   **11.** 25 mo. = _____ yr.   **12.** 52 wk. = _____ days

13. 5 centuries = _____ yr.   **14.** 17 decades = _____ yr.

15. 4,000 yr. = _____ millennia   **16.** 350 yr. = _____ decades

17. 3 wk. 5 days = _____ days   **18.** 5 wk. 4 days = _____ wk.

19. 3 yr. 4 mo. = _____ yr.   **20.** 4 yr. 3 mo. = _____ mo.

B. *Solve these reading problems.*

21. How many seconds are in 1 day?

22. How many minutes are in 1 week?

23. The average life expectancy in the United States is about 75 years 6 months. How many months is that?

24. In 1920, the average life expectancy was only about 54 years 1 month. Express 54 years 1 month as years.

25. In Psalm 90:10, the normal life span of a man is stated as "threescore years and ten." How many months is that? (1 score = 20)

26. Every morning during family devotions, the Nolt family spends 10 minutes singing. How many hours does that amount to in a 365-day year?

REVIEW EXERCISES

C. *Change these measures as indicated.* (Lessons 25–28)

27. 6 sq. ft. = _____ sq. in.   **28.** 3,840 a. = _____ sq. mi.   **29.** 15 sq. ft. = _____ sq. yd.

30. 20 pk. = _____ bu.   **31.** 3 cups = _____ fl. oz.   **32.** 23 lb. = _____ oz.

33. 17 ft. = _____ yd.   **34.** 11 ft. 2 in. = _____ in.   **35.** 3 tons 500 lb. = _____ lb.

36. 5 tons 1,000 lb. = _____ tons

D. *Find the average of each set of numbers. Express any remainder as a fraction.* (Lesson 19)

37. 45, 42, 57, 35, 48   **38.** 82, 96, 87, 74, 82

E. *Solve these multiplication problems. Label each part of the problems, including the intermediate steps and answers. Check by casting out nines, and show your check numbers.* (Lessons 12, 13)

39.   376 _____   **40.**   5,421 _____
       × 415 _____   × 761 _____

30. Time Zones

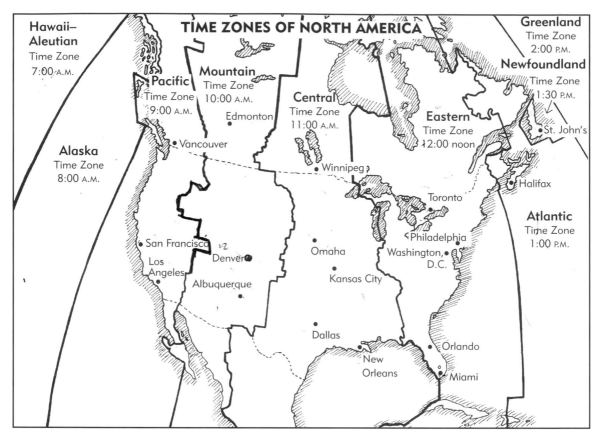

Memorize the order of the time zones.

Time Zone	City	Time	
Newfoundland	St. John's, Newfoundland	1:30	P.M.
Atlantic (A.S.T.)	Halifax, Nova Scotia	1:00	P.M.
Eastern (E.S.T.)	Washington, D.C.	12:00	noon
Central (C.S.T.)	Kansas City, Missouri	11:00	A.M.
Mountain (M.S.T.)	Denver, Colorado	10:00	A.M.
Pacific (P.S.T.)	Los Angeles, California	9:00	A.M.
Alaska	Anchorage, Alaska	8:00	A.M.
Hawaii–Aleutian	Honolulu, Hawaii	7:00	A.M.

The time on our clocks is based on the assumption that the sun is directly overhead at 12:00 noon. The sun is always directly overhead somewhere in the world, so it is always noon somewhere. If clocks in each location were set so that the sun is directly overhead at noon, there would be so many different times that it would be confusing.

To avoid this confusion, the world has been divided into 24 different time zones. The time is the same throughout any given time zone. Each time zone is one hour ahead of its neighboring zone to the west and one hour behind its neighboring zone to the east.

The United States and Canada have eight time zones. One of these zones, Newfoundland, is only $\frac{1}{2}$ hour ahead of the next time zone to the west, the Atlantic Time Zone.

When changing time from one time zone to the next, subtract time when moving from east to west and add time when moving from west to east. Because the hour hand circles a clock twice during a day, the hours on the clock start over at noon.

The abbreviation A.M. means "before noon" and is used for times from midnight till noon. The abbreviation P.M. means "after noon" and is used for times from noon until midnight. Twelve o'clock noon is written as 12:00 noon, and twelve o'clock midnight as 12:00 midnight.

In changing from one time zone to the next, subtract time when moving from east to west and add time when moving from west to east.

Example A

If it is 4:30 P.M. in Halifax, Nova Scotia, what time is it in Denver, Colorado?
Solution: Denver, Colorado is 3 time zones west of Halifax, so 3 hours must be subtracted from 4:30.   Time in Denver: 1:30 P.M.

Example B

If it is 9:00 A.M. in Honolulu, Hawaii, what time is it in St. John's, Newfoundland?
Solution: St. John's is 6 time zones plus $\frac{1}{2}$ hour east of Honolulu, so $6\frac{1}{2}$ hours must be added to 9:00 A.M.   Time in St. John's: 3:30 P.M.

CLASS PRACTICE

Give the correct time for each blank.

a. 5:00 P.M. in Halifax, Nova Scotia; _____ in Chicago, Illinois

b. 6:00 A.M. in Anchorage, Alaska; _____ in New York City

c. 11:30 P.M. in Albuquerque, New Mexico; _____ in the Eastern Time Zone

d. 11:30 P.M. in Honolulu, Hawaii; _____ in St. John's, Newfoundland

WRITTEN EXERCISES

A. Halifax, Nova Scotia, is in the Atlantic Time Zone. Find the correct time in the following cities when it is 6:00 P.M. in Halifax.

1. Omaha, Nebraska
2. Orlando, Florida
3. Vancouver, British Columbia
4. New Orleans, Louisiana
5. Anchorage, Alaska
6. Honolulu, Hawaii

B. Omaha, Nebraska is in the Central Time Zone. Find the correct time in the following cities when it is 9:00 A.M. in Omaha.

7. Winnipeg, Manitoba
8. Denver, Colorado
9. St. John's, Newfoundland
10. Nome, Alaska
11. San Francisco, California
12. Dallas, Texas

C. *Denver, Colorado is in the Mountain Time Zone. Find the correct time in the following time zones when it is 12:00 noon in Denver.*

13. Eastern Time Zone

14. Central Time Zone

15. Newfoundland Time Zone

16. Aleutian–Hawaii Time Zone

17. Pacific Time Zone

18. Alaska Time Zone

D. *Solve these reading problems.*

19. How often will a person need to reset his watch if he is traveling from Halifax, Nova Scotia, to Anchorage, Alaska?

20. The Martin family traveled from Miami, Florida, to Albuquerque, New Mexico, and visited there for 1 week before returning. How many times did they need to reset their watches on the round trip?

21. Brother Friesen plans to make a business telephone call from his home near Edmonton, Alberta, to Toronto, Ontario. He wants to call the business as soon as it opens at 8:00 A.M. (E.S.T.). What time should he call from his home?

22. The Metzlers live in Ohio (E.S.T.). Their son is teaching school in British Columbia (P.S.T.), and they would like to call him at 7:30 A.M. (P.S.T.). At what time should they call him from their home?

23. When Brother Martin was returning from visiting a mission in the Philippines, the plane needed to make an unexpected stop at Honolulu, Hawaii. At 9:00 P.M., he called his family near Edmonton, Alberta, to tell them that he would be delayed. What time was it at his home when he called?

24. Brother Lehman flew from Philadelphia, Pennsylvania, to Vancouver, British Columbia. He left at 9:00 A.M. and was enroute for 6 hours. What time was it in Vancouver when he arrived?

REVIEW EXERCISES

E. *Change these measures as indicated.* (Lessons 25–29)

25. 13 decades = _____ yr.

26. 25 centuries = _____ yr.

27. 15 wk. = _____ days

28. 26 mo. = _____ yr.

29. 3 tons = _____ lb.

30. 115 oz. = _____ lb.

31. 15 pk. = _____ bu.

32. 4 cups = _____ fl. oz.

33. 13 ft. = _____ in.

34. 17 ft. = _____ yd.

F. *Use the rules of divisibility to answer these questions.* (Lesson 20)

35. Is 348 divisible by 2?   by 3?   by 4?   by 5?

36. Is 445 divisible by 5?   by 6?   by 9?

G. *Solve these problems mentally.* (Lesson 20)

37. $168 \div 14$ **38.** $550 \div 50$ **39.** $700 \div 25$ **40.** $168 \div 24$

H. *Solve by horizontal multiplication.* (Lesson 12)

41. 482×7 **42.** $3,722 \times 8$

31. Mental Conversion of English Units

The lessons in this chapter include tables to use for changing measures from one unit to another. In everyday life, tables are not always available. There is a definite advantage in memorizing the relationships between the various units so that you can convert measures without using a table. For example, a carpet layer does not refer to a table every time he needs to change square feet to square yards.

Many of the measure conversions in everyday life can be done mentally. Your mother probably often doubles or triples recipes without using pencil and paper. Carpenters can easily calculate mentally how high a roof will be if they know the length of the rafters and the steepness of the roof. All that is needed is plenty of practice.

CLASS PRACTICE

Change these measures mentally by using shortcuts as indicated.

a. 25 ft. = _____ in. (rule for multiplying by 25)

b. 112 oz. = _____ lb. (divide-and-divide rule)

c. 50 lb. = _____ oz. (double-and-divide rule)

d. 15 ft. = _____ in. (double-and-divide rule)

e. 40 ft. = _____ in. (rule for multiplying by a multiple of 10)

f. 144 oz. = _____ lb. (divide-and-divide rule)

WRITTEN EXERCISES

A. *Make these conversions mentally, using the shortcuts you learned in lessons 14, 15, and 20 as much as you can. Do as many as you can without looking back.*

Linear measures

1. 7 ft. = _____ in.
2. 50 ft. = _____ in.
3. 30 ft. = _____ in.
4. 144 in. = _____ ft.
5. 63 ft. = _____ yd.
6. 168 in. = _____ ft.

Measures of weight

7. 4 lb. = _____ oz.
8. 12 tons = _____ lb.
9. 5 lb. = _____ oz.
10. 96 oz. = _____ lb.
11. 128 oz. = _____ lb.
12. 20 lb. = _____ oz.

Measures of capacity

13. 5 gal. = _____ qt.
14. 36 pk. = _____ bu.
15. 5 cups = _____ tbsp.
16. 18 qt. = _____ pk.
17. 25 cups = _____ tbsp.
18. 15 qt. = _____ pt.
19. 4 gal. 3 qt. = _____ qt.
20. 4 bu. 2 pk. = _____ bu.

Measures of area

21. 7 sq. yd. = _____ sq. ft.

22. 20 sq. ft. = _____ sq. in.

23. 180 sq. ft. = _____ sq. yd.

24. 2 sq. mi. = _____ a.

B. *Solve these reading problems.*

25. One morning at the Stony Brook Market, James received a 25-pound package of one-ounce pieces of candy. How many pieces of candy were in the package?

26. The living room in the Martin home has an area of 270 square feet. How many square yards is that?

27. Baby Joel weighed 9 pounds when he was 2 weeks old. That day when Susan fed him with the bottle, he drank 3 ounces of milk. How many times as much did Joel weigh as the milk he drank?

28. Thomas works at the Mill Creek Feed Mill. One morning he opened a 50-pound bag of medication, which was to be used at a rate of 4 ounces per ton of finished feed. The 50-pound bag was enough medication for how many tons of feed?

29. The Wengers bought 12 bushels of peaches, which they will be selling by the peck. How many pecks of peaches should they have to sell? Subtract 5 pecks from your answer to allow for extra peaches that will be used in heaping each of the peck baskets.

30. Darlene is helping Mother bake a cake that requires $\frac{1}{2}$ cup of shortening. On the side of the container, Darlene read that the shortening has 100 calories per tablespoon. How many calories are in $\frac{1}{2}$ cup of shortening?

REVIEW EXERCISES

C. *New York City is in the Eastern Standard Time Zone. Using the map in Lesson 30, find the correct time in the cities named when it is 11:00 A.M. in New York City.*

31. Los Angeles, California

32. Halifax, Nova Scotia

33. Albuquerque, New Mexico

34. Nome, Alaska

D. *Change these measures as indicated.* (Lessons 25–29)

35. 5 yr. = _____ mo.

36. 160 yr. = _____ decades

37. 24 sq. ft. = _____ sq. yd.

38. 13 yd. = _____ ft.

39. 12 lb. = _____ oz.

40. 14 qt. = _____ gal.

E. *Estimate the products. You do not need to find the exact answers.* (Lesson 14)

41.   451
           × 74

42.   891
           × 326

43.   3,124
           × 490

44.   5,166
           × 3,812

32. Distance, Rate, and Time

Study these three problems. How are they alike? How are they different?

1. Father drove 3 hours at an average speed of 50 miles per hour. How far did he travel?
2. Father drove 150 miles in 3 hours. What was his average speed?
3. Father drove 150 miles at an average speed of 50 miles per hour. How long did it take for the trip?

All three problems deal with one set of facts: Father drove 150 miles in 3 hours at an average speed of 50 miles per hour. They are also the same in that each contains two of the three facts (150 miles, 3 hours, and 50 miles per hour). The problems are different in that the first one asks for the **distance** traveled, the second asks for the average speed or **rate** of travel, and the third asks for the **time** of travel. In each problem, the answer can be calculated from the facts that are given.

Distance, rate, and time are the three parts in any math problem that deals with a distance traveled in a certain amount of time. There is a certain relationship among these three parts, and it can be stated in a formula.

A **formula** is an equation that gives a rule for solving a certain type of problem. The formula may use words or letters. Applying the proper formula will yield the answer to any problem of a given type. The formulas below can be used to solve problems involving distance, rate, and time.

Formula for Solving Problem 1

(This is the basic formula for distance–rate–time problems.)

distance = rate × time or $d = rt$

d = unknown r = 50 m.p.h. t = 3 hr

$d = 50 \times 3 = 150$ mi.

Formula for Solving Problem 2

rate = $\dfrac{\text{distance}}{\text{time}}$ or $r = \dfrac{d}{t}$

r = unknown d = 150 mi. t = 3 hr.

$r = \dfrac{150}{3} = 50$ m.p.h.

Formula for Solving Problem 3

time = $\dfrac{\text{distance}}{\text{rate}}$ or $t = \dfrac{d}{r}$

t = unknown d = 150 mi. r = 50 m.p.h.

$t = \dfrac{150}{50} = 3$ hr.

CLASS PRACTICE

Find the missing numbers.

	time	rate	distance		time	rate	distance
a.	6 hr.	45 m.p.h.	_____ mi.	b.	12 hr.	_____ m.p.h.	630 mi.
c.	_____ hr.	40 m.p.h.	620 mi.	d.	4 hr.	_____ m.p.h.	1,375 mi.

e. r = 45 m.p.h.   f. d = 625 mi.   g. d = 435 mi.
   t = 3 hr. t = 6 hr. r = 45 m.p.h.
   d = _____ r = _____ t = _____

WRITTEN EXERCISES

A. Write and memorize these formulas.

1. Write the formula for finding the rate.

2. Write the formula for finding the time.

3. Write the formula for finding the distance.

B. Find the missing numbers. Write any remainder as a fraction.

	time	rate	distance		time	rate	distance
4.	4 hr.	45 m.p.h.	_____ mi.	5.	6 hr	48 m.p.h.	_____ mi.
6.	5 hr.	55 m.p.h.	_____ mi.	7.	4 hr.	_____ m.p.h.	636 mi.
8.	7 hr.	_____ m.p.h.	315 mi.	9.	15 hr.	_____ m.p.h.	785 mi.
10.	_____ hr.	37 m.p.h.	703 mi.	11.	_____ hr.	50 m.p.h.	775 mi.
12.	_____ hr.	350 m.p.h.	1,470 mi.				

13. d = 220 mi..   14. t = 7 hr.   15. d = 3,192 mi.
    t = 4 hr r = 46 m.p.h. r = 456 m.p.h.
    r = _____ d = _____ t = _____

C. Solve these reading problems.

16. According to Ezra 7, it took about 4 months for Ezra and the people with him to travel from Babylon to Jerusalem. If they traveled 85 days and the distance was 800 miles, what was the average distance they traveled each day?

17. The Smith family flew to Guatemala City to visit their cousins who were serving as missionaries there. If they were in the air 4 hours and flew a distance of 1,358 miles, what was their average speed?

18. In Bible times, distance was sometimes measured in days' journeys. For example, a man on a three-days' journey might walk 3 m.p.h. for 11 hours the first day, 3 m.p.h. for 9 hours the second day, and 2 m.p.h. for 11 hours the third day. How many miles long would his journey be?

19. The Kauffman family was on a trip to visit their grandparents in a distant state. They left home at 6:00 A.M. and drove until 12:00 noon at an average speed of 53 m.p.h. After lunch they drove at an average speed of 59 m.p.h from 1:30 until they reached their destination at 7:30. How many miles did the Kauffmans travel?

20. On the way home from their grandparents, the Kauffmans took a different route. From 7:00 A.M. until 12:30 P.M., they drove 332 miles and stopped to visit some friends for the rest of the day. The next day, they drove 465 miles in $9\frac{1}{2}$ hours to arrive at home. What was their average speed for the entire trip home?

21. Some turtles crawl at a speed of about 500 feet per hour. At that rate, how long would it take for a turtle to crawl 1,000 yards?

REVIEW EXERCISES

D. Change these measures by mental calculation. *(Lesson 31)*

22. 15 lb. = _____ oz.

23. 40 sq. yd. = _____ sq. ft.

24. 144 oz. = _____ lb.

25. 240 in. = _____ ft.

26. 4 ft. 5 in. = _____ ft.

27. 7 lb. 14 oz. = _____ lb.

E. St. Louis, Missouri, is in the Central Time Zone. What time is it in these time zones if it is 4:00 A.M. in St. Louis? *(Lesson 30)*

28. Hawaii–Aleutian Time Zone

29. Eastern Time Zone

30. Newfoundland Time Zone

31. Pacific Time Zone

F. Change these measures as indicated. *(Lessons 25–29)*

32. 15 sq. yd. = _____ sq. ft.

33. 22 pk. = _____ bu.

34. 24 oz. = _____ lb.

35. 15 wk. = _____ days

36. 4 mi. = _____ ft.

37. 23 qt. = _____ gal.

38. 4 cups = _____ fl. oz.

39. 64 fl. oz. = _____ cups

On the first day of the fifth month came he to Jerusalem, according to the good hand of his God upon him.

Ezra 7:9

33. Distance, Rate, and Time in Reading Problems

This lesson will give you more practice in working with distance, rate, and time, especially in reading problems. The three formulas are shown in the box.

distance = rate × time or $d = r\,t$	
rate = $\dfrac{\text{distance}}{\text{time}}$ or $r = \dfrac{d}{t}$	
time = $\dfrac{\text{distance}}{\text{rate}}$ or $t = \dfrac{d}{r}$	

CLASS PRACTICE

Find the missing numbers.

a. $d = 115$ mi.
   $t = 2$ hr.
   $r =$ _____

b. $t = 4$ hr.
   $r = 58$ m.p.h.
   $d =$ _____

c. $d = 325$ mi.
   $r = 50$ m.p.h.
   $t =$ _____

WRITTEN EXERCISES

A. Find the missing number in each problem. Express any remainder as a fraction.

1. $d = 360$ mi.
   $r = 60$ m.p.h.
   $t =$ _____

2. $t = 6$ hr.
   $r = 45$ m.p.h.
   $d =$ _____

3. $d = 275$ mi.
   $t = 5$ hr.
   $r =$ _____

4. $t = 7$ hr.
   $r = 38$ m.p.h.
   $d =$ _____

5. $d = 232$ mi.
   $r = 52$ m.p.h.
   $t =$ _____

6. $d = 255$ mi.
   $t = 7$ hr.
   $r =$ _____

B. Solve these reading problems relating to distance, rate, and time.

7. Brother Carl traveled 410 miles in 8 hours. What was his average speed?

8. How far is it from Carlton to Newburg if a car can travel the distance in 4 hours at an average speed of 52 miles per hour?

9. How long will a 475-mile trip take at an average speed of 50 miles per hour?

10. Transportation has become much faster in the last 150 years. Before the invention of the steam locomotive, people often traveled by stagecoaches that went about 10 miles per hour. Horses were changed at relay stations every 15 or 20 miles. At 10 miles per hour, how long would it take the stage to travel 15 miles?

11. In the early 1800s, it took two weeks to travel from New York to Indiana by stagecoach. Suppose a stage covered the 720 miles from New York City to Indianapolis, Indiana, by traveling 8 hours each day for 12 days. What would be its average speed in miles per hour? Reduce any fraction to lowest terms.

12. With the invention of the steam engine, the speed of travel increased considerably. By 1900 it was possible to travel from New York City to Los Angeles, California, in about 4 days. What was the average speed in miles per hour of a train that traveled 2,784 miles in four 24-hour days?

13. Today it is typical to fly the 2,451 air miles from New York City to Los Angeles in about 6 hours. What is the average speed of a plane that makes such a flight?

14. An airplane maintaining an average speed of 375 miles per hour flew over a city at 6 A.M. At what time will it come to a city 1,125 miles away? Assume that both cities are in the same time zone.

15. A jet leaves an airport at 9:00 A.M. and travels west at 425 miles per hour. At the same time, another jet leaves the same airport and travels east at 375 miles per hour. How far apart will the airplanes be at 11:00 A.M.?

16. When Brother Mark left home, his odometer reading was 41,324.7. At the end of his trip, the reading was 41,656.7. If his travel time was 6 hours, what was his average speed?

17. To visit his parents, Mr. Martin must travel 18 miles to the expressway and then drive 3 hours at an average speed of 55 miles per hour. After leaving the expressway, he has another 23 miles to their home. How many miles does he travel to his parents' home?

18. On a trip, Mr. Lewis averaged 52 miles per hour for the first 3 hours and 45 miles per hour for the last 2 hours. How many miles did he travel?

REVIEW EXERCISES

C. *Change these measures by mental calculation.* (*Lesson 31*)

19. 15 ft. = _____ in.
20. 30 sq. yd. = _____ sq. ft.
21. 128 oz. = _____ lb.
22. 30 ft. = _____ in.
23. 50 lb. = _____ oz.
24. 25 yd. = _____ in.

D. *Halifax, Nova Scotia, is in the Atlantic Time Zone. Using the map in Lesson 30, find the correct time in these cities when it is 12:00 noon in Halifax.*

25. Honolulu, Hawaii
26. Orlando, Florida
27. St. John's, Newfoundland
28. Los Angeles, California

E. *Solve these division problems, and check by casting out nines. Show your check numbers.* (*Lessons 16, 17*)

29. $82\overline{)4,591}$
30. $324\overline{)14,512}$

F. *Write these numbers, using words.* (*Lesson 1*)

31. 4,500,000
32. 6,007,000,000
33. 5,700,200,000
34. 8,300,000,000,000

34. Working With Graphs: The Line Graph

Reading Line Graphs

Line graphs usually show changes over a period of time. The line graph above shows the average temperature in Barrow, Alaska, for each month of the year. A reader can tell at a glance during which months the temperature is highest and during which months it is lowest. A reader can also tell quickly which times of the year the temperature changes fastest.

To read the line graph above, follow the grid line for one month to the point where the graph line intersects it. By looking at the scale to the left of the intersection, you can see what the average temperature is for that month.

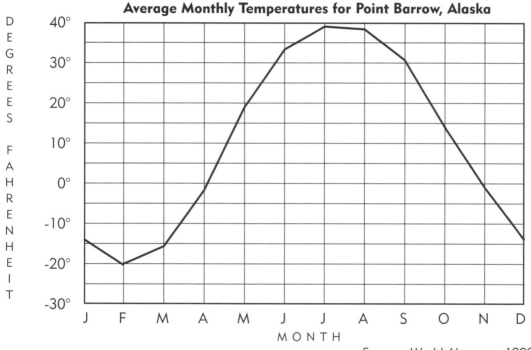

Average Monthly Temperatures for Point Barrow, Alaska

Source: *World Almanac, 1992*

Drawing Line Graphs

To draw a line graph, use the following steps.

1. Decide what range you will need for the scale at the left edge of your graph (such as 70°–82° in the following example). Number this scale, using the same increment (amount of increase) from one mark to the next. For example, the numbers should all increase by 10's or by 25's; they should not begin with one increment and suddenly change to another. Label the scale one line higher than what you will need for the greatest amount to be shown.

2. Write labels for the vertical lines, spacing them evenly across the bottom of the graph.
3. Label the vertical scale and the horizontal scale.
4. Plot accurately each point to be shown by placing a small dot at the correct place on each labeled vertical line.
5. Use a straightedge to connect all the points you have plotted.
6. Write a title for the graph.

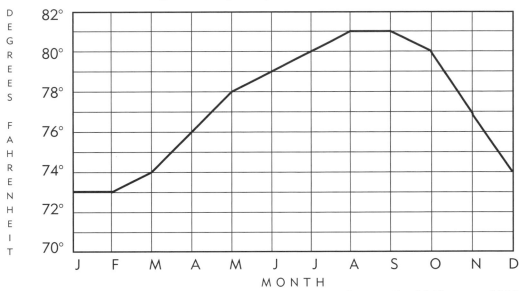

Source: *World Almanac, 1992*

CLASS PRACTICE

Answer these questions by referring to the line graph showing temperatures in Honolulu.

a. What is the title of the graph?

b. What is the average temperature during each of these months?

January   March   May   July   September   November

c. Which are the two warmest months of the year?

d. Which are the two coolest months of the year?

e. What is the difference in temperature between the warmest and the coolest months?

Answer this question by comparing the two line graphs in the lesson.

f. How are seasonal temperature changes in Honolulu different from those in Point Barrow?

WRITTEN EXERCISES

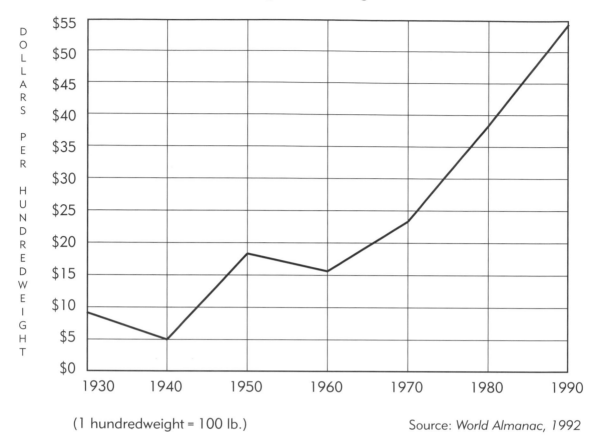

Average Price of Hogs in U.S.A

(1 hundredweight = 100 lb.)   Source: *World Almanac, 1992*

A. Study the graph above. Then give the price of hogs per hundredweight in the following years.

1. 1930   **2.** 1940   **3.** 1950   **4.** 1960   **5.** 1970   **6.** 1980   **7.** 1990

B. Use the graph above to answer these questions.

8. What was the approximate price increase per hundredweight between 1930 and 1990?

9. During which two decades did the price per hundredweight increase the most? Write the beginning and ending years of each decade.

10. The price of hogs in 1950 was about how many times greater than the price in 1930?

11. About how many times higher was the price of hogs in 1990 than it was in 1940? Use a whole number for your answer.

12. What was the average price of a 230-pound hog in 1930? Estimate the price per pound to the nearest whole cent. Allowance will be given if your answer is off by 1 cent per pound.

13. What was the average price of a 230-pound hog in 1990? Estimate the price per pound to the nearest whole cent. Allowance will be given if your answer is off by 1 cent per pound.

C. Construct line graphs to show the following information.

14. The average prices per dozen eggs received by United States farmers are listed below. On your graph, the vertical scale should begin at 10 cents and increase by 5-cent increments.

1930 . . . . . . 24 cents	1960 . . . . 36 cents	1980 . . . . . . 56 cents
1940 . . . . . . 18 cents	1970 . . . . 39 cents	1990 . . . . . . 71 cents
1950 . . . . . . 36 cents		Source: *World Almanac, 1992*

15. The average monthly temperatures for Nome, Alaska, are listed below. On your graph, the vertical scale should begin at 0 degrees Fahrenheit and increase by 5-degree increments.

January . . . . . . 9°F	May . . . . 36°F	September . . . 42°F
February . . . . . 3°F	June . . . . 45°F	October . . . . . 28°F
March . . . . 7°F	July . . . . 51°F	November . . . .16°F
April . . . . .18°F	August . . . . . .50°F	December . . . . 4°F
		Source: *World Almanac, 1992*

REVIEW EXERCISES

D. Solve these distance-rate-time problems. *(Lesson 32)*

16. d = 110 mi.
    t = 3 hr.
    r = _____

17. d = 155 mi.
    r = 40 m.p.h.
    t = _____

18. d = 950 mi.
    r = 400 m.p.h.
    t = _____

19. t = 6 hr.
    r = 185 m.p.h.
    d = _____

E. Change these measures as indicated. *(Lessons 25–29)*

20. 9 hr. = _____ min.

21. 18 wk. = _____ days

22. 17 centuries = _____ yr.

23. 15 bu. = _____ pk.

24. 78 oz. = _____ lb.

25. 71 ft. = _____ yd.

F. Solve these problems by short division. *(Lesson 17)*

26. $3\overline{)7,182}$ 27. $5\overline{)8,215}$ 28. $7\overline{)8,283}$ 29. $9\overline{)6,213}$

G. Write the value of each underlined digit. *(Lesson 2)*

30. 4<u>4</u>5,931,812

31. <u>8</u>7,912,000,000,000

35. Chapter 3 Review

A. Write the measurement of each line in inches. *(Lesson 25)*

1. _____

2. _____

B. Write the abbreviation for each English unit. *(Lessons 25–29)*

3. inch   4. fluid ounce   5. yard   6. acre

7. bushel   8. square mile   9. pound   10. quart

C. Change these measures as indicated. *(Lessons 25–30)*

11. 17 yd. = _____ ft.   12. 38 ft. = _____ yd.

13. 4 mi. = _____ ft.   14. 9 tons = _____ lb.

15. 7 lb. = _____ oz.   16. 208 oz. = _____ lb.

17. 9 gal. = _____ qt.   18. 11 pt. = _____ qt.

19. 20 pk. = _____ bu.   20. 160 mo. = _____ yr

21. 20 yr. = _____ mo.   22. 9 days = _____ hr.

23. 7 decades = _____ yr.   24. 2,000 yr. = _____ centuries

25. 7 sq. ft. = _____ sq. in.   26. 6 sq. yd. = _____ sq. ft.

27. 5 a. = _____ sq. ft.   28. 4 yr. 2 mo. = _____ yr.

29. 3 yr. 8 mo. = _____ mo.   30. 5 ft. 7 in. = _____ ft.

31. 7 ft. 4 in. = _____ in.   32. 4 lb. 6 oz. = _____ oz.

33. 4 tons 600 lb. = _____ lb.   34. 7 bu. 3 pk. = _____ bu.

35. 3 cups 4 fl. oz. = _____ cups   36. 4 cups 3 fl. oz. = _____ fl. oz.

37. 5 sq. mi. 300 a. = _____ a.   38. 9 sq. yd. 3 sq. ft. = _____ sq. yd.

D. Change these measures by using mental calculation as much as you can.
(Lesson 31)

39. 50 lb. = _____ oz.   40. 30 ft. = _____ in.   41. 25 cups = _____ tbsp.

42. 30 lb. = _____ oz.   43. 84 pk. = _____ bu.   44. 15 cups = _____ tbsp.

45. 12 sq. yd. = _____ sq. ft.   46. 450 sq. ft. = _____ sq. yd.

E. Find the missing numbers. Write any remainder as a fraction. *(Lesson 33)*

47. d = 464 mi.   48. t = 8 hr.   49. t = 7 hr.   50. d = 216 mi.

    t = 4 hr. r = 32 m.p.h. r = 217 m.p.h. r = 48 m.p.h.

    r = _____ d = _____ d = _____ t = _____

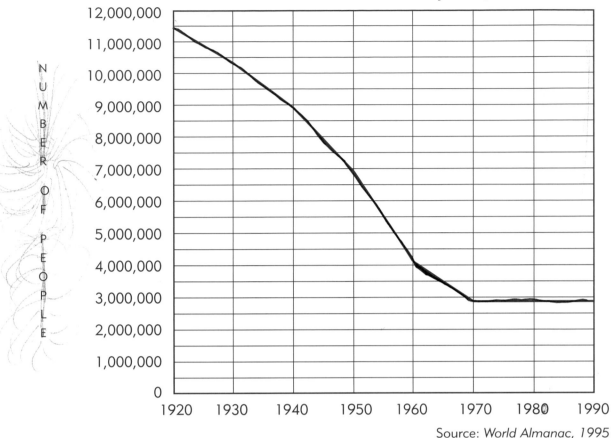

Number of Persons in Farm Occupations, 1920–1990

Source: *World Almanac, 1995*

F. Study the line graph above. Then write the approximate number of people involved in farming occupations in each of the following years. *(Lesson 34)*

51. 1920   **52.** 1930   **53.** 1950   **54.** 1980

G. Refer to the line graph above to do the following exercises. *(Lesson 34)*

55. To the nearest whole number, how many times more people were involved in farming occupations in 1940 than in 1990?

56. From 1920 to 1990, the population of the United States increased from 106,021,537 to 248,709,873. Using these numbers and the information shown on the line graph, compare the efficiency of the average farm worker in 1990 with that in 1920. It is clear that the amount of food produced by the average farmer in 1990 was _____ in 1920.

    a. much less than   **d.** a little more than

    b. a little less than   **e.** much more than

    c. about the same as

H. Answer the questions about time in the places indicated. *(Lesson 30)*

What is the time in the following time zones when it is 11:00 A.M. in the Pacific Time Zone?

57. Hawaii–Aleutian Time Zone

58. Mountain Time Zone

59. Newfoundland Time Zone

60. Alaska Time Zone

Detroit, Michigan, is in the Eastern Time Zone. What is the time in the following cities when it is 3:00 P.M. in Detroit?

61. Halifax, Nova Scotia

62. Los Angeles, California

I. Solve these reading problems.

63. The Millers are planning to attend an ordination at a church that is 275 miles away. If they average 50 miles per hour, how much time should they plan for the trip? Add $\frac{1}{2}$ hour to your answer to allow for unexpected delays.

64. Another family drove 325 miles to the ordination. Because of heavy traffic, it took them 7 hours to make the trip. What was their average rate of speed?

65. The Troyers are moving to another state. Their furniture is loaded on a semitrailer, which will need to travel 11 hours at 45 miles per hour to arrive at their new home. How long will it take the Troyers to drive the same distance in their car at 55 miles per hour?

66. How long will it take a train averaging 120 miles per hour to make a 90-mile trip?

67. Mr. Shirk bought 5 bushels of apples at $5.00 per bushel and sold them at $1.50 per peck. What was his profit on the apples?

68. Mr. Shirk sold 1 bushel of early sugar peas for $1.25 per quart. How much did he receive for the entire bushel?

36. Chapter 3 Test

Chapter 4

Working With Fractions

He shall deliver thee in six troubles:
yea, in seven there shall no evil touch thee.
(Job 5:19)

37. Finding Prime Factors

A **prime number** is not divisible by any number except 1 and itself. Five is a prime number because it is divisible only by 1 and 5. A **composite number** (kəm · poz' it) is divisible by numbers other than 1 and itself. Fifteen is a composite number because it is divisible by 3 and 5 as well as 1 and 15.

Recognizing the difference between prime and composite numbers is useful when working with fractions. Composite numbers in fractions can sometimes be reduced to lowest terms. They can also sometimes be canceled when multiplying and dividing fractions. A prime number in a fraction cannot be reduced or canceled unless it is a prime factor of the other number in the fraction.

Composite numbers can be separated into their prime factors by using the factoring process, as shown in Example C below. Finding the prime factors of composite numbers is beneficial when reducing or canceling parts of fractions and also when finding the greatest common factors and lowest common multiples of several composite numbers.

Example A
7 is prime because it is divisible only by 1 and 7.
Example B
8 is composite because it is divisible by 2 and 4 as well as 1 and 8.

Example C: Using Division by Primes to Find Prime Factors

Step 1: Divide the composite number by its smallest prime factor. First try dividing by 2, by 3, by 5, and so on.	Find the prime factors of 24.
Step 2: Repeat Step 1 until the quotient of the last division is a prime number.	$\dfrac{2\,\overline{)24}}{2\,\overline{)12}}$ $2\,\overline{)6}$
Step 3: The prime factors of the composite number are all the divisors and the final quotient. The answer is expressed by writing the composite number, the equal sign, and all the prime factors joined by multiplication signs.	3 Answer: $24 = 2 \times 2 \times 2 \times 3$

CLASS PRACTICE

Identify these numbers as prime or composite.

  a. 23   b. 25   c. 27   d. 29

Find the prime factors of these composite numbers.

  e. 16   f. 28   g. 42   h. 81

WRITTEN EXERCISES

A. *Identify each number as prime or composite.*

1. 3   **2.** 21   **3.** 39   **4.** 17
5. 29   **6.** 47   **7.** 49   **8.** 51

B. *The sieve of Eratosthenes* (ĕr´· ə· tŏs´· thə· nēz´) *is a simple way to find prime numbers. Write the numbers from 1 to 100 as shown below. Follow the directions in crossing out composite numbers. If you complete the sieve correctly, the circled numbers will be all the prime numbers from 1 to 100.*

```
 1   2   3   4   5   6   7   8   9  10
11  12  13  14  15  16  17  18  19  20
21  22  23  24  25  26  27  28  29  30
31  32  33  34  35  36  37  38  39  40
41  42  43  44  45  46  47  48  49  50
51  52  53  54  55  56  57  58  59  60
61  62  63  64  65  66  67  68  69  70
71  72  73  74  75  76  77  78  79  80
81  82  83  84  85  86  87  88  89  90
91  92  93  94  95  96  97  98  99 100
```

9. Cross out 1 because it is neither prime nor composite.

10. Circle 2 because it is a prime number. Cross out all the other even numbers because they are divisible by 2.

11. Circle 3 because it is prime. Cross out all the multiples of 3 that are not already crossed out.

12. Circle 5 because it is prime. Cross out all the multiples of 5 that are not already crossed out.

13. Circle 7 because it is prime. Cross out all the multiples of 7 that are not already crossed out.

14. Circle all the numbers that are not crossed out. If you completed the sieve correctly, the circled numbers are all the prime numbers from 1 to 100. Now use the table to check that you correctly identified all the numbers in exercises 1–8.

C. *Divide by primes to find the prime factors of these composite numbers. Your answers should be number sentences as shown in Example C.*

15. 14   **16.** 26
17. 35   **18.** 57
19. 99   **20.** 75
21. 130   **22.** 220

D. Solve these reading problems.

23. A fraction cannot be reduced unless the numerator and the denominator have at least one common factor. Use prime factors to discover if $\frac{51}{68}$ can be reduced. Can it?

24. Using the same procedure as in problem 23, answer this question: Can the fraction $\frac{27}{85}$ be reduced?

25. Can $\frac{35}{50}$ be reduced?

26. Can $\frac{29}{61}$ be reduced?

27. In the first report card period of the school year, Mark received these spelling test grades: 100%, 95%, 95%, 100%, 85%, 90%. During the second report card period he received these spelling test grades: 95%, 95%, 100%, 90%, 95%, 95%. In the second period, was Mark's average grade better or worse than in the first period?

28. Dwight was born in MCMLXXXI. Find his age in the year MM, and write your answer in Roman numerals.

REVIEW EXERCISES

E. Change these measures as indicated. *(Lesson 27)*

29. 2 cups = _____ fl. oz.

30. 14 qt. = _____ gal.

31. 18 bu. = _____ pk.

32. 42 qt. = _____ pk.

33. 9 tsp. = _____ tbsp.

34. 7 cups = _____ pt.

F. Find the average of each set of numbers. Express any remainder as a fraction. *(Lesson 19)*

35. 42, 48, 53, 47

36. 928, 915, 943, 900

G. Express the Roman numerals as Arabic numerals, and the Arabic numerals as Roman numerals. *(Lesson 4)*

37. CLIV

38. $\overline{\text{XIII}}$

39. 578

40. 1,659

38. Finding Greatest Common Factors

The **greatest common factor** (*g.c.f.*) is the largest number that is a factor of a set of numbers. For example, 10 is the largest number by which both 20 and 30 are divisible. This makes 10 the greatest common factor of 20 and 30.

Because the greatest common factor is a factor of both numbers, it is never larger than the smaller number.

Knowing the greatest common factor of a number is helpful in reducing fractions to lowest terms. Fractions are reduced to lowest terms by dividing both the numerator and the denominator by their greatest common factor.

To find the greatest common factor of a set of numbers, first determine whether the smaller number is the greatest common factor. If it is not, find the prime factors of each number. The product of the prime factors that the numbers have in common is the greatest common factor.

To find the greatest common factor, use the following steps.

Step 1: Look at the smaller number. Is it a factor of the larger number? If not, go to Step 2.

Step 2: List the prime factors of both numbers.

Step 3: Find all the factors that the two numbers have in common, and draw lines between them. If the same factor is in both sets more than once, continue drawing lines between the factors until all the common factors are joined by lines.

Step 4: Multiply all the factors that the composite numbers have in common. The product is the greatest common factor.

Example A	**Example B**
Find the greatest common factor of 8 and 24.	Find the greatest common factor of 84 and 280.
1. Is 8 a factor of 24? It is, so the greatest common factor of 8 and 24 is 8.	1. Is 84 a factor of 280? No, it is not.
Steps 2, 3, and 4 are not needed because the greatest common factor was found in Step 1.	2. $2\overline{)84}$ $\quad$ $2\overline{)280}$ $\\ 2\overline{)42}$ $\quad$ $2\overline{)140}$ $\\ 3\overline{)21}$ $\quad$ $2\overline{)70}$ $\\ \quad 7 \quad\quad 5\overline{)35}$ $\\ \quad\quad\quad\quad 7$
g.c.f. = 8	3. $84 = 2 \times 2 \times 3 \times 7$ $\\ 280 = 2 \times 2 \times 2 \times 5 \times 7$
	4. $2 \times 2 \times 7 = 28$
	g.c.f. = 28

CLASS PRACTICE

Find the greatest common factors of these pairs.

   a. 12, 16   b. 14, 42   c. 15, 25   d. 27, 36

WRITTEN EXERCISES

   A. *Find the greatest common factor (g.c.f.) of each pair of numbers.*

   1. 12, 15   2. 16, 28   3. 18, 36

   4. 30, 50   5. 18, 30   6. 21, 33

   7. 24, 60   8. 45, 75   9. 26, 39

   10. 35, 49   11. 28, 42   12. 38, 95

   B. *Solve these reading problems.*

13. To reduce fractions, find the greatest common factor of the numerator and the denominator and divide both parts of the fraction by it. What is the greatest common factor of 54 and 81?

14. Brother Wenger gave his students the following problem. "My age is two times the greatest common factor of 51 and 68. How old am I?"

15. Daryl said, "My father is 42 years old, and my grandfather is 70 years old. My age is 2 years less than the greatest common factor of my father's and my grandfather's ages. How old am I?"

16. One Sunday, 72 of the 90 people who usually come to church were able to come despite the heavy snowfall. What is the greatest common factor of these two numbers? The greatest common factor can be used to reduce to lowest terms the fraction of the congregation who could come to church.

I was glad when they said unto me, Let us go into the house of the Lord.
Psalms 122:1

17. Father drove to an ordination service early one Saturday morning. For the first several hours, he drove an average of 45 miles per hour. He then drove an average of 55 miles per hour for the same number of hours until he arrived at the church. The number of hours he drove at each speed was the greatest common factor of 45 and 55. How far was it to the ordination?

18. On the return trip from the ordination service, Father drove the first 320 miles in 7 hours. What was his average rate of speed?

REVIEW EXERCISES

C. Identify these numbers as prime or composite. *(Lesson 37)*

19. 41   20. 43   21. 45

22. 47   23. 49   24. 51

D. Change these measures as indicated. *(Lesson 28)*

25. 7 sq. yd. = _____ sq. ft.   26. 7 sq. ft. = _____ sq. yd.

27. 3 sq. ft. = _____ sq. in.   28. 4 sq. mi. = _____ a.

E. Use the rules of divisibility to answer these questions. *(Lesson 20)*

29. Is 457 divisible by 2?   by 3?   by 4?

30. Is 585 divisible by 5?   by 6?   by 9?

F. Solve these division problems mentally. *(Lesson 20)*

31. 800 ÷ 25   32. 1,300 ÷ 50   33. 216 ÷ 24

34. 242 ÷ 22   35. 900 ÷ 25   36. 1,500 ÷ 50

G. Copy and solve these addition problems. *(Lesson 5)*

37. $3,812.74
     + 7,821.85

38.   6,753,812
     + 7,723,712

39. Finding Lowest Common Multiples

The **lowest common multiple** ($l.c.m.$) is the smallest number that is a multiple of a set of numbers. This number is helpful in finding a common denominator when changing unlike fractions to like fractions. The lowest common multiple is never smaller than the largest number in the set.

Two ways of finding lowest common multiples are described below. Use Method 1 first to see if the lowest common multiple can easily be found by that method. If the lowest common multiple has not been found after the third step, use Method 2.

Method 1: Finding the lowest common multiple by trial and error
 	
1. Look at the larger number. Is it a multiple of the smaller number? If not, go to step 2.
2. Multiply the larger number by 2. Is the answer a multiple of the smaller number? If not, go to step 3.
3. Multiply the larger number by 3. Is the answer a multiple of the smaller number? If not, use Method 2.
	Example A
	  Find the lowest common multiple of 12 and 18.
	  1. 18 is not a multiple of 12.
	  2. $18 \times 2 = 36$. 36 is a multiple of 12.
	  $l.c.m. = 36$
	  3. (Step 3 is not needed.)

Method 2: Finding the lowest common multiple by factoring
 	
1. Find the prime factors of both numbers.
2. Draw lines to connect the common factors in the two sets.
3. Cross out one factor in each pair of factors.
4. Multiply all the remaining prime factors. The product is the lowest common multiple.
	Example B
	  Find the lowest common multiple of 10 and 12.
	  1. $2\overline{)10}$ $\quad$ $2\overline{)12}$
	  $\quad$ 5 $\qquad$ $2\overline{)6}$
	  $\qquad\qquad\qquad$ 3
	  2,3. $10 = 2 \times 5$
	  $\qquad$ $12 = 2 \times 2 \times 3$
	  4. $2 \times 5 \times 2 \times 3 = 60$
	  $l.c.m. = 60$

CLASS PRACTICE

Find the lowest common multiples by using Method 1.

   a. 8, 12   b. 10, 15   c. 6, 10

Find the lowest common multiples by using Method 2.

   d. 10, 18   e. 15, 18   f. 12, 22

Find the lowest common multiples by using Method 1 and then Method 2 if necessary.

   g. 12, 15   h. 15, 45   i. 15, 20

WRITTEN EXERCISES

A. Use Method 1 to find the lowest common multiple of each set.

1. 6, 9   **2.** 16, 24   **3.** 9, 15   **4.** 12, 20   **5.** 18, 24   **6.** 18, 30

B. Use Method 2 to find the lowest common multiple of each set. Show your work.

7. 8, 14   **8.** 20, 35   **9.** 32, 40   **10.** 20, 24   **11.** 15, 21   **12.** 24, 30

C. Find the lowest common multiples by using Method 1 and then Method 2 if necessary.

13. 16, 40   **14.** 6, 8   **15.** 12, 21   **16.** 24, 36   **17.** 18, 21   **18.** 9, 21

D. Solve these reading problems.

19. Lowest common multiples are useful in adding and subtracting unlike fractions. When you are adding $\frac{5}{12}$ and $\frac{9}{14}$, the first step is to find the lowest common multiple of the denominators 12 and 14. What is it?

20. What is the lowest common multiple of 8 and 10 in the fractions $\frac{7}{8}$ and $\frac{7}{10}$?

21. There are 10 seventh grade students and 14 eighth grade students in the upper grade classroom. The number of students in the entire school is the lowest common multiple of 10 and 14. How many students is that?

22. In their garden last spring, the Zook family planted the rows 28 inches apart. How many inches wide was the planted portion when it was an exact number of yards wide? To find the answer, find the lowest common multiple of 28 and 36.

23. Jonathan cuts a 20-inch swath when he mows the lawn. How many inches wide will the area be that he has mowed when its width is an exact number of yards? See problem 22 for a hint on how to solve this problem.

24. Each time Jonathan mows a swath the entire length of the lawn, he mows 108 square feet. How many square feet is the area of the lawn if he mows 24 equal-length swaths in all?

REVIEW EXERCISES

E. Find the greatest common factor of each set. *(Lesson 38)*

25. 27, 45   **26.** 42, 70   **27.** 32, 96   **28.** 39, 65

F. Identify these numbers as prime or composite. *(Lesson 37)*

29. 90   **30.** 91   **31.** 92   **32.** 93

G. Change these measures as indicated. *(Lesson 29)*

33. 14 min. = _____ sec.   **34.** 90 min. = _____ hr.

35. 25 decades = _____ yr.   **36.** 7 mo. = _____ yr.

H. Do these additions mentally. *(Lesson 6)*

37. 48 + 34   **38.** 53 + 68   **39.** 46 + 58   **40.** 114 + 58

40. Introduction to Common Fractions

Fractions like $\frac{1}{2}$ and $\frac{3}{4}$ are known as common fractions. The upper number is the **numerator** and the lower number is the **denominator**. The two numbers are also called the **terms** of the fraction. (In Chapter 5 you will study decimal fractions, which have a different form.)

Fractions are used to express parts of whole numbers. In Example A, $\frac{3}{20}$ of the squares are shaded.

Example A

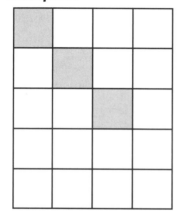

Example B

Fractions are also used to compare whole numbers. In Example B, 3 out of 5 squares are shaded. The fraction $\frac{3}{5}$ compares the number of shaded squares with the total number of squares.

Fractions and division problems are different ways of expressing the same numbers. The fraction $\frac{3}{5}$ is the same as the quotient of the problem $3 \div 5$. A large fraction such as $\frac{23}{39}$ may be easier to read as "Twenty-three divided by thirty-nine."

Various terms are used in working with fractions. **Proper fractions** have a numerator that is smaller than the denominator. The value of these fractions is less than 1. **Improper fractions** have a numerator equal to or larger than the denominator. The value of these fractions is equal to or greater than 1. **Whole numbers** do not include any fractions. **Mixed numbers** include a whole number and a fraction.

Example C

Proper Fractions	Improper Fractions	Whole Numbers	Mixed Numbers
$\frac{3}{4}$ $\frac{5}{8}$ $\frac{8}{9}$	$\frac{3}{2}$ $\frac{5}{5}$ $\frac{8}{7}$	3 5 8	$3\frac{1}{4}$ $5\frac{3}{8}$

Equivalent fractions have equal value. An equivalent fraction can be obtained by multiplying or dividing both the numerator and the denominator by the same number. Fractions are usually reduced to **lowest terms** if possible by dividing both the numerator and the denominator by their greatest common factor.

Reducing fractions to lowest terms makes them simpler to understand. The fractions $\frac{368}{736}$ and $\frac{1}{2}$ have the same value, but $\frac{1}{2}$ is much simpler to work with. For this reason, reducing fractions is also known as **simplifying** fractions.

In Example D, the first fraction is expanded to higher terms. The other three fractions are reduced to lowest terms.

Example D

$\frac{3}{4} \times \frac{2}{2} = \frac{6}{8}$	$\frac{15}{25} \div \frac{5}{5} = \frac{3}{5}$	$\frac{12}{18} \div \frac{6}{6} = \frac{2}{3}$	$\frac{21}{36} \div \frac{3}{3} = \frac{7}{12}$

CLASS PRACTICE

Expand these fractions.

a. $\frac{2}{3}$ b. $\frac{1}{6}$ c. $\frac{3}{4}$ d. $\frac{4}{7}$ e. $\frac{7}{9}$

Reduce these fractions to lowest terms.

f. $\frac{16}{20}$ g. $\frac{6}{10}$ h. $\frac{10}{15}$ i. $\frac{24}{32}$ j. $\frac{76}{95}$

WRITTEN EXERCISES

A. Answer these questions about fractions.

1. What is the denominator of the fraction $\frac{7}{8}$?

2. Which of these is a mixed number?   5 $\frac{3}{4}$ $\frac{4}{1}$ $3\frac{1}{4}$

3. What is the numerator of the fraction $\frac{15}{4}$?

4. Which of these is an improper fraction?   7 $\frac{5}{6}$ $\frac{9}{8}$ $1\frac{1}{2}$

5. Which of these is a whole number?   15 $\frac{3}{5}$ $\frac{5}{2}$ $5\frac{7}{8}$

B. Expand these fractions by multiplying both the numerator and the denominator by 7.

6. $\frac{1}{2}$ 7. $\frac{2}{3}$ 8. $\frac{5}{6}$ 9. $\frac{5}{8}$ 10. $\frac{4}{9}$ 11. $\frac{3}{11}$

C. Reduce these fractions to lowest terms by dividing the numerator and denominator by their greatest common factor.

12. $\frac{9}{12}$ 13. $\frac{9}{15}$ 14. $\frac{6}{9}$ 15. $\frac{15}{18}$

16. $\frac{18}{24}$ 17. $\frac{21}{28}$ 18. $\frac{15}{45}$ 19. $\frac{12}{30}$

20. $\frac{14}{35}$ 21. $\frac{18}{45}$ 22. $\frac{36}{48}$ 23. $\frac{36}{54}$

D. *Solve these reading problems. Give all fraction answers in lowest terms.*

24. Mother baked 5 pies and gave three of them to the Brossmans because the mother in the family was ill. What fraction of the pies did Mother give to the Brossmans?

25. Dwight sawed 8 inches off a 96-inch board. What fraction of the board did Dwight saw off?

26. One Sunday, 72 of the 90 people who attend Lakeside Church were able to come in spite of the flu epidemic. What fraction of the people who usually attend church were present that Sunday?

27. The Hillview Mennonite School has 128 pupils. Of these, 32 children are in the seventh and eighth grades. What fraction of the entire student body is in these grades?

28. Michael is 12 years old and his father is 42. Write a fraction comparing Michael's age with his father's age.

29. Write a fraction comparing Michael's age with his father's age when they are three years older than they are now. (See problem 28.)

REVIEW EXERCISES

E. *Find the lowest common multiple of each set.* (Lesson 39)

30. 9, 18   **31.** 14, 20   **32.** 24, 36   **33.** 15, 35

F. *Find the greatest common factor of each set.* (Lesson 38)

34. 24, 36   **35.** 34, 85   **36.** 42, 98   **37.** 48, 80

G. *Indianapolis, Indiana is in the Eastern Time Zone. Use the map in Lesson 30 to discover what time it is in the following cities when it is 12:00 midnight in Indianapolis.*

38. Halifax   **39.** Vancouver

H. *Solve these subtraction problems. Write the label for each number beside it, including answers.* (Lesson 7)

40.   4,361,351 _____
         - 2,577,921 _____

41. $3,912.93 _____
         - 1,866.49 _____

41. Simplifying and Comparing Fractions

The fractions $\frac{2}{3}$ and $\frac{82}{123}$ have the same value, but $\frac{2}{3}$ is much simpler to understand because it is reduced to lowest terms. Remember that reducing fractions means the same thing as simplifying fractions.

Which is larger, $\frac{5}{9}$ or $\frac{7}{12}$? When you are comparing two unlike fractions, the fractions need to be changed so that they have like denominators. This is usually done by expanding one or both fractions.

Comparing Unlike Fractions	Compare $\frac{5}{9}$ and $\frac{7}{12}$.
1. Find the lowest common multiple for the denominators of the fractions.	1. *l.c.m.* of 9 and 12 = 36
2. Express the fractions as like fractions. To do this, use the lowest common multiple of the denominators. This **lowest common denominator** will be the denominator of the like fractions to which you change the unlike fractions.	2. $\frac{5}{9} \times \frac{4}{4} = \frac{20}{36}$ $\frac{7}{12} \times \frac{3}{3} = \frac{21}{36}$
3. Compare the fractions. Place the "greater than" symbol (>) between the two if the first number is larger than the second one. Place the "less than" symbol (<) between the two if the first number is smaller than the second one.	3. $\frac{20}{36} < \frac{21}{36}$ so $\frac{5}{9} < \frac{7}{12}$

CLASS PRACTICE

Compare these fractions by using the < and > symbols.

a. $\frac{5}{8}$ _____ $\frac{9}{16}$ b. $\frac{5}{6}$ _____ $\frac{13}{15}$ c. $\frac{5}{8}$ _____ $\frac{13}{20}$ d. $\frac{7}{12}$ _____ $\frac{11}{18}$

WRITTEN EXERCISES

A. *Reduce these fractions to lowest terms.*

1. $\frac{27}{36}$ 2. $\frac{21}{49}$ 3. $\frac{32}{48}$ 4. $\frac{34}{85}$

5. $\frac{45}{63}$ 6. $\frac{22}{77}$ 7. $\frac{39}{65}$ 8. $\frac{63}{84}$

B. *Compare these fractions by using the < and > symbols.*

9. $\frac{5}{6}$ _____ $\frac{13}{16}$ 10. $\frac{5}{8}$ _____ $\frac{7}{12}$ 11. $\frac{3}{4}$ _____ $\frac{11}{14}$ 12. $\frac{2}{3}$ _____ $\frac{7}{12}$

13. $\frac{7}{10}$ _____ $\frac{11}{15}$ 14. $\frac{3}{8}$ _____ $\frac{1}{3}$ 15. $\frac{5}{12}$ _____ $\frac{7}{15}$ 16. $\frac{7}{12}$ _____ $\frac{9}{20}$

C. Solve these reading problems.

17. When Susan was buying cinnamon, she noticed that two different brands each sold for $2.09. One can contained $\frac{7}{16}$ pound and the other $\frac{5}{12}$ pound. Which can contained more?

18. Mr. Martin needs a screw to repair a door that has a thickness of $1\frac{5}{8}$ inches. He has three screws of the following lengths: $1\frac{1}{4}$ inches, $1\frac{1}{2}$ inches, and $1\frac{3}{4}$ inches. Which one should he use if he wants to use the longest screw possible without going through the other side of the door?

19. Brenda is $12\frac{3}{8}$ years old, Mary is $12\frac{5}{12}$ years old, and Alice is $12\frac{1}{3}$ years old. Which of the girls is oldest?

20. In Carol's school, $\frac{1}{3}$ of the students are in grades 1–3, $\frac{3}{10}$ of them are in grades 4–6, and $\frac{11}{30}$ are in grades 7–10. Which room has the most students?

21. One morning Father estimated that there were 1,500 pounds of feed in a bin. That evening only 700 pounds were left. Write a fraction in lowest terms to show what part of the feed was eaten that day.

22. One day Deborah had 36 out of 40 math answers correct. What fraction of her answers were correct? (Be sure your answer is in lowest terms.)

REVIEW EXERCISES

D. Answer these questions about fractions. *(Lesson 40)*

23. Which of these fractions is an improper fraction? $\frac{3}{4}$ $1\frac{3}{4}$ $\frac{4}{3}$

24. Which of these fractions is a proper fraction? $\frac{5}{6}$ $\frac{3}{2}$ $3\frac{3}{4}$

E. Find the lowest common multiple of each set. *(Lesson 39)*

25. 14, 18   **26.** 16, 24   **27.** 25, 40   **28.** 22, 33

F. Write whether each number is prime or composite. *(Lesson 37)*

29. 61   **30.** 63   **31.** 65   **32.** 67

G. Solve these subtraction problems mentally. *(Lesson 8)*

33. 72 – 45   **34.** 63 – 37   **35.** 81 – 29   **36.** 92 – 68

42. Adding Common Fractions

Adding fractions, like comparing fractions, can be done only if all the fractions have like denominators. Fractions with like denominators are known as like fractions. To add like fractions, add the numerators. The denominator of the sum is the same as those of the addends. The answer should always be expressed in lowest terms.

Example A	**Example B**
$\frac{1}{6} = \frac{2}{12}$ $+\frac{3}{4} = \frac{9}{12}$ $\frac{11}{12}$	$\frac{7}{12} = \frac{7}{12}$ $+\frac{3}{4} = \frac{9}{12}$ $\frac{16}{12} = 12\overline{)16}^{\,1\frac{4}{12}} = 1\frac{1}{3}$

If the sum is an improper fraction, it is changed to a whole or mixed number by dividing the numerator by the denominator and expressing the remainder as a fraction in lowest terms. (See Example B.) Such a mixed number is said to be in **simplest form**.

Mixed numbers are added in much the same way as proper fractions. If the fractions are unlike, change them to like fractions. Add the fractions together, and then add the whole numbers. If the fractional part of the sum is an improper fraction, change it to a mixed number in simplest form and add it to the whole number in the sum.

Example C	**Example D**
$3\frac{1}{6} = 3\frac{2}{12}$ $+2\frac{3}{4} = 2\frac{9}{12}$ $5\frac{11}{12}$	$3\frac{3}{4} = 3\frac{9}{12}$ $+2\frac{11}{12} = 2\frac{11}{12}$ $5\frac{20}{12} = 5+1\frac{8}{12} = 5+1\frac{2}{3} = 6\frac{2}{3}$

CLASS PRACTICE

Add these fractions.

a. $\frac{3}{5}$ $+\frac{7}{10}$

b. $\frac{3}{4}$ $+\frac{5}{6}$

c. $3\frac{1}{3}$ $+2\frac{2}{5}$

d. $2\frac{2}{3}$ $+2\frac{7}{8}$

e. $1\frac{7}{8}$ $+2\frac{7}{12}$

WRITTEN EXERCISES

A. Add these fractions. Write the answers in simplest form.

1. $\frac{1}{6}$ $+\frac{1}{3}$

2. $\frac{1}{4}$ $+\frac{1}{2}$

3. $\frac{1}{3}$ $+\frac{3}{5}$

4. $\frac{1}{7}$ $+\frac{2}{5}$

5. $\frac{5}{6}$ $+\frac{1}{8}$

6. $\frac{3}{4}$ $+\frac{7}{8}$

7. $\frac{5}{6}$ $+\frac{2}{3}$

8. $\frac{7}{8}$ $+\frac{5}{6}$

9. $\frac{2}{3}$ $+\frac{3}{4}$

10. $\frac{7}{9}$ $+\frac{1}{2}$

11. $3\frac{1}{5}$ 12. $2\frac{3}{8}$ 13. $2\frac{3}{7}$ 14. $3\frac{2}{5}$ 15. $1\frac{1}{6}$
   $+1\frac{1}{10}$ $+1\frac{1}{4}$ $+2\frac{1}{3}$ $+2\frac{1}{4}$ $+2\frac{5}{8}$

16. $2\frac{4}{5}$ 17. $3\frac{2}{3}$ 18. $1\frac{7}{8}$ 19. $1\frac{5}{6}$ 20. $2\frac{3}{7}$
   $+1\frac{1}{3}$ $+2\frac{1}{2}$ $+2\frac{3}{4}$ $+1\frac{3}{10}$ $+1\frac{3}{4}$

B. Solve these reading problems.

21. One morning, John picked $1\frac{2}{3}$ bushels of peas for Mother, and Carla picked $1\frac{3}{8}$ bushels. How many peas did they pick in all?

22. Last year the Martins planted $73\frac{1}{2}$ acres of corn. This year they are planting the same amount of corn on their own land as well as $25\frac{1}{4}$ acres on rented land. How much corn are they planting in all?

23. As a place for hanging garden tools, Father nailed a strip of three two-by-four boards along the garage wall. If the boards measured $2\frac{1}{3}$ feet, $1\frac{7}{8}$ feet, and $2\frac{5}{12}$ feet, how long a strip did he nail on the wall?

24. When the cooler in the milk tank stopped working, Uncle David suggested that they make butter from the cream, since they couldn't sell the milk. Aunt Sarah made three batches of butter, yielding $4\frac{3}{4}$ pounds, $5\frac{1}{2}$ pounds, and $3\frac{7}{8}$ pounds. How many pounds of butter did she make?

25. Father sold 3 chickens to a neighbor. If the chickens weighed $7\frac{9}{16}$ pounds, $8\frac{3}{4}$ pounds, and $6\frac{3}{8}$ pounds, what was their total weight?

26. When Brother Leonard was planning to fly to a mission in Paraguay, he was told that he could take along no more than 60 pounds of luggage. He wanted to take the following items; suitcase $4\frac{3}{4}$ lb., nails $14\frac{5}{8}$ lb., clothes $12\frac{3}{4}$ lb., and books $27\frac{1}{2}$ lb. What was their total weight?

REVIEW EXERCISES

C. Answer these questions about fractions. *(Lesson 40)*

27. Which of these numbers is a mixed number?   3 $\frac{4}{3}$ $\frac{3}{4}$ $3\frac{3}{4}$

28. The numerator of a fraction is 9. For the fraction to be an improper fraction, what must be true about the denominator?

D. Find the greatest common factor of each set. *(Lesson 38)*

29. 36, 63   30. 28, 44   31. 24, 44   32. 54, 90

E. Solve these problems about distance, rate, and time. *(Lesson 32)*

33. t = 4 hr.   34. d = 120 mi.   35. d = 117 mi.   36. d = 178 mi.
   r = 45 m.p.h. r = 48 m.p.h. r = 52 m.p.h. t = 4 hr.
   d = _____ t = _____ t = _____ r = _____

43. Subtracting Common Fractions

Subtracting fractions is done by much the same procedure as adding fractions. For like fractions, the numerator of the subtrahend is subtracted from the numerator of the minuend (Example A). If the fractions are unlike, they must be changed to like fractions and then subtracted (Example B). As usual, the answer should be reduced to lowest terms.

Example A	Example B
$\dfrac{5}{7}$	$\dfrac{7}{12} = \dfrac{7}{12}$
$-\dfrac{2}{7}$	$-\dfrac{1}{3} = \dfrac{4}{12}$
$\dfrac{3}{7}$	$\dfrac{3}{12} = \dfrac{1}{4}$

Subtractions that include whole numbers and mixed numbers are done much like those with proper fractions. If the mixed numbers contain unlike fractions, first change them to like fractions. Find the difference, and express the answer in simplest form.

Examples C shows how to borrow when you are subtracting from a whole number. Borrow 1 from the ones' place in the minuend, and change it to an improper fraction with the same denominator as that in the subtrahend. The numerator of this improper fraction will be the same as the denominator, since $1 = \frac{2}{2}, \frac{3}{3}, \frac{4}{4}$, and so on.

Example D shows how to borrow when you are subtracting from a mixed number. Subtract 1 from the whole number in the minuend, change it to an improper fraction, and add it to the fraction in the minuend. Subtract the fraction from the fraction and the whole number from the whole number, and express the difference in simplest form.

Example C	Example D
$5 \quad = 4\frac{7}{7}$	$3\frac{3}{4} = 3\frac{9}{12} = 2\frac{12}{12} + \frac{9}{12} = 2\frac{21}{12}$
$-2\frac{5}{7} = 2\frac{5}{7}$	$-1\frac{11}{12} \qquad\qquad\qquad = 1\frac{11}{12}$
$2\frac{2}{7}$	$\qquad\qquad\qquad\qquad 1\frac{10}{12} = 1\frac{5}{6}$

CLASS PRACTICE

Subtract these fractions.

a. $\dfrac{5}{8}$ $-\dfrac{1}{4}$ b. $\dfrac{5}{7}$ $-\dfrac{1}{3}$ c. 7 $-3\frac{1}{3}$ d. 5 $-3\frac{3}{4}$ e. $8\frac{2}{3}$ $-1\frac{3}{4}$ f. $9\frac{1}{6}$ $-3\frac{1}{2}$

WRITTEN EXERCISES

A. Copy and subtract these fractions. Write the answers in simplest form.

1. $\dfrac{3}{4}$ $-\dfrac{3}{8}$ 2. $\dfrac{3}{5}$ $-\dfrac{1}{3}$ 3. $\dfrac{2}{3}$ $-\dfrac{1}{2}$ 4. $\dfrac{5}{6}$ $-\dfrac{3}{4}$ 5. $\dfrac{7}{9}$ $-\dfrac{1}{6}$ 6. $\dfrac{5}{6}$ $-\dfrac{7}{9}$

7. $\frac{9}{10}$ 8. $\frac{7}{8}$ 9. $\frac{6}{7}$ 10. $\frac{2}{3}$ 11. $\frac{11}{12}$ 12. $\frac{7}{9}$
$-\frac{3}{4}$ $-\frac{5}{6}$ $-\frac{1}{4}$ $-\frac{1}{4}$ $-\frac{5}{8}$ $-\frac{3}{4}$

B. Copy and subtract. Express your answers in simplest form.

13. 3 14. 4 15. 8 16. 10 17. $2\frac{3}{4}$
$-1\frac{3}{8}$ $-1\frac{5}{6}$ $-3\frac{7}{10}$ $-5\frac{11}{12}$ $-1\frac{1}{2}$

18. $4\frac{5}{6}$ 19. $3\frac{1}{4}$ 20. $4\frac{3}{5}$ 21. $5\frac{5}{8}$ 22. $4\frac{1}{6}$
$-1\frac{2}{3}$ $-2\frac{1}{2}$ $-2\frac{3}{4}$ $-2\frac{2}{3}$ $-2\frac{2}{3}$

C. Solve these reading problems.

23. In the early 1960s, approximately $\frac{2}{5}$ of all Mennonites lived in the United States and $\frac{1}{8}$ lived in Canada. What part more lived in the United States than in Canada?

24. During the same period, $\frac{11}{20}$ of all Mennonites lived in North and Central America. Using the figures given in number 23, find what fraction lived in Central America.

25. Approximately $\frac{9}{16}$ of the Mennonites lived in the Western Hemisphere. If $\frac{11}{20}$ lived in North and Central America, what fraction lived in South America?

26. The remaining $\frac{7}{16}$ of the Mennonites lived in the Eastern Hemisphere, with about $\frac{9}{40}$ of the total number living in Europe. What fraction lived in parts of the Eastern Hemisphere outside of Europe?

27. Sister Alice bought $9\frac{1}{3}$ yards of material to sew dresses for the sewing circle. She used $2\frac{7}{8}$ yards to make one dress. How much material did she have left?

28. Sister Mary bought $8\frac{1}{4}$ yards of material to sew dresses for the sewing circle. She used $3\frac{1}{3}$ yards to make the first dress and $3\frac{1}{6}$ yards to make the second one. How much material did she have left?

REVIEW EXERCISES

D. Add these fractions. Express the answers in simplest form. *(Lesson 42)*

29. $\frac{5}{8}$ 30. $\frac{5}{7}$ 31. $2\frac{3}{4}$ 32. $3\frac{8}{9}$
$+\frac{5}{6}$ $+\frac{3}{5}$ $+1\frac{3}{5}$ $+2\frac{1}{6}$

E. Find the lowest common multiple of each set. *(Lesson 39)*

33. 12, 16 34. 20, 25 35. 18, 22 36. 14, 18

F. Change these measures as indicated. *(Lesson 25)*

37. 17 ft. = _____ in. 38. 14 yd. = _____ in.

39. 3 ft. 6 in. = _____ ft. 40. 5 yd. 10 in. = _____ yd.

44. Mental Multiplication of Whole Numbers and Fractions

One evening while the Martins were milking cows, Father said, "We have milked $\frac{1}{4}$ of our 56 cows. How many is that?"

Doris thought, " $\frac{1}{4}$ of 56 is the same as 56 ÷ 4. 56 ÷ 4 = 14. We have milked 14 cows."

Later Doris thought, "I wonder how many cows we need to milk in order to have $\frac{3}{4}$ of them milked? If $\frac{1}{4}$ of 56 is 14, $\frac{3}{4}$ of 56 is 3 times as many: 3 × 14 = 42. Three-fourths of our cows is 42 cows."

Doris was multiplying fractions mentally. The word *of* in problems such as $\frac{1}{4}$ of 56 and $\frac{3}{4}$ of 56 means $\frac{1}{4}$ × 56 and $\frac{3}{4}$ × 56.

Fractions in which 1 is the numerator are called **unit fractions**. To mentally multiply a whole number by a unit fraction, divide the whole number by the denominator of the fraction.

Example A	Example B
$\frac{1}{4}$ of 36 = 36 ÷ 4 = 9	$\frac{1}{5}$ of 20 = 20 ÷ 5 = 4

To mentally multiply a whole number by a fraction that is not a unit fraction, first divide the whole number by the denominator of the fraction and then multiply that answer by the numerator of the fraction.

Example C	Example D
$\frac{3}{4}$ of 36 = 36 ÷ 4 × 3 = 27	$\frac{3}{5}$ of 20 = 20 ÷ 5 × 3 × 12

CLASS PRACTICE

Find the answers mentally.

a. $\frac{1}{3}$ of 18   b. $\frac{1}{8}$ of 40   c. $22 \times \frac{1}{11}$ d. $18 \times \frac{1}{9}$

e. $\frac{2}{3}$ of 24   f. $\frac{5}{8}$ of 32   g. $33 \times \frac{7}{11}$ h. $36 \times \frac{7}{9}$

WRITTEN EXERCISES

A. *Mentally solve these multiplications containing unit fractions.*

1. $\frac{1}{6}$ of 36   2. $\frac{1}{7}$ of 56   3. $\frac{1}{2}$ of 42   4. $\frac{1}{8}$ of 72

5. $72 \times \frac{1}{12}$ 6. $55 \times \frac{1}{11}$ 7. $90 \times \frac{1}{10}$ 8. $60 \times \frac{1}{15}$

B. *Find the answers mentally.*

9. $\frac{3}{8}$ of 24

10. $\frac{4}{7}$ of 14

11. $\frac{5}{9}$ of 36

12. $\frac{7}{10}$ of 60

13. $30 \times \frac{5}{6}$

14. $66 \times \frac{7}{11}$

15. $60 \times \frac{5}{12}$

16. $96 \times \frac{7}{12}$

17. $\frac{1}{16}$ of 32

18. $\frac{1}{20}$ of 80

19. $\frac{3}{20}$ of 80

20. $\frac{9}{16}$ of 32

21. $56 \times \frac{7}{8}$

22. $48 \times \frac{11}{12}$

23. $88 \times \frac{8}{11}$

24. $108 \times \frac{5}{12}$

C. *Solve these reading problems.*

25. How much would you pay for $\frac{1}{2}$ pound of bologna at $2.20 per pound?

26. What is the price of $\frac{1}{4}$ ton of feed at $160.00 per ton?

27. One snowy morning, $\frac{8}{9}$ of the 72 students were able to come to school on time. How many students were there on time?

28. During Thanksgiving week, Belmont Christian Day School was in session only $2\frac{1}{2}$ days. How many school days was school closed that week? Remember that a school week has 5 days.

29. To find the weight of his dog, Samuel weighed himself and his dog together. The combined weight of the two was $138\frac{1}{2}$ pounds. Samuel's weight was $110\frac{3}{4}$ pounds. What was the weight of the dog?

30. The Martins' cucumber field needed to be hoed. Joel and Lois hoed $\frac{4}{5}$ acre one morning. By noon they still had $\frac{2}{3}$ acre to hoe. How large was the cucumber field?

REVIEW EXERCISES

D. *Copy and solve these problems.* (Lessons 42, 43)

31.
$$4\frac{3}{5}$$
$$+1\frac{1}{2}$$

32.
$$5\frac{3}{4}$$
$$+3\frac{2}{3}$$

33.
$$2\frac{3}{8}$$
$$+1\frac{5}{6}$$

34.
$$3\frac{6}{7}$$
$$+1\frac{1}{2}$$

35.
$$4\frac{4}{5}$$
$$-2\frac{1}{3}$$

36.
$$5\frac{1}{4}$$
$$-2\frac{3}{5}$$

37.
$$6\frac{5}{9}$$
$$-3\frac{5}{6}$$

38.
$$3\frac{4}{9}$$
$$-1\frac{5}{6}$$

E. *Change these measures as indicated.* (Lesson 26)

39. 4 lb. 5 oz. = _____ oz.

40. 5 lb. 12 oz. = _____ lb.

41. 6 tons 1,000 lb. = _____ tons

42. 85 oz. = _____ lb.

45. Multiplication Problems With Fractions

There are several kinds of multiplication problems that contain fractions. In Lesson 44 you worked with multiplying whole numbers by proper fractions. Multiplication problems involving fractions also include multiplying proper fractions by proper fractions, multiplying proper fractions by mixed numbers, and multiplying mixed numbers by mixed numbers. Of course, not all these kinds of multiplication problems can be solved mentally.

Though there is a variety of multiplication problems involving fractions, one basic method can be used to solve them all. The steps in that method are listed below. After the steps are some examples showing how to apply the steps to several kinds of fraction problems.

Solving Multiplication Problems With Fractions

Step 1: Express all whole numbers and mixed numbers as improper fractions.

Step 2: If possible, use cancellation to simplify the problem.

Step 3: Multiply numerators by numerators and denominators by denominators.

Step 4: Write the answer in simplest form.

Multiplying Whole Numbers and Proper Fractions

When multiplying a proper fraction and a whole number, you may need to use all four of the steps listed above.

Example A

	Steps 1 & 2	Step 3	Step 4

$$6 \times \frac{3}{4} = \frac{6}{1} \times \frac{3}{4} = \frac{9}{2} = 9 \div 2 = 4\frac{1}{2}$$

$(6 \div 2) \rightarrow 3$; $(4 \div 2) \rightarrow 2$

Multiplying Proper Fractions

Step 1 is not used when multiplying a proper fraction by a proper fraction. If all the cancellation is done that is possible (Step 2), only Steps 2 and 3 will be necessary. Because both factors are less than 1, multiplying a proper fraction by a proper fraction always results in a product less than 1.

Example B	**Example C**
$\frac{3}{4} \times \frac{2}{5} = \frac{3}{10}$	$\frac{5}{8} \times \frac{2}{5} = \frac{1}{4}$

Multiplying Whole Numbers and Mixed Numbers

Step 1 is used in multiplying most mixed numbers. The only exception is a problem in which the other factor is a whole number that can be multiplied mentally.

> **Example D**
>
> | Steps 1 & 2 | Step 3 | Step 4 |
> |---|---|---|
> | $3\frac{1}{6} \times 3 = \frac{19}{\overset{1}{\cancel{6}}_{2}} \times \frac{\cancel{3}}{1}$ | $= \quad \frac{19}{2}$ | $= \quad 19 \div 2 = 9\frac{1}{2}$ |

Multiplying Proper Fractions and Mixed Numbers

> **Example E**
>
> | Steps 1 & 2 | Step 3 | Step 4 |
> |---|---|---|
> | $2\frac{5}{8} \times \frac{4}{7} = \frac{\overset{3}{\cancel{21}}}{\underset{2}{\cancel{8}}} \times \frac{\overset{1}{\cancel{4}}}{\underset{1}{\cancel{7}}}$ | $= \quad \frac{3}{2}$ | $= \quad 3 \div 2 = 1\frac{1}{2}$ |

CLASS PRACTICE

Solve these problems.

a. $9 \times \frac{3}{4}$ b. $\frac{5}{6} \times \frac{3}{5}$ c. $1\frac{3}{5} \times 10$ d. $3\frac{3}{7} \times \frac{1}{6}$

WRITTEN EXERCISES

A. Copy and solve these problems.

1. $2 \times \frac{3}{4}$ 2. $3 \times \frac{3}{4}$ 3. $6 \times \frac{2}{7}$ 4. $5 \times \frac{2}{3}$

5. $12 \times \frac{5}{6}$ 6. $12 \times \frac{7}{10}$ 7. $15 \times \frac{3}{10}$ 8. $7 \times \frac{2}{3}$

9. $\frac{5}{7} \times \frac{4}{5}$ 10. $\frac{2}{3} \times \frac{9}{10}$ 11. $\frac{4}{9} \times \frac{3}{8}$ 12. $\frac{5}{6} \times \frac{8}{15}$

13. $\frac{3}{5} \times \frac{5}{7}$ 14. $\frac{7}{8} \times \frac{5}{6}$ 15. $\frac{7}{12} \times \frac{10}{11}$ 16. $\frac{4}{9} \times \frac{5}{6}$

17. $1\frac{1}{3} \times 4$ 18. $2\frac{1}{2} \times 7$ 19. $3\frac{3}{5} \times \frac{5}{9}$ 20. $4\frac{1}{2} \times \frac{2}{3}$

B. Solve these reading problems.

21. When Jacob finished picking lima beans, his $\frac{1}{2}$ bushel basket was $\frac{2}{3}$ full. What part of a bushel of lima beans did he have?

22. The Martins' tomato field contained $\frac{4}{5}$ acre. Marvin and Matthew hoed $\frac{2}{3}$ of the field one day. What part of an acre did they hoe?

23. Last Tuesday the Martins took 15 bushels of tomatoes to a roadside stand to sell. By the end of the day, $\frac{3}{4}$ of them were sold. How many bushels of tomatoes were sold?

24. On Wednesday the Martins took $12\frac{1}{2}$ bushels to the stand and sold $\frac{4}{5}$ of them. How many tomatoes did they sell that day?

25. What was the difference between the number of bushels taken to the stand on Tuesday and on Wednesday? (See problems 23 and 24.)

26. At the end of the week, all but $2\frac{3}{4}$ bushels of tomatoes had been sold. One bushel was in a bushel basket, and the rest were in peck baskets. How many peck baskets were filled with tomatoes?

REVIEW EXERCISES

C. *Solve these multiplication problems mentally.* *(Lesson 44)*

27. $\frac{1}{5}$ of 55

28. $\frac{1}{3}$ of 36

29. $25 \times \frac{4}{5}$

30. $35 \times \frac{5}{7}$

D. *Solve these subtraction problems.* *(Lesson 43)*

31. $3\frac{3}{4}$
$-1\frac{2}{3}$

32. $5\frac{5}{6}$
$-2\frac{3}{4}$

33. $4\frac{1}{5}$
$-3\frac{2}{3}$

34. $5\frac{2}{7}$
$-2\frac{1}{2}$

E. *Identify these numbers as prime or composite.* *(Lesson 37)*

35. 18

36. 19

37. 20

38. 21

F. *Change these measures as indicated.* *(Lesson 27)*

39. 4 pk. = _____ qt.

40. 5 fl. oz. = _____ cups

41. 6 gal. = _____ qt.

42. 5 gal. 2 qt. = _____ gal.

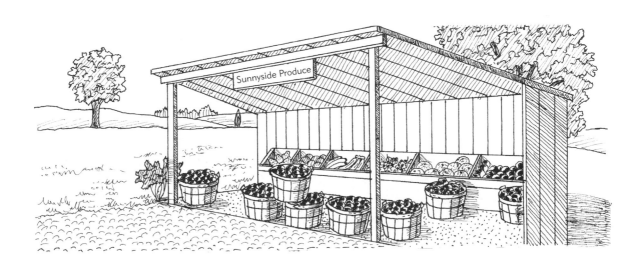

46. Multiplication With More Challenging Fractions

Multiplying Mixed Numbers

In Lesson 45 you studied the following steps for solving multiplication problems with fractions.

Step 1: Express all whole numbers and mixed numbers as improper fractions.

Step 2: If possible, use cancellation to simplify the problem.

Step 3: Multiply numerators by numerators and denominators by denominators.

Step 4: Write the answer in simplest form.

These steps are also used to multiply mixed numbers. Often all four steps will be needed to solve such problems.

Example A

$$\text{Steps 1 \& 2} \qquad \text{Step 3} \qquad \text{Step 4}$$

$$4\tfrac{1}{2} \times 2\tfrac{2}{3} = \dfrac{\overset{3}{\cancel{9}}}{\underset{1}{\cancel{2}}} \times \dfrac{\overset{4}{\cancel{8}}}{\underset{1}{\cancel{3}}} \quad = \quad \dfrac{12}{1} \quad = \quad 12 \div 1 = 12$$

Example B

$$\text{Steps 1 \& 2} \qquad \text{Step 3} \qquad \text{Step 4}$$

$$1\tfrac{3}{7} \times 2\tfrac{3}{5} = \dfrac{10}{7} \times \dfrac{\overset{2}{13}}{\underset{1}{\cancel{5}}} \quad = \quad \dfrac{26}{7} \quad = \quad 26 \div 7 = 3\tfrac{5}{7}$$

Vertical Multiplication of Whole Numbers by Mixed Numbers

Multiplication with mixed numbers is usually done by the method shown above and in Lesson 45. But sometimes a whole number is multiplied by a mixed number with a denominator that is a factor of the whole number. Then it is often easier to solve the problem by vertical multiplication as shown in Examples C and D.

Step 1: Copy the problem, using the mixed number as the multiplier.

Step 2: Multiply the whole number by the fraction in the multiplier.

Step 3: Multiply the whole number by the ones digit in the multiplier. Write the ones digit of the partial product directly below that of the first partial product.

Step 4: If the multiplier has two digits, multiply the whole number by the tens digit. Write the first digit of the partial product in the tens place. (See Example D.)

Step 5: Add the partial products to obtain the final product.

Example C	Example D
$\begin{array}{r} 12 \\ \times 2\frac{1}{3} \\ \hline 4 \\ 24 \\ \hline 28 \end{array}$	$\begin{array}{r} 15 \\ \times 12\frac{1}{2} \\ \hline 7\frac{1}{2} \\ 30 \\ 15 \\ \hline 187\frac{1}{2} \end{array}$

In Example D, the denominator 2 is not a factor of the whole number 15. But $\frac{1}{2}$ is such a simple fraction that the vertical method can also be used to solve this problem.

CLASS PRACTICE

Solve these horizontal multiplication problems with mixed numbers.

a. $4\frac{1}{2} \times 3\frac{2}{3}$ b. $2\frac{5}{6} \times 1\frac{1}{8}$ c. $3\frac{3}{4} \times 4\frac{3}{5}$ d. $5\frac{5}{9} \times 3\frac{1}{5}$

These are simple problems in which a whole number is multiplied by a mixed number. Solve them by vertical multiplication.

e. $\begin{array}{r} 9 \\ \times 3\frac{1}{3} \\ \hline \end{array}$ f. $\begin{array}{r} 10 \\ \times 4\frac{3}{5} \\ \hline \end{array}$ g. $\begin{array}{r} 12 \\ \times 11\frac{3}{4} \\ \hline \end{array}$ h. $\begin{array}{r} 17 \\ \times 12\frac{1}{2} \\ \hline \end{array}$

WRITTEN EXERCISES

A. Copy and solve these problems by the standard method shown first in this lesson.

1. $17 \times \frac{2}{3}$
2. $13 \times \frac{3}{4}$
3. $\frac{4}{5} \times \frac{5}{8}$
4. $\frac{7}{9} \times \frac{15}{16}$
5. $4\frac{1}{3} \times 8$
6. $5\frac{3}{5} \times 8$
7. $3\frac{5}{7} \times \frac{9}{10}$
8. $2\frac{8}{9} \times \frac{11}{13}$
9. $1\frac{1}{2} \times 2\frac{2}{3}$
10. $3\frac{1}{5} \times 2\frac{5}{6}$
11. $5\frac{5}{8} \times 1\frac{1}{9}$
12. $3\frac{6}{7} \times 2\frac{1}{6}$
13. $2\frac{1}{12} \times 3\frac{1}{5}$
14. $1\frac{5}{16} \times 2\frac{1}{14}$

B. Copy and solve these problems by the vertical method.

15. $\begin{array}{r} 8 \\ \times 4\frac{1}{4} \\ \hline \end{array}$ 16. $\begin{array}{r} 9 \\ \times 8\frac{2}{3} \\ \hline \end{array}$ 17. $\begin{array}{r} 12 \\ \times 7\frac{5}{6} \\ \hline \end{array}$

18. $\begin{array}{r} 16 \\ \times 2\frac{3}{4} \\ \hline \end{array}$ 19. $\begin{array}{r} 13 \\ \times 12\frac{1}{2} \\ \hline \end{array}$ 20. $\begin{array}{r} 15 \\ \times 11\frac{1}{2} \\ \hline \end{array}$

C. Solve these reading problems.

21. About $\frac{5}{12}$ of the total land area in the Americas is in South America. Nearly $\frac{1}{2}$ of the land in South America lies within the borders of Brazil. What fraction of the land area in the Americas is found in Brazil?

22. Brother Dwight purchased $3\frac{1}{2}$ tons of coal and gave $\frac{1}{10}$ of it to an elderly neighbor. How much coal did Brother Dwight give to the neighbor?

23. The $3\frac{1}{2}$ tons of coal cost $120 per ton. What was the total cost of the coal? Use the vertical method to solve this problem.

24. Brother Dwight hauled the $3\frac{1}{2}$ tons of coal on a truck that weighed $6\frac{1}{8}$ tons. What was the gross (total) weight of the coal and the truck?

25. Mother bought $5\frac{1}{2}$ yards of material at $3 per yard. What was the total cost of the material? Use the vertical method to solve this problem.

26. Miller's Auto Supply received a shipment of 50 cases of motor oil. Each case weighed $48\frac{1}{2}$ pounds. What was the total weight of the motor oil?

But to do good and to communicate forget not.   *Hebrews 13:16*

REVIEW EXERCISES

D. Copy and add. *(Lesson 42)*

27.
$$\begin{array}{r} \frac{7}{9} \\ + \frac{11}{12} \end{array}$$

28.
$$\begin{array}{r} \frac{11}{15} \\ + \frac{11}{18} \end{array}$$

29.
$$\begin{array}{r} 2\frac{1}{5} \\ + 3\frac{2}{3} \end{array}$$

30.
$$\begin{array}{r} 5\frac{3}{4} \\ + 3\frac{4}{9} \end{array}$$

E. Find the greatest common factor for each set. *(Lesson 38)*

31. 9, 15   32. 18, 42   33. 21, 56   34. 52, 91

F. Change these measures. *(Lesson 28)*

35. 3 sq. ft. = _____ sq. in.   36. 3 sq. ft. = _____ sq. yd.

37. 4 sq. mi. = _____ a.   38. 12 sq. ft. = _____ sq. yd.

G. Solve by horizontal multiplication. *(Lesson 12)*

39. 352×7 40. 782×5 41. $1,251 \times 6$ 42. $3,518 \times 8$

47. Using Reciprocals to Divide by Fractions

Study the three multiplication problems below. They are alike in that each product is 1. All the products are 1 because in each problem, a number is multiplied by its **reciprocal**. Multiplying a number by its reciprocal always results in a product of 1.

$$\frac{3}{4} \times \frac{4}{3} = 1 \qquad \frac{5}{2} \times \frac{2}{5} = 1 \qquad \frac{7}{1} \times \frac{1}{7} = 1$$

Every number except zero and one has a reciprocal. A reciprocal is simple to find if the number is first expressed as a fraction. To find the reciprocal of a fraction, simply invert the fraction. The reciprocal of a proper fraction is always an improper fraction. If the reciprocal is an improper fraction, do not change it to a mixed number.

Example A: The reciprocal of $\frac{3}{8}$ is $\frac{8}{3}$.

Example B: The reciprocal of $\frac{7}{9}$ is $\frac{9}{7}$.

To find the reciprocal of a whole number, first express the whole number as an improper fraction with the denominator 1. Then invert the improper fraction.

Example C: Find the reciprocal of 7.

Step 1:   Change 7 to an improper fraction: $7 = \frac{7}{1}$.

Step 2:   The reciprocal of $\frac{7}{1}$ is $\frac{1}{7}$.

To find the reciprocal of a mixed number, first express the mixed number as an improper fraction. Then invert the improper fraction.

Example D: Find the reciprocal of $7\frac{1}{3}$.

Step 1:   Change $7\frac{1}{3}$ into an improper fraction: $7\frac{1}{3} = \frac{22}{3}$.

Step 2:   The reciprocal of $\frac{22}{3}$ is $\frac{3}{22}$.

Reciprocals are most commonly used in dividing fractions. To divide a whole number by a fraction, multiply the dividend by the reciprocal of the divisor. In Example E, notice that dividing a whole number by a unit fraction is the same as multiplying the whole number by the denominator of the fraction.

Example E: Solve. $6 \div \frac{1}{3}$ $6 \div \frac{1}{3} = \frac{6}{1} \times \frac{3}{1} = 6 \times 3 = 18$

Example F: Solve. $8 \div \frac{3}{4}$ $8 \div \frac{3}{4} = \frac{8}{1} \times \frac{4}{3} = \frac{32}{3} = 10\frac{2}{3}$

CLASS PRACTICE

Find the reciprocals of these numbers.

a. $\frac{9}{11}$
b. 11
c. $3\frac{1}{2}$
d. $4\frac{5}{6}$

Find these answers mentally by multiplying the whole number by the denominator of the fraction.

e. $4 \div \frac{1}{2}$
f. $7 \div \frac{1}{8}$
g. $6 \div \frac{1}{16}$
h. $9 \div \frac{1}{11}$

Find these answers by multiplying the dividend by the reciprocal of the divisor.

i. $4 \div \frac{2}{3}$
j. $6 \div \frac{5}{6}$
k. $8 \div \frac{3}{5}$
l. $7 \div \frac{7}{9}$

Solve this reading problem.

Mother bought five pounds of butter in $\frac{1}{4}$-pound sticks. How many sticks of butter were there? (Solve as a division problem.)

WRITTEN EXERCISES

A. *Find the reciprocals of these numbers.*

1. $\frac{4}{5}$
2. $\frac{7}{12}$
3. $\frac{27}{2}$
4. 12
5. 29
6. 57
7. 100
8. $5\frac{5}{8}$
9. $3\frac{7}{9}$
10. $5\frac{3}{4}$

B. *Find the answers to these division problems mentally by multiplying the whole numbers by the denominators of the unit fractions.*

11. $5 \div \frac{1}{6}$
12. $7 \div \frac{1}{7}$
13. $8 \div \frac{1}{9}$
14. $11 \div \frac{1}{2}$
15. $12 \div \frac{1}{7}$
16. $16 \div \frac{1}{3}$

C. *Solve these problems by multiplying the dividend by the reciprocal of the divisor.*

17. $3 \div \frac{3}{4}$
18. $6 \div \frac{3}{4}$
19. $5 \div \frac{4}{5}$
20. $2 \div \frac{3}{4}$
21. $7 \div \frac{5}{9}$
22. $9 \div \frac{6}{7}$

D. *Solve these reading problems.*

23. Mother cut 4 apples into halves to make apple dumplings. How many halves did she have? Write this problem as a division problem. Show your work.

24. At a roadside stand, there were $23 worth of quarters in the cash box at the end of one day. How many quarters was that? Write this problem as a division problem. Show your work.

25. To find the diameter of a circle when the circumference is known, the circumference is divided by pi, or $3\frac{1}{7}$. What is the reciprocal of $3\frac{1}{7}$?

26. The Millers harvested 1,533 bushels of corn from a $10\frac{1}{2}$-acre field. To find the number of bushels per acre, James is dividing 1,533 by $10\frac{1}{2}$. The first step is to find the reciprocal of $10\frac{1}{2}$. What is it?

27. The Millers also planted corn in a $25\frac{1}{4}$-acre field. How much larger was that field than their $10\frac{1}{2}$-acre field?

28. The $10\frac{1}{2}$-acre field was larger before the Millers donated $3\frac{1}{3}$ acres to build the Rockville Mennonite School. How large was the field before the school was built?

REVIEW EXERCISES

E. *Find these products mentally.* (Lesson 44)

29. $6 \times \frac{1}{3}$ **30.** $8 \times \frac{1}{4}$ **31.** $10 \times \frac{2}{5}$ **32.** $12 \times \frac{2}{3}$

F. *Solve these subtraction problems.* (Lesson 43)

33. $3\frac{1}{4}$
    $-1\frac{1}{8}$

34. $5\frac{1}{3}$
    $-2\frac{3}{4}$

G. *Find the lowest common multiple of each set.* (Lesson 39)

35. 6, 14   **36.** 16, 18

H. *Change these measures as indicated.* (Lesson 29)

37. 9 wk. = _____ days   **38.** 38 mo. = _____ yr.

39. 3 millennia = _____ yr.   **40.** 35 decades = _____ yr.

48. More Practice With Dividing Fractions

Compare the two problems shown below. In the first problem, 81 is divided by 9; and in the second problem, 81 is multiplied by $\frac{1}{9}$, the reciprocal of 9.

In both problems, the answer is 9. Multiplying a number by the reciprocal of the divisor is the same as dividing it by the divisor.

$$81 \div 9 = 9 \qquad\qquad 81 \times \frac{1}{9} = \frac{\overset{9}{\cancel{81}}}{1} \times \frac{1}{\cancel{9}} = 9$$

Division is done to find how many times one number is contained in another number. In the division problem above, $81 \div 9$ means "How many 9's are in 81?"

In Example A below, $2 \div \frac{1}{4}$ means "How many $\frac{1}{4}$'s are in 2?" When dividing by a fraction, multiply by the reciprocal of the divisor. Follow the steps below.

1. Express both the dividend and the divisor as fractions.
2. Change the divisor to its reciprocal by inverting it.
3. Cancel whenever possible.
4. Multiply.
5. Write the answer in simplest form.

Example A	**Example B**
$2 \div \frac{1}{4} = \frac{2}{1} \times \frac{4}{1} = \frac{8}{1} = 8$	$5 \div \frac{3}{4} = \frac{5}{1} \times \frac{4}{3} = \frac{20}{3} = 6\frac{2}{3}$

Whenever whole numbers or mixed numbers are part of the division problem, first change them to improper fractions and then solve.

Example C

$$3\frac{1}{8} \div \frac{1}{4} = \frac{25}{8} \div \frac{1}{4} = \frac{25}{\underset{2}{\cancel{8}}} \times \frac{\overset{1}{\cancel{4}}}{1} = \frac{25}{2} = 12\frac{1}{2}$$

Example D

$$4\frac{1}{5} \div 1\frac{1}{10} = \frac{21}{5} \div \frac{11}{10} = \frac{21}{\underset{1}{\cancel{5}}} \times \frac{\overset{2}{\cancel{10}}}{11} = \frac{42}{11} = 3\frac{9}{11}$$

CLASS PRACTICE

Solve these division problems.

a. $8 \div \frac{3}{4}$ b. $\frac{7}{8} \div \frac{2}{3}$ c. $\frac{3}{4} \div \frac{7}{8}$ d. $1\frac{3}{4} \div \frac{1}{4}$

e. $4\frac{1}{2} \div 1\frac{1}{5}$ f. $3\frac{1}{5} \div 2\frac{1}{4}$ g. $2\frac{2}{3} \div 1\frac{1}{8}$

WRITTEN EXERCISES

A. *Solve these division problems.*

1. $5 \div \frac{1}{4}$ 2. $6 \div \frac{1}{3}$ 3. $8 \div \frac{2}{3}$ 4. $9 \div \frac{4}{5}$

5. $\frac{5}{6} \div \frac{1}{3}$ 6. $\frac{7}{8} \div \frac{3}{8}$ 7. $\frac{7}{9} \div \frac{2}{3}$ 8. $\frac{3}{7} \div \frac{1}{3}$

9. $\frac{3}{5} \div \frac{3}{4}$ 10. $\frac{5}{8} \div \frac{7}{8}$ 11. $1\frac{1}{4} \div \frac{1}{4}$ 12. $3\frac{5}{8} \div \frac{3}{8}$

13. $2\frac{1}{2} \div 1\frac{1}{4}$ 14. $3\frac{3}{8} \div 1\frac{1}{4}$ 15. $4\frac{1}{3} \div 2\frac{1}{2}$ 16. $2\frac{1}{7} \div 1\frac{1}{2}$

B. *Solve these reading problems.*

17. Janet wants to cut a 4-yard piece of elastic into $\frac{1}{6}$-yard lengths. How many pieces will she be able to cut?

18. Anna's bread recipe calls for $\frac{3}{4}$ cup shortening. If Anna has $2\frac{1}{2}$ cups of shortening, how many batches of bread can she make?

19. Carl has $\frac{3}{4}$ bushel of shelled peas. He plans to sell them by the pint ($\frac{1}{64}$ bushel). How many pints of shelled peas does Carl have?

20. From a 9-foot length of shelving, John wants to cut shelves $1\frac{1}{2}$ feet long. How many such boards will he be able to cut?

21. Marcia gathered $27\frac{1}{2}$ dozen eggs. How many flats will the eggs fill if each flat holds $2\frac{1}{2}$ dozen eggs?

22. Mother froze 80 pints of corn, putting $2\frac{1}{2}$ pints in each freezer bag. How many bags of corn did she have?

REVIEW EXERCISES

C. *Solve these fraction problems mentally.* (Lesson 44)

23. $\frac{1}{4} \times 24$ 24. $\frac{1}{5} \times 35$ 25. $\frac{3}{8} \times 24$ 26. $\frac{5}{7} \times 28$

D. *Boston, Massachusetts, is in the Eastern Time Zone. Use the map in Lesson 30 to discover what time it is in the following cities when it is 2:00 P.M. in Boston.*

27. St. John's, Newfoundland   28. Honolulu, Hawaii

E. *Do these multiplications mentally.* (Lesson 15)

29. 22×6 30. 14×50 31. 28×25 32. 18×6

F. *Estimate the products to these multiplication problems. You do not need to find exact answers.* (Lesson 14)

33. $\begin{array}{r} 32 \\ \times\,48 \end{array}$ 34. $\begin{array}{r} 425 \\ \times\,36 \end{array}$ 35. $\begin{array}{r} 528 \\ \times\,489 \end{array}$ 36. $\begin{array}{r} 3{,}260 \\ \times\,4{,}771 \end{array}$

49. Finding a Number When a Fraction of It Is Known

Example A

David is 12 years old. He is twice as old as his younger sister Joanna. How old is Joanna?

Example B

David is 12 years old. He is $\frac{2}{3}$ as old as his older brother Mark. How old is Mark?

Study the reading problems above. The facts are very nearly alike. The main difference is that in the first reading problem, David is two times as old as his younger sister, and in the second reading problem, he is $\frac{2}{3}$ as old as his older brother.

Example A is solved by dividing 12 by 2. Because David is 2 times Joanna's age, his age is divided by 2: $12 \div 2 = 6$.

Example B is solved by dividing 12 by $\frac{2}{3}$. Because David is $\frac{2}{3}$ times Mark's age, David's age is divided by $\frac{2}{3}$ to discover Mark's age.

$$12 \div \frac{2}{3} = \overset{6}{\underset{1}{\cancel{\frac{12}{1}}}} \times \frac{3}{\cancel{2}} = 18$$

You know that *of* means "times." Think of the word *is* as an equal sign. Thus the question *12 is $\frac{2}{3}$ of what number?* can be written as the number sentence $12 = \frac{2}{3} \times$ ___. You can find the missing factor by dividing.

To find a number when a fractional part of it is known, divide the known number by the fractional part.

Example C

6 is $\frac{3}{4}$ of what number? $6 \div \frac{3}{4} = \overset{2}{\underset{1}{\cancel{\frac{6}{1}}}} \times \frac{4}{3} = 8$; 6 is $\frac{3}{4}$ of 8

Example D

9 is $\frac{5}{8}$ of what number? $9 \div \frac{5}{8} = \frac{9}{1} \times \frac{8}{5} = \frac{72}{5} = 14\frac{2}{5}$; 9 is $\frac{5}{8}$ of $14\frac{2}{5}$

These problems can be checked by multiplying as shown below.

Check for Example C	**Check for Example D**
$8 \times \frac{3}{4} = 6$	$14\frac{2}{5} \times \frac{5}{8} = \overset{9}{\underset{1}{\cancel{\frac{72}{5}}}} \times \frac{\overset{1}{\cancel{5}}}{\cancel{8}} = 9$

CLASS PRACTICE

Solve these problems.

a. 4 is $\frac{1}{2}$ of _____

b. 5 is $\frac{5}{6}$ of _____

c. 6 is $\frac{4}{9}$ of _____

d. There are $\frac{2}{3}$ as many students in seventh grade as in eighth grade. If 8 students are in seventh grade, how many are in eighth grade?

WRITTEN EXERCISES

A. *Find the unknown numbers.*

1. 2 is $\frac{1}{2}$ of _____

2. 4 is $\frac{1}{3}$ of _____

3. 6 is $\frac{2}{3}$ of _____

4. 6 is $\frac{3}{8}$ of _____

5. 9 is $\frac{3}{4}$ of _____

6. 7 is $\frac{3}{5}$ of _____

7. 8 is $\frac{4}{5}$ of _____

8. 12 is $\frac{3}{7}$ of _____

9. 10 is $\frac{2}{9}$ of _____

10. 14 is $\frac{7}{12}$ of _____

11. 16 is $\frac{4}{5}$ of _____

12. 18 is $\frac{9}{10}$ of _____

B. *Solve these reading problems.*

13. The robin of eastern North America is an average of about 10 inches long, or about $\frac{1}{2}$ the average length of a crow. What is the average length of a crow?

14. The robin is about $\frac{5}{6}$ as long as a blue jay. What is the average length of a blue jay?

15. A canvasback duck lays eggs that are $2\frac{1}{2}$ inches long. A ruby-throated hummingbird lays eggs whose length is the reciprocal of the length of a canvasback duck egg. How long is the egg of a ruby-throated hummingbird?

16. Canvasback duck eggs are $2\frac{1}{2}$ inches long. That is $\frac{5}{7}$ as long as the eggs of the common loon. How long are the eggs of the common loon?

17. Bald eagles are large birds that are 35 inches long. But they are only $\frac{7}{12}$ as long as mute swans. What is the length of the mute swan?

18. The whistling swan, the most common swan in North America, has a length of 54 inches. Its length is $\frac{2}{3}$ as great as its wingspan. What is the wingspan of the whistling swan?

REVIEW EXERCISES

C. *Solve these division problems.* (*Lesson 48*)

19. $8 \div \frac{5}{6}$

20. $\frac{3}{5} \div \frac{2}{3}$

21. $3\frac{1}{4} \div \frac{2}{5}$

22. $4\frac{1}{2} \div 2\frac{1}{3}$

D. *Find the reciprocals of these numbers.* (*Lesson 47*)

23. $\frac{5}{12}$

24. $\frac{13}{12}$

25. 9

26. $4\frac{1}{5}$

E. *Solve these problems about distance, rate, and time.* (*Lesson 32*)

27. $t = 4\frac{1}{2}$ hr.
$r = 52$ m.p.h.
$d =$ _____

28. $d = 120$ mi.
$r = 45$ m.p.h.
$t =$ _____

29. $t = 7$ hr.
$r = 278$ m.p.h.
$d =$ _____

30. $d = 160$ mi.
$t = 3$ hr.
$r =$ _____

50. Reading Problems: Problems With Extra Information

When math is used in everyday life, the problems are not neatly arranged in columns and rows as they often are in a math textbook. Neither do problems come with only the information needed to solve them. Instead, you need to select the information that you will use to solve the problem. Consider the following example.

> A car drove 135 miles at an average rate of 45 miles per hour. It traveled 18 miles on each gallon of gasoline it used. How many gallons of gasoline did the car use on the trip?

It is not necessary to know the average speed in order to calculate how many gallons of gasoline were used. The answer can be found by dividing 135 by 18. The car used $7\frac{1}{2}$ gallons of gasoline.

So far this year, most of the reading problems in your math book gave you only the information needed to solve the problems. The reading problems in this lesson include extra information. Study each problem carefully in order to use only the needed facts to find the solution.

CLASS PRACTICE

In each problem, first identify the numbers that are not needed to find the solution. Then solve the problem.

a. A mechanic paid $2,300 for a used car that had an odometer reading of 78,581 miles. He spent $375 to repair the car and then sold it for $2,725. By then the odometer reading was 79,151 miles. How much profit did he make?

b. One day the Maple Hill Orchard sold 35 bushels of apples at $7.00 per bushel and 60 pecks of apples at $2.25 per peck. How many apples were sold in all?

WRITTEN EXERCISES

A. *In each reading problem, first find the numbers that are not needed and write them on your paper. Then solve the problem.*

1. A mission board bought a van for missionaries to use in traveling to their homes. When the vehicle was purchased, the odometer showed 45,321 miles. One year the odometer showed 68,439 miles on January 1 and 92,312 miles on December 31. By the end of that year, how many miles had the van been driven since it was purchased?

2. On one round trip to Central America, the beginning odometer reading on the vehicle was 72,121 miles. The oil was changed at 75,124 miles, and at the end of the trip the odometer showed 79,115 miles. At 11 miles per gallon, how many gallons of fuel did the vehicle use on the trip?

3. While visiting Rod and Staff Publishers at Crockett, Kentucky, Father purchased *The New Unger's Bible Dictionary* for $42.35 to use at home. If he had bought the book for a school library, he would have received a discount of $4.24. Kentucky sales tax on his purchase was $2.54. How much did Father pay in all?

4. God created an abundance of insects in the world. Scientists have identified at least 800,000 different kinds of insects. Some scientists have estimated that there are at least 2,000,000 different kinds of insects. One insect census reported that only 235 kinds of insects caused damage on farms and in cities. How many of the identified kinds of insects are not harmful?

5. Insects vary greatly in size. The smallest insects are less than $\frac{1}{100}$ inch long, and the largest ones are about 12 inches long. The largest dragonflies have a wingspan of 7 inches. How many times longer are the longest insects than the shortest ones?

6. Some insects can be very destructive. The corn earworm has been estimated to eat 2,000,000 acres of corn per year. One year the boll weevil was the most expensive pest, doing damage of $200,000,000. At 130 bushels of corn per acre, how many bushels of corn are lost to the corn earworm?

7. Bees are helpful insects because they pollinate fruit trees and other plants. It has been estimated that without bees, 100,000 kinds of flowering plants would die. It has also been estimated that bees may need to travel 13,000 miles to make one pound of honey. If the average speed of a bee is 12 miles per hour, how many hours of flying time are needed to make one pound of honey?

8. Some bee colonies have 80,000 members. An average honeybee produces only about $\frac{1}{10}$ pound of honey during its entire life, which varies from 6 weeks to several months. Since bees may need to travel 13,000 miles to make 1 pound of honey, what is the average distance that a bee travels in producing $\frac{1}{10}$ pound of honey?

How sweet are thy words unto my taste! Yea, sweeter than honey to my mouth!
Psalms 119:103

9. Butterflies are another of God's amazing creatures. Some large butterflies may have 1,000,000 scales on their wings. The Queen Alexandria's birdwing is the largest butterfly in the world, with a wingspread of about 11 inches. One of the largest butterflies in North America, the tiger swallowtail, has a wingspread of about 5 inches. That is $13\frac{1}{3}$ times greater than the wingspread of the western pygmy blue butterfly. What is the wingspread of the western pygmy blue butterfly?

10. The painted lady is a butterfly that migrates 2,500 miles to its winter home, sometimes in large swarms numbering in the millions. One large swarm was 600 feet high, 1 mile wide, and many miles long. How many times greater was the width of the swarm than its height?

REVIEW EXERCISES

B. Find the unknown numbers. *(Lesson 49)*

11. 12 is $\frac{6}{7}$ of _____

12. 15 is $\frac{1}{3}$ of _____

13. 10 is $\frac{5}{6}$ of _____

14. 16 is $\frac{3}{4}$ of _____

C. Add these fractions and mixed numbers. *(Lesson 42)*

15.
$$\begin{array}{r} \frac{5}{6} \\ + \frac{3}{4} \\ \hline \end{array}$$

16.
$$\begin{array}{r} 2\frac{1}{3} \\ + 3\frac{3}{4} \\ \hline \end{array}$$

17.
$$\begin{array}{r} 3\frac{7}{9} \\ + 2\frac{5}{6} \\ \hline \end{array}$$

18.
$$\begin{array}{r} 5\frac{4}{5} \\ + 2\frac{2}{3} \\ \hline \end{array}$$

D. Solve these division problems. Write any remainders as whole numbers. *(Lesson 16)*

19. $41\overline{)683}$

20. $89\overline{)735}$

21. $115\overline{)6,529}$

22. $311\overline{)12,271}$

51. Working With Graphs: The Bar Graph

Reading Bar Graphs

A bar graph is much like a picture graph. The lengths of the bars on a bar graph are used to compare quantities just as the numbers of symbols are on a picture graph. Bar graphs and picture graphs differ from line graphs in that bar graphs and picture graphs usually compare different items, but line graphs compare changing amounts over a period of time.

For example, the first bar graph below compares the size of the five largest cities in Texas. The same facts could be presented on a picture graph. If a line graph were made, it would not be used to compare the five cities but rather to show the growth of one city over a given period of time.

Bar graphs are convenient for making comparisons. On the first graph below, comparing the lengths of the bars shows that Houston is about three times as large as El Paso.

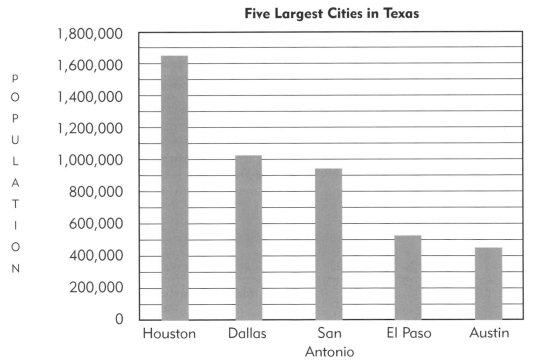

Five Largest Cities in Texas

Source: *1990 Census*

Five Largest Cities in Ohio

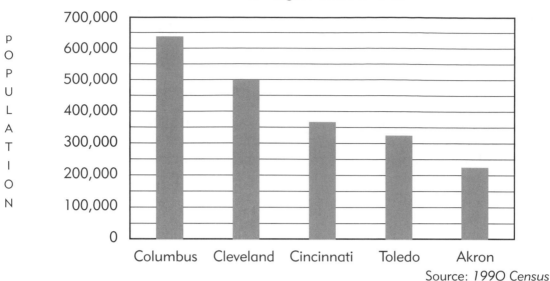

Source: *1990 Census*

Drawing Bar Graphs

To draw a bar graph, use the following steps.

1. Look over the facts to be shown on the graph, and find the largest number.
2. Decide what scale you will use. For example, if the largest number is 900, you should number your scale by hundreds from 0 to 1,000. If the largest number is 90,000, your scale should be numbered by ten thousands from 0 to 100,000.
3. Start with zero, and mark off the scale you chose in step 2. The scale must increase at a constant rate. For example, if you are labeling by hundreds, the distance from each mark to the next should represent 100. Do not use an inconsistent scale, such as starting with hundreds and changing to thousands.
4. Label the vertical scale.
5. Draw each bar to the correct height, and label it. The bars should all be the same width, and the distance between them should be consistent.
6. Write a title for the graph.
7. Write the source of the information in the lower right corner of the graph.

WRITTEN EXERCISES

A. *Use the graphs in the lesson to answer these questions.*

1. Estimate the population of Columbus, Ohio.
2. Which city is closest to twice as large as Akron?
3. Which city is closest to twice as large as Toledo?
4. Estimate how many more people live in Cleveland than in Cincinnati.
5. Which two cities are most nearly equal in size?
6. Which two cities have a combined population nearest to 1,000,000?

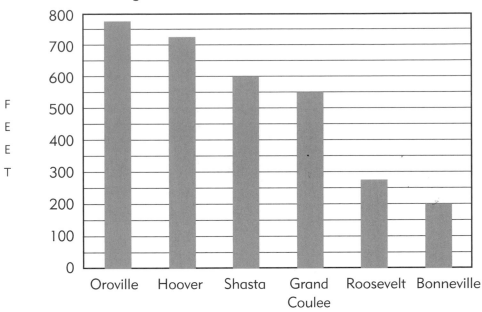

Height of Six Well-Known Dams in the United States

Source: *World Book Encyclopedia*

B. Use the graph above to answer these questions.

7. Which dam is about three times as high as the Bonneville Dam?

8. Which dam is about twice as high as the Roosevelt Dam?

9. Which dam is nearly four times as high as the Bonneville Dam?

10. Estimate how much higher the Shasta Dam is than the Bonneville Dam.

11. Estimate how much higher the Shasta Dam is than the Grand Coulee Dam.

12. Estimate how much higher the Hoover Dam is than the Shasta Dam.

C. Draw a bar graph for each set of facts. Label every other horizontal line on your graph paper. Allow three blank squares between each bar, and make each bar two squares wide.

13. The five largest cities in the province of Saskatchewan have populations as listed below.

    Saskatoon 177,641
    Regina 175,064
    Moose Jaw 35,073
    Prince Albert 33,686
    Lloydminster 17,356

    Source: *Rand McNally Road Atlas, 1995*

14. The ages of five early Anabaptist leaders at their deaths are listed below. The cause of death is for your information only; do not include it on the graph.

> *Leader (Cause of Death)   Age at Death*
> Conrad Grebel (illness) 28
> Felix Manz (martyrdom) 29
> George Blaurock (martyrdom) 37
> Michael Sattler (martyrdom) 37
> Menno Simons (natural causes) 65
>
> Source: *Mennonite Encyclopedia*

(Ages are approximate because dates of birth are uncertain.)

REVIEW EXERCISES

D. Write the reciprocal of each number. *(Lesson 47)*

15. $\frac{3}{5}$ **16.** $\frac{5}{3}$ **17.** 6   **18.** 19   **19.** $5\frac{1}{2}$ **20.** $4\frac{5}{6}$

E. Solve these subtraction problems. *(Lesson 43)*

21. $\frac{3}{5}$ **22.**   7   **23.** $3\frac{3}{5}$ **24.** $4\frac{1}{6}$
       $-\frac{1}{4}$ $-1\frac{3}{4}$ $-1\frac{1}{3}$ $-1\frac{5}{9}$

F. Solve these problems by short division, without copying them. Write remainders as whole numbers. *(Lesson 17)*

25. $5\overline{)8{,}214}$ **26.** $4\overline{)3{,}156}$ **27.** $8\overline{)7{,}321}$ **28.** $7\overline{)2{,}612}$

52. Chapter 4 Review

A. Identify each number as prime or composite. *(Lesson 37)*

1. 15   **2.** 17   **3.** 19   **4.** 21

B. Find the prime factors of these composite numbers. *(Lesson 37)*

5. 18   **6.** 28   **7.** 32   **8.** 81

C. Find the greatest common factor (g.c.f.) of each pair. *(Lesson 38)*

9. 12, 18   **10.** 16, 40   **11.** 24, 48   **12.** 40, 70

D. Find the lowest common multiple of each pair by using Method 1 and then Method 2 if necessary. *(Lesson 39)*

13. 8, 12   **14.** 9, 12   **15.** 16, 18   **16.** 20, 24

E. Answer these questions about fractions. *(Lesson 40)*

17. What is the denominator of the fraction $\frac{5}{6}$?

18. Which of these numbers is a mixed number? $\frac{5}{8}$ 4 $4\frac{1}{5}$ $\frac{31}{7}$

19. Which of these numbers is an improper fraction? $\frac{5}{3}$ 9 $\frac{7}{8}$ $3\frac{3}{4}$

20. Which of these numbers is a whole number? $\frac{7}{2}$ $\frac{4}{7}$ 6 $3\frac{12}{17}$

F. Reduce these fractions to lowest terms. *(Lesson 41)*

21. $\frac{16}{18}$ **22.** $\frac{35}{77}$ **23.** $\frac{24}{40}$ **24.** $\frac{36}{54}$

G. Compare these fractions by using the < and > symbols. *(Lesson 41)*

25. $\frac{9}{16}$ _____ $\frac{7}{12}$ **26.** $\frac{4}{7}$ _____ $\frac{5}{8}$

H. Solve by mental multiplication. *(Lesson 44)*

27. $\frac{1}{5}$ of 35   **28.** $\frac{1}{9}$ of 54   **29.** $72 \times \frac{7}{12}$ **30.** $45 \times \frac{8}{15}$

I. Copy and solve these problems by the vertical method. *(Lesson 46)*

31. $\begin{array}{r} 6 \\ \times\, 5\frac{1}{2} \\ \hline \end{array}$ **32.** $\begin{array}{r} 12 \\ \times\, 6\frac{3}{4} \\ \hline \end{array}$

J. Find the reciprocals of these numbers. *(Lesson 47)*

33. $\frac{3}{8}$ **34.** $\frac{9}{17}$ **35.** $\frac{41}{6}$ **36.** 29

K. Solve mentally by multiplying the whole number by the denominator of the divisor. *(Lesson 47)*

37. $5 \div \frac{1}{6}$ **38.** $7 \div \frac{1}{7}$ **39.** $8 \div \frac{1}{9}$ **40.** $3 \div \frac{1}{11}$

L. Solve these fraction problems. *(Lessons 42–48)*

41. $\begin{array}{r} \frac{1}{2} \\ + \frac{1}{3} \\ \hline \end{array}$ **42.** $\begin{array}{r} \frac{1}{5} \\ + \frac{1}{3} \\ \hline \end{array}$ **43.** $\begin{array}{r} \frac{2}{9} \\ + \frac{5}{6} \\ \hline \end{array}$ **44.** $\begin{array}{r} \frac{5}{8} \\ + \frac{1}{3} \\ \hline \end{array}$

45. $\begin{array}{r} \frac{1}{2} \\ - \frac{3}{8} \\ \hline \end{array}$ **46.** $\begin{array}{r} \frac{5}{6} \\ - \frac{3}{4} \\ \hline \end{array}$ **47.** $\begin{array}{r} 7 \\ - 2\frac{4}{5} \\ \hline \end{array}$ **48.** $\begin{array}{r} 11 \\ - 6\frac{3}{10} \\ \hline \end{array}$

49. $4 \times \frac{3}{7}$ **50.** $6 \times \frac{4}{5}$ **51.** $\frac{3}{4} \times \frac{4}{7}$ **52.** $\frac{5}{6} \times \frac{4}{5}$

53. $3\frac{1}{2} \times 6$ **54.** $4\frac{3}{4} \times 9$ **55.** $2\frac{1}{4} \times 2\frac{1}{2}$ **56.** $4\frac{2}{5} \times 4\frac{1}{6}$

57. $\frac{4}{7} \div \frac{2}{5}$ **58.** $\frac{3}{4} \div \frac{6}{7}$ **59.** $2\frac{1}{2} \div \frac{3}{4}$ **60.** $3\frac{5}{9} \div \frac{4}{9}$

61. $5\frac{1}{3} \div 1\frac{1}{5}$ **62.** $3\frac{3}{5} \div 1\frac{1}{15}$

M. Find the unknown numbers. *(Lesson 49)*

63. 3 is $\frac{1}{3}$ of _____   **64.** 9 is $\frac{3}{4}$ of _____

65. 8 is $\frac{4}{9}$ of _____   **66.** 12 is $\frac{4}{7}$ of _____

N. In each reading problem, first find the numbers that are not needed and write them on your paper. Then solve the problem. *(Lesson 50)*

67. Darlene is $1\frac{7}{8}$ times as tall and 2 times as old as her younger brother. Her younger brother is $2\frac{2}{3}$ feet tall. How tall is Darlene?

68. Marilyn is $\frac{4}{7}$ the age of her brother Michael and is $\frac{4}{5}$ his height. Marilyn is 8 years old and 50 inches tall. How tall is Michael?

69. Sister Miller makes little boys' shirts to send to the mission field. She uses $\frac{1}{4}$ yard of fabric and 5 buttons for each shirt. A store owner gave her $9\frac{3}{4}$ yards of fabric to use. The cost of the fabric would have been $2.45 per yard. How many shirts could she make from the fabric?

70. After the Ebys finished painting their house, there was a little paint left in three of the cans. One can had about $\frac{1}{8}$ gallon, another $\frac{3}{16}$ gallon, and the third about $\frac{1}{16}$ gallon. The price of the paint was $15.95 per gallon. What was the total amount of paint remaining?

71. Carl purchased 25 yards of poultry wire and used some of it to make a yard for his 25 chickens. The chicken yard was a triangle with sides measuring $6\frac{1}{3}$ yards, $4\frac{3}{4}$ yards, and $7\frac{1}{2}$ yards. How many yards of wire were left?

72. The Wrights have an orchard with 45 trees. At the end of one season, $17\frac{1}{2}$ bushels of apples were left over. They had these apples pressed for cider, and the total yield was 56 gallons. How many gallons of cider per bushel did the apples produce?

O. Use the graph to answer the following questions. *(Lesson 51)*

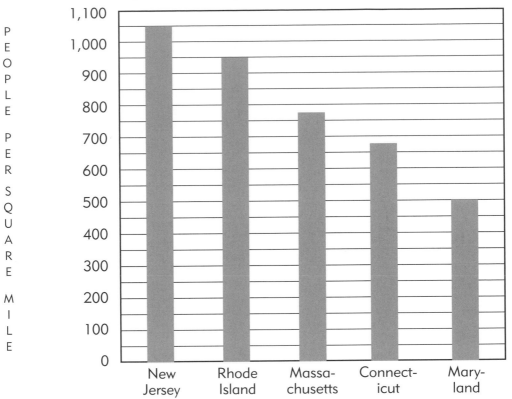

Population Density of Five Most Crowded States in the U.S.

Source: *World Almanac, 1995*

73. What is the population density of New Jersey?

74. What is the difference in population density between Massachusetts and Connecticut?

75. California has 190 people per square mile. What fraction is that of the population density in Rhode Island?

76. Which state has the nearest to half as many people per square mile as New Jersey?

53. Chapter 4 Test

Chapter 5

Decimal Fractions

Seven times a day do I praise thee because of thy righteous judgments.
(Psalm 119:164)

54. Introduction to Decimals

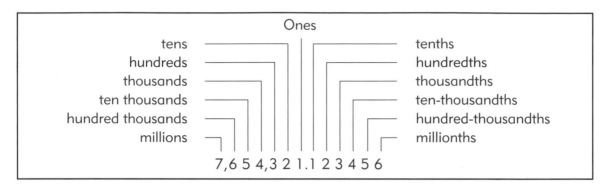

The Arabic number system is a place-value system. In the number 303, the first 3 at the right means 3 ones or 3 because it is in the ones' place. The third 3 from the right means 3 hundreds or 300 because it is in the hundreds' place. The zero shows that there are no tens in this number.

The place-value system also extends to the right of the ones' place to express fractions. One place to the *left* of the ones' place is the tens' place, and one place to the *right* of the ones' place is the tenths' place. Two places to the left of the ones' place is the hundreds' place, and two places to the right of the ones' place is the hundredths' place. Thus the ones' place is the center of the decimal system.

The decimal point is used to show where the ones' place is. There is an infinite number of places to the right of the ones' place, the same as to the left of the ones' place. No commas are used to the right of the decimal point.

In Chapter 4 you studied fractions that are written with a numerator and a denominator, separated by a division sign (such as $\frac{1}{4}$ and $\frac{3}{5}$). These are common fractions. Fractions expressed by using a decimal point are **decimal fractions**, or simply "decimals." Common fractions and decimals are two ways of expressing the same numbers. If a decimal has a value less than 1, a zero is placed before the decimal point so that the decimal fraction is not misread as a whole number.

Reading Decimals	Read 0.0625.
1. Read the number to the right of the decimal point just the same as a number to the left of the decimal point. This is the numerator of the fraction.	1. The numerator is 625.
2. Determine the denominator of the decimal by counting the number of places to the right of the decimal point.	2. There are four places to the right of the decimal point. The denominator of the fraction is ten-thousandths.
The number is read "Six hundred twenty-five ten-thousandths."	

CLASS PRACTICE

Read these decimals orally.

a. 0.15   b. 0.375   c. 0.017

d. 0.1432   e. 0.01415   f. 0.161666

Express these decimals as common fractions. Do not reduce your answers.

g. 0.7   h. 0.61   i. 0.08

j. 0.088   k. 0.161513   l. 0.00011

Express these common fractions as decimals.

m. $\frac{3}{10}$ n. $\frac{41}{100}$ o. $\frac{7}{100}$

p. $\frac{4,151}{10,000}$ q. $\frac{33,771}{100,000}$ r. $\frac{315,577}{1,000,000}$

WRITTEN EXERCISES

A. *Express these decimals as common fractions. Have as many zeroes in the denominator of the common fraction as there are decimal places in the decimal.*

1. 0.17   **2.** 0.09

3. 0.107   **4.** 0.7177

5. 0.0872   **6.** 0.349

7. 0.616111   **8.** 0.78731

B. *Write these decimals, using words.*

9. 0.9   **10.** 0.16

11. 0.616   **12.** 0.079

13. 0.3406   **14.** 0.01103

15. 0.100006   **16.** 0.000009

C. *Express these common fractions as decimals. Be sure there are as many places to the right of the decimal point as there are zeroes in the denominator of the common fraction.*

17. $\frac{17}{100}$ **18.** $\frac{899}{1,000}$

19. $\frac{57}{1,000}$ **20.** $\frac{99}{1,000}$

21. $\frac{71}{10,000}$ **22.** $\frac{349}{10,000}$

23. $\frac{11,111}{100,000}$ **24.** $\frac{778,918}{1,000,000}$

D. Solve these reading problems.

25. Many of the living things created by God are extremely small. One kind of parasitic wasp measures only eight thousandths of an inch in length and has a wing span of only four hundredths of an inch. Write the length of the wasp in decimal form.

26. This same wasp may weigh as little as 0.005 milligram or 0.00000018 ounce. Write in word form the numerical value of the metric unit of weight.

27. One of the largest living things known to man is the General Sherman Tree, found in California. Although the estimated weight of this sequoia is 6,167 tons, the sequoia seed weighs only 0.000321 ounce. Write the weight of the seed in word form.

28. If the General Sherman Tree weighed exactly 6,167 tons, how many pounds would it weigh?

29. The smallest seed known to man is that of the epiphytic orchid. A single seed of this plant weighs only 0.7986 microgram or 0.00000002875 ounce. Write in word form the metric weight of the epiphytic orchid seed.

30. Another interesting fact about God's creation is the speed at which some plants grow. Some species of bamboo grow at a rate of 0.125 foot per hour. One variety of kelp has been found to grow as fast as 0.0616 foot per hour. Write the bamboo's rate of growth as a common fraction. Reduce your answer to lowest terms.

He hath made everything beautiful in his time.
Ecclesiastes 3:11

REVIEW EXERCISES

E. Find the unknown numbers. *(Lesson 49)*

31. 15 is $\frac{3}{4}$ of _____   **32.** 22 is $\frac{1}{2}$ of _____   **33.** 10 is $\frac{2}{3}$ of _____

34. 9 is $\frac{3}{5}$ of _____   **35.** 16 is $\frac{8}{9}$ of _____   **36.** 12 is $\frac{4}{7}$ of _____

F. Find the average of each set. *(Lesson 19)*

37. 5, 6, 5, 8, 7, 4   **38.** 17, 15, 19, 18, 19

39. 47, 76, 56, 58   **40.** 90, 97, 92, 85

55. Comparing and Rounding Decimals

Comparing Decimals

Decimals are much easier to compare than unlike common fractions are. To compare unlike common fractions, you must use the lowest common multiple to change them to like fractions. But you can compare decimals by simply annexing zeroes. In this way you can give them the same denominator so that the decimals can be compared.

> **Example A**
>
> Annexing zeroes to the right of a decimal does not change its value.
> $$0.1 = 0.10 = 0.100 = 0.1000 = 0.10000 = 0.100000$$

To compare decimals, use the following steps.

1. If the decimals do not have the same number of digits, annex zeroes to the shorter one until it matches the longer.
2. Compare the resulting decimals, and then rewrite them in the original form.

Example B	**Example C**
Compare 0.9104 and 0.92.	Compare 0.031 and 0.030999.
$\quad$ 0.9104 $<$ 0.9200	$\quad$ 0.031000 $>$ 0.030999
$\quad$ 0.9104 $<$ 0.92	$\quad$ 0.031 $\quad$ $>$ 0.030999

Rounding Decimals

Numbers are sometimes rounded because it is not necessary to know the exact amount. You have already studied the procedure for rounding whole numbers. The procedure for rounding decimals is nearly the same and is shown below.

Step 1: Determine the place value to which the number will be rounded. Underline the digit in that place.

Step 2: Look at the digit one place to the right. If it is 5 or more, round the underlined digit to the next higher number. If it is less than 5, leave the underlined digit the same.

Step 3: Drop all digits to the right of the underlined digit. If the underlined digit is zero or is rounded to zero, do not drop that zero. Rather, leave it there to show that the decimal was rounded to that place.

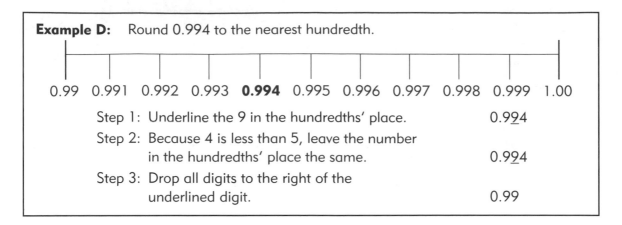

Example D: Round 0.994 to the nearest hundredth.

Step 1: Underline the 9 in the hundredths' place.	0.9<u>9</u>4
Step 2: Because 4 is less than 5, leave the number in the hundredths' place the same.	0.9<u>9</u>4
Step 3: Drop all digits to the right of the underlined digit.	0.99

The decimal 0.994 is nearer to the next lower hundredth, 0.99, than it is the next higher hundredth, 1.00, as shown by the number line above.

Example E

Round 0.831 and 0.899 to the nearest tenth.

0.<u>8</u>31 = 0.8 to the nearest tenth (3 < 5)
0.<u>8</u>99 = 0.9 to the nearest tenth (9 > 5)

Example F

Round 0.831 and $4.899 to the nearest hundredth.

0.8<u>3</u>1 = 0.83 to the nearest tenth (1 < 5)
$4.8<u>9</u>9 = $4.90 to the nearest cent (nearest hundredth) (9 > 5)

Example G

Round 3.4137 and 2.7998 to the nearest thousandth.

3.41<u>3</u>7 = 3.414 to the nearest thousandth (7 > 5)
2.79<u>9</u>8 = 2.800 to the nearest thousandth (8 > 5)

Some prices, such as those for gasoline and fuel oil, may include tenths of a cent. When you are calculating with such prices, it is easier if the tenths of a cent are expressed as parts of a dollar. Because a tenth of a cent is equal to a thousandth of a dollar, write the number of tenth cents in the third place (thousandths) to the right of the decimal point.

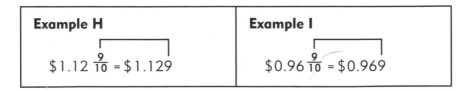

Example H	**Example I**
1.12\frac{9}{10}$ = $1.129	0.96\frac{9}{10}$ = $0.969

CLASS PRACTICE

Compare each set of decimals, and write < or > between them.

  a. 0.456 ____ 0.45   b. 2.107 ____ 2.1101   c. 2.0007 ____ 2.1

Write the tenth just before and just after each number. Then write the hundredth just before and just after each number.

  d. 2.713   e. 5.522
  f. 2.836   g. 1.994

Round each decimal to the nearest tenth, hundredth, and thousandth.

  h. 5.4274   i. 4.7138
  j. 1.0019   k. 2.9999

Express these fractions of cents as decimal parts of a dollar.

  l. 1.15\frac{9}{10}$ m. 2.65\frac{4}{10}$
  n. 0.69\frac{1}{10}$ o. 0.07\frac{8}{10}$

WRITTEN EXERCISES

A. *Copy each set of decimals, compare them, and write < or > between them.*

  1. 0.787 ____ 0.8   **2.** 1.303 ____ 1.2999
  3. 2.7077 ____ 2.7   **4.** 4.4 ____ 3.99
  5. 1.8 ____ 1.8511   **6.** 3.8984 ____ 3.899

B. *Write the tenth just before and just after each number.*

  Example: 4.74   *Answer:* 4.7, 4.8

  7. 3.53   **8.** 4.08
  9. 6.97   **10.** 9.91

C. *Write the hundredth just before and just after each number.*

  Example: 5.749   *Answer:* 5.74, 5.75

  11. 3.857   **12.** 4.498
  13. 5.712   **14.** 3.717

D. *Write the thousandth just before and just after each number.*

  Example: 3.1774   *Answer:* 3.177, 3.178

  15. 0.7971   **16.** 2.5957
  17. 1.9992   **18.** 4

E. *Round these numbers as indicated.*

Round to the nearest tenth.

19. 7.73   **20.** 6.595   **21.** 3.27   **22.** 0.899

Round to the nearest hundredth.

23. 0.477   **24.** 3.695   **25.** 3.8871   **26.** 4.2277

Round to the nearest cent.

27. $0.877   **28.** $5.699   **29.** $2.008   **30.** $7.999

Round to the nearest thousandth.

31. 3.9796   **32.** 4.1122   **33.** 5.77769   **34.** 5.31119

F. *Express these fractions of cents as decimal parts of a dollar.*

35. $1.18 $\frac{9}{10}$ **36.** $1.25 $\frac{3}{10}$ **37.** $0.77 $\frac{9}{10}$ **38.** $0.64 $\frac{7}{10}$

G. *Solve these reading problems.*

39. After a heavy downpour, Philip saw that the rain gauge had 1.5 inches of water in it. The local weather station recorded 1.609 inches of rainfall during the same downpour. Was the measurement at the weather station more or less than at Philip's home?

40. Some species of bamboo grow at a rate of 0.125 foot per hour, one variety of kelp grows as fast as 0.0616 foot per hour, and one species of eucalyptus tree may grow 0.003244 foot per hour. Which of these plants grows the fastest?

41. In the last year, Gerald has grown 1.5 inches, or an average of 0.00411 inch per day. To the nearest thousandth of an inch, how much did Gerald grow each day?

42. In the United States, the average boy gains 99.5 pounds during the first 14 years of his life, or about 0.019458 pound per day. Round the average weight gain per day to the nearest thousandth.

43. Use words to state the average weight gain per day in problem 42.

44. Write the growth per day in problem 41 as a common fraction.

REVIEW EXERCISES

H. *Multiply these mixed numbers.* (*Lesson 46*)

45. $5\frac{1}{2} \times 3\frac{3}{4}$ **46.** $6\frac{2}{3} \times 1\frac{1}{2}$

I. *Write whether each number is prime or composite.* (*Lesson 37*)

47. 33   **48.** 35   **49.** 37   **50.** 39

J. *Find the answers. Work mentally if you can.* (*Lesson 20*)

51. 144 ÷ 18   **52.** 128 ÷ 16   **53.** 850 ÷ 50   **54.** 450 ÷ 25

56. Fractions and Terminating Decimals

Memorize the following equivalents.

$$\frac{1}{2} = 0.5 \qquad \frac{1}{3} = 0.33\frac{1}{3} \qquad \frac{2}{3} = 0.66\frac{2}{3} \qquad \frac{1}{4} = 0.25 \qquad \frac{3}{4} = 0.75$$

$$\frac{1}{5} = 0.2 \qquad \frac{2}{5} = 0.4 \qquad \frac{3}{5} = 0.6 \qquad \frac{4}{5} = 0.8$$

$$\frac{1}{8} = 0.125 \qquad \frac{3}{8} = 0.375 \qquad \frac{5}{8} = 0.625 \qquad \frac{7}{8} = 0.875$$

Common fractions and decimal fractions are two different methods of expressing parts of 1. Every decimal fraction is equal to a common fraction.

Sometimes it is necessary to find the decimal equivalent of a common fraction. For example, a calculator uses decimals rather than common fractions. Mental calculation is sometimes easier with a common fraction than with its equivalent decimal. Therefore, it is valuable to know how to change decimals to common fractions and common fractions to decimals.

Changing Decimals to Common Fractions

To change a decimal to a common fraction, write it in fraction form just as you would read it. Then reduce the fraction to lowest terms.

Example A $0.72 = \frac{72}{100} \div \frac{4}{4} = \frac{18}{25}$

Changing Common Fractions to Decimals

If you cannot change a common fraction to a decimal mentally, divide the numerator by the denominator. Use the following steps.

Step 1: Write a division problem with the numerator as the dividend and the denominator as the divisor.

Step 2: Place a decimal point after the dividend, and annex a zero.

Step 3: Place a decimal point in the quotient above the decimal point in the dividend.

Step 4: Divide. Annex zeroes and continue dividing until there is no remainder. (In Lesson 57 you will work with fractions that never divide evenly.)

Example B

$$\frac{7}{8} = 8 \overline{)7.000} \quad \frac{0.875}{}$$
```
       0.875
  8)7.000
    6 4
      60
      56
       40
       40
        0
```

Example C

$$2\frac{1}{40} = 2 + 40\overline{)1.000} = 2 + 0.025 = 2.025$$
```
         0.025
  40)1.000
      80
     200
     200
       0
```

CLASS PRACTICE

Change these decimals to common fractions in lowest terms.

  a. 0.31   b. 0.24   c. 0.52   d. 0.84

Change these common fractions to decimals.

  e. $\frac{11}{25}$ f. $\frac{13}{20}$ g. $\frac{9}{40}$ h. $\frac{11}{40}$

WRITTEN EXERCISES

A. Change these decimals to common fractions or mixed numbers in simplest form.

  1. 0.77   2. 0.91   3. 0.35   4. 0.88

  5. 3.22   6. 5.12   7. 0.002   8. 0.006

B. Change these common fractions to decimals. They all divide evenly to the tenths' or hundredths' place.

  9. $\frac{3}{4}$ 10. $\frac{3}{5}$ 11. $\frac{19}{20}$ 12. $\frac{1}{20}$

  13. $\frac{19}{25}$ 14. $\frac{27}{50}$ 15. $2\frac{13}{20}$ 16. $3\frac{17}{25}$

C. Change these common fractions to decimals. They all divide evenly to the thousandths' place or sooner.

  17. $\frac{7}{20}$ 18. $\frac{7}{40}$ 19. $\frac{17}{40}$ 20. $\frac{19}{40}$

  21. $\frac{23}{40}$ 22. $\frac{3}{40}$ 23. $1\frac{9}{40}$ 24. $2\frac{1}{8}$

D. Solve these reading problems.

25. David's father mixes hog feed in a hammermill. One mix is a finisher feed that is $\frac{17}{20}$ corn by weight. What decimal part of the feed is corn?

26. The hog grower feed he prepares is $\frac{31}{40}$ corn by weight. What decimal part of the grower feed is corn?

27. The grower feed he mixes is 0.13 soybean meal by weight. The finisher feed is 0.085 soybean meal. Which batch of feed has the greater part of soybean meal?

28. David's father added 3,400 pounds of corn to a batch of finisher feed. How large a batch is he mixing if the corn is $\frac{17}{20}$ of the entire batch?

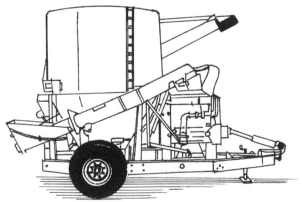

29. In one batch of feed, the weight of the medication he adds is $\frac{1}{125}$ of the weight of the entire batch. What decimal part of the entire batch is medication?

30. In another batch of feed, David's father is adding another type of medication to the feed. The medication is $\frac{1}{400}$ the weight of the entire batch. What decimal part of the entire batch is the medication?

REVIEW EXERCISES

E. Round these decimals as indicated. *(Lesson 55)*

31. 0.867 *(tenth)*

32. 1.487 *(hundredth)*

33. 6.5855 *(thousandth)*

34. 0.715 *(tenth)*

35. 7.89432 *(thousandth)*

36. $6.546 *(cent)*

F. Divide these fractions. *(Lesson 48)*

37. $5 \div 1\frac{3}{4}$

38. $5\frac{1}{2} \div 3\frac{1}{3}$

G. Find the greatest common factor of each set. *(Lesson 38)*

39. 42, 28

40. 45, 75

57. Fractions and Nonterminating Decimals

Each of the common fractions in Lesson 56 has an exact decimal equivalent. But that is not true of many common fractions. Their decimal equivalents are known as **nonterminating decimals**.

Because nonterminating decimals cannot be expressed as exact decimals, several methods are used to express them as nearly as possible. Three of these are shown below.

Method 1: Calculating a nonterminating decimal to the hundredths' place and expressing the remainder as a fraction.	
1. Divide the fraction to the hundredths' place. 2. Express the remainder as a fraction in lowest terms.	**Example A:** Change $\frac{1}{11}$ to a decimal. $\begin{array}{r} 0.09\frac{1}{11} \\ 11\overline{)1.00} \\ \underline{99} \\ 1 \end{array}$

Method 2: Rounding a nonterminating decimal to the nearest thousandth.	
1. Divide the fraction to the ten-thousandths' place. 2. Round the answer to the nearest thousandth.	**Example B:** Change $\frac{2}{3}$ to a decimal. $\begin{array}{r} 0.6666 \\ 3\overline{)2.0000} \\ \underline{18} \\ 20 \\ \underline{18} \\ 20 \\ \underline{18} \\ 20 \\ \underline{18} \\ 2 \end{array}$ = 0.667 to the nearest thousandth

When a nonterminating decimal is obtained by division, certain digits begin repeating themselves. Such a quotient is known as a repeating decimal. This is illustrated by the repeating 6 in Example B. The repetition may be shown by placing a bar above the digits that are repeated. In Example B, this would have been shown by placing a line above the 6 in the tenths' place ($0.\overline{6}$).

Method 3:   Using a bar to indicate the repeating digits.

After there are only zeroes to bring down, divide until the remainder repeats itself. As soon as that happens, the digits in the quotient will begin repeating. In Example C, the remainder 20 is a repetition of the 20 in the second step of the division process. So the repeating digits are 3 and 6 (0.2363636 . . .).	**Example C:** Change $\frac{13}{55}$ to a decimal.

$$\overset{\overline{}}{0.2\overline{36}} \text{ (Bar)}$$
$$55\overline{)13.000}$$
$$\underline{110}$$

After there are only zeroes to bring down, 20 is the first remainder that repeats.

After	200 ←
there are	165
only zeroes	350
to bring down,	330
20 is the first	20 ←
remainder that repeats.	

CLASS PRACTICE

Change each fraction to a nonterminating decimal by all three methods shown in the lesson.

a. $\frac{1}{6}$ b. $\frac{4}{15}$ c. $\frac{7}{9}$ d. $\frac{8}{11}$ e. $\frac{11}{12}$ f. $\frac{17}{24}$

WRITTEN EXERCISES

A. *Change these fractions to nonterminating decimals. Divide to the hundredths' place, and express the remainder as a fraction.*

1. $\frac{5}{6}$ 2. $\frac{4}{7}$ 3. $\frac{5}{9}$ 4. $\frac{3}{11}$

5. $\frac{7}{12}$ 6. $\frac{7}{15}$ 7. $\frac{13}{24}$ 8. $\frac{17}{30}$

B. *Change each fraction to a decimal rounded to the nearest thousandth.*

9. $\frac{1}{7}$ 10. $\frac{6}{7}$ 11. $\frac{8}{9}$ 12. $\frac{7}{11}$

13. $\frac{1}{12}$ 14. $\frac{1}{15}$ 15. $\frac{5}{24}$ 16. $\frac{7}{30}$

C. *Change each fraction to a decimal. Carry the decimal to six places to show the pattern of repeating digits.*

17. $\frac{1}{9}$ 18. $\frac{9}{11}$ 19. $\frac{10}{11}$ 20. $\frac{5}{12}$

D. *Change each fraction to a repeating decimal. When you can identify the repeating digits, draw a bar above them.*

21. $\frac{11}{15}$ 22. $\frac{2}{15}$ 23. $\frac{7}{22}$ 24. $\frac{5}{33}$

E. Solve these reading problems.

25. The Constitution of the United States was ratified by the Constitutional Convention on September 17, 1787. To become effective, the Constitution had to be approved by 9 of the 13 states. By the end of 1787, 3 out of the 13 states had ratified it. What decimal fraction of the 13 states had ratified the Constitution by the end of 1787? (Answer to the nearest thousandth.)

26. On June 21, 1788, New Hampshire became the ninth state to ratify the Constitution. Write as a decimal the part of the 13 states that had ratified the Constitution by this point. Calculate your answer to the hundredths' place, and express the remainder as a fraction.

27. The first amendment to the United States Constitution states that no law may be made against freedom to worship God. This amendment is one of 10 amendments known as the Bill of Rights, which was ratified on December 15, 1791. In all, 26 amendments have been made to the Constitution. Write as a decimal the number of amendments in the Bill of Rights compared to the total number of amendments made. Round your answer to the nearest thousandth.

28. Christians in Canada have enjoyed religious freedom under the British North America Act and since that, under the Constitution Act of 1982. The Constitution Act was approved by 11 of the 12 provinces and territories in Canada during the 1980s. What decimal fraction of the provinces and territories approved the Constitution Act of 1982? (Draw a bar above the repeating part of the decimal.)

29. The Witmers are painting the block walls in their basement. They used 8 gallons of paint to put one coat on $\frac{5}{8}$ of the surface area of the walls. How many gallons will they use in all to paint the first coat? Remember to round your answer to the next higher gallon.

30. The Witmers' basement walls have a surface area of 1,216 square feet. When the Witmers put the second coat of paint on the walls, each gallon of paint covered 140 square feet. At that rate, how many gallons of paint did they need for the second coat? Remember to round your answer to the next higher gallon.

REVIEW EXERCISES

F. Round these decimals as indicated. *(Lesson 55)*

31. 0.2419 *(tenth)*   **32.** 0.71759 *(hundredth)*

33. 0.98739 *(thousandth)*   **34.** $3.8992 *(cent)*

G. Find the unknown numbers. *(Lesson 49)*

35. 9 is $\frac{3}{4}$ of _____   **36.** 4 is $\frac{2}{5}$ of _____

37. 6 is $\frac{5}{6}$ of _____   **38.** 7 is $\frac{7}{8}$ of _____

H. Find the lowest common multiple of each pair. *(Lesson 39)*

39. 6, 8   **40.** 9, 18   **41.** 10, 11   **42.** 14, 16

58. Adding and Subtracting Decimals

Adding Decimals

Decimals are added and subtracted in much the same way as whole numbers. Only two things are different.

1. All the decimal points must be kept in line.
2. If the decimals do not have the same number of places to the right of the decimal point, zeroes should be annexed so that they have the same number of places.

Example A   Add 5.3, 0.003, and 0.9804.

$$
\begin{array}{r}
5.3000 \\
0.0030 \\
+\ 0.9804 \\
\hline
6.2834
\end{array}
$$

Subtracting Decimals

The same two differences given under "Adding Decimals" apply to subtracting decimals. When the subtrahend has more places to the right of the decimal point than the minuend does, annex zeroes to the minuend to equal the number of decimal places in the subtrahend.

Example B	**Example C**
Find 4.2 – 3.763.	Find 7 – 0.0968.
$\begin{array}{r} 4.200 \\ -\ 3.763 \\ \hline 0.437 \end{array}$	$\begin{array}{r} 7.0000 \\ -\ 0.0968 \\ \hline 6.9032 \end{array}$

CLASS PRACTICE

Add or subtract these decimals.

a. $\begin{array}{r} 17.71 \\ +\ 2.7386 \\ \hline \end{array}$
  b. $\begin{array}{r} 13.003 \\ +\ 6.8162 \\ \hline \end{array}$
  c. $\begin{array}{r} 4.14 \\ -\ 2.8746 \\ \hline \end{array}$
  d. $\begin{array}{r} 3 \\ -\ 1.8942 \\ \hline \end{array}$

e. 4.5 + 6.09 + 2.0101   f. 4 – 2.2222   g. 4.1 – 0.8938

WRITTEN EXERCISES

A. *Add these decimals.*

1. $3.72
    + 5.82

2. $6.82
    + 3.95

3.   4.7
    + 5.317

4.   3.0021
    + 2.021

5.   4.002
     0.0019
    + 2.20021

6.   157
      0.1818
    + 3.07

7. 2.3 + 5.72 + 12 + 0.011

8. 3.11 + 0.0003 + 1 + 53

B. *Subtract these decimals.*

9. $13.07
    - 5.87

10. $90.05
    - 15.69

11.   3.62
    - 1.924

12.   7.1
    - 2.985

13. 4.2 - 2.675

14. 3.711 - 0.0088

15. 5 - 3.456

16. 17 - 0.0078

C. *Solve these problems.*

17.   14.82
    - 3.0609

18. 15
    + 7.7872

19. 3.2 + 1.15 + 1.0054

20. 7 - 3.9381

21. 5.3 - 3.6721

22.   3
      7.778
    + 1.23

D. *Solve these reading problems.*

23. Concord, New Hampshire has an average annual precipitation of 36.53 inches. About 100 miles from Concord on Mount Washington, New Hampshire, the average annual precipitation is 89.92 inches. During an average year, how much more precipitation falls on Mount Washington than on Concord?

24. The region of Seattle, Washington, has an average annual precipitation of 38.1 inches. East of the Cascade Range in Spokane, Washington, the average annual precipitation is 16.64 inches. How much more precipitation falls on Seattle than on Spokane?

25. In an average year, Spokane receives precipitation on about $\frac{5}{16}$ of the days. What decimal fraction of the days is that? (Divide until the decimal comes out evenly.)

26. Atlanta, Georgia, receives precipitation on about 23 out of every 73 days. What decimal part is that? Express the answer to hundredths, with the remainder as a fraction.

27. In Seattle, Washington, the average precipitation from April through October is as follows: April, 2.5 inches; May, 1.8 inches; June, 1.6 inches; July, 0.9 inch; August, 1.2 inches; September, 1.9 inches; and October, 3.3 inches. What is the total rainfall during these months?

28. The winter months generally bring more moisture to the Seattle area than the summer months do. Average precipitation from November through March is as follows: November, 5.7 inches; December, 6.0 inches; January, 5.4 inches; February, 4.0 inches; and March, 3.5 inches. What is the total precipitation during these months?

REVIEW EXERCISES

E. Change these fractions to nonterminating decimals. Follow the instructions for how to treat the remainder. *(Lesson 57)*

Round the answers to the nearest thousandth.

29. $\frac{9}{14}$ 30. $\frac{3}{19}$

Use a bar to show the repeating part of the decimal.

31. $\frac{5}{18}$ 32. $\frac{3}{22}$

F. Change these common fractions to decimals. If you cannot do them mentally, review the memory chart in Lesson 56.

33. $\frac{4}{5}$ 34. $\frac{2}{3}$ 35. $\frac{1}{8}$ 36. $\frac{7}{8}$

G. Reduce these fractions to lowest terms. *(Lesson 40)*

37. $\frac{16}{36}$ 38. $\frac{24}{48}$ 39. $\frac{16}{48}$ 40. $\frac{27}{63}$

For as the rain cometh down . . . So shall my word be . . . it shall accomplish that which I please, and it shall prosper in the thing whereto I sent it.

Isaiah 55:10, 11

59. Multiplying and Dividing Decimals by Powers of Ten

Because our number system is based on tens, multiplying or dividing by 10 is very simple. To multiply a number by 10, move the decimal point 1 place to the right. To divide by 10, move the decimal point 1 place to the left.

The same rule applies for multiplying and dividing by all powers of 10 (10; 100; 1,000; 10,000; and so forth). The decimal point is moved as many places as there are zeroes in the power of ten being used.

When multiplying by a power of ten, move the decimal point as many places to the right as there are zeroes in the power of ten. Annex zeroes to the right when necessary so that the decimal point can be moved the required number of places.

Example A	$10 \times 3.5 = 35$	1 zero: Move decimal point 1 place to the right.
Example B	$100 \times 2.7 = 270$	2 zeroes: Move decimal point 2 places to the right.
Example C	$1,000 \times 0.145 = 145$	3 zeroes: Move decimal point 3 places to the right.

When dividing by a power of ten, move the decimal point as many places to the left as there are zeroes in the power of ten. Annex zeroes to the left when necessary so that the decimal point can be moved the required number of places.

Example D	$3.5 \div 10 = 0.35$	1 zero: Move decimal point 1 place to the left.
Example E	$2.7 \div 100 = 0.027$	2 zeroes: Move decimal point 2 places to the left.
Example F	$14.5 \div 1,000 = 0.0145$	3 zeroes: Move decimal point 3 places to the left.

CLASS PRACTICE

Find the answers mentally.

a. 100×3.089 b. 10×45.0925 c. $1,000 \times 37.1$

d. $25.0403 \div 10$ e. $2.8749 \div 100$ f. $3.0089 \div 1,000$

WRITTEN EXERCISES

A. *Multiply these decimals as indicated.*

1. 10×1.3 2. 10×0.74 3. 100×0.1876

4. 100×0.077 5. $1,000 \times 0.03$ 6. $1,000 \times 0.089$

7. 100×0.0097 8. $1,000 \times 3.07091$

B. Divide these decimals as indicated.

9. 5.3 ÷ 10

10. 0.27 ÷ 10

11. 14.05 ÷ 100

12. 14.0937 ÷ 100

13. 0.007 ÷ 100

14. 0.099 ÷ 100

15. 35.089 ÷ 1,000

16. 10.802 ÷ 1,000

C. Find the answers mentally.

17. 234.784 ÷ 10

18. 100 × 13.507

19. 315.097 ÷ 1,000

20. 42.5687 ÷ 10

21. 3.8907 × 10

22. 41.09 ÷ 100

23. 0.51 ÷ 1,000

24. 3.099 × 100

25. 0.0789 × 1,000

26. 4.217 × 1,000

27. 2.99 × 10

28. 1.012 ÷ 10

D. Solve these reading problems mentally.

29. There are one hundred centimeters in a meter. How many meters are in 476 centimeters?

30. Goliath's height is given in 1 Samuel 17:4 as 6 cubits 1 span. Because the cubit and the span are not standard units of measure, we do not know exactly how tall Goliath was. Based on the approximate length of the cubit, however, Goliath is estimated to have been about 3 meters tall. How many centimeters is that?

31. Mark's father is 178 centimeters tall. How many meters is that?

32. A metric ton equals 1,000 kilograms. If an elephant weighs 6,850 kilograms, what is his weight in metric tons?

33. Whales may weigh as much as 200 metric tons. Which is heavier, a very large elephant weighing 6,900 kilograms or a newborn blue whale calf that weighs 7.1 metric tons?

34. Some of the largest ants are about 25 millimeters long. Which is longer, an ant that is 23 millimeters long or one that is 0.021 meter long? (One meter = 1,000 millimeters.)

> For every beast of the forest is mine,
> and the cattle upon a thousand hills.
> I know all the fowls of the mountains:
> and the wild beasts of the field are mine.
> (Psalm 50:10, 11)

REVIEW EXERCISES

E. Solve these problems. *(Lesson 58)*

35.   11.66
           − 2.9191

36.   22
           + 6.8231

37. 2.2 + 4.09 + 3.7008

38. 9 − 2.7767

39. 2.7 − 1.1412

40.   5
           6.8266
           + 2.77

F. Change these fractions to nonterminating decimals as indicated. *(Lesson 57)*

Divide to the hundredths' place, and express the remainder as a fraction.

41. $\frac{5}{12}$

42. $\frac{7}{13}$

Use a bar to show the repeating part of the decimal.

43. $\frac{6}{11}$

44. $\frac{11}{27}$

G. Round these decimals as indicated. *(Lesson 55)*

45. 0.7179 *(hundredth)*

46. 0.3456 *(thousandth)*

47. 0.4499 *(tenth)*

48. 0.6989 *(hundredth)*

60. Multiplying Decimals

Multiplying decimals is much like multiplying whole numbers. The only difference is the placing of the decimal point in the product.

To multiply decimals, use the following steps.

Step 1: Multiply the factors as usual.

Step 2: Determine the position of the decimal point by counting the total number of decimal places in both factors. Place the decimal point in the product the same number of places from the right as the total number of decimal places in both factors.

Sometimes the product does not have as many digits as are needed to place the decimal point correctly. In that case, annex enough zeroes to the left of the product so that the decimal point can be placed in the product. (See Example B.)

In multiplying decimals, the answer can be checked by casting out nines. When casting out nines, do not consider the decimal point. Its placement can be checked by recounting the decimal places in the factors.

When the product contains final zeroes to the right of the decimal point, they may be dropped without affecting the value of the product. (See Example C.)

Example A		Example B		Example C	
3.2	(1 place)	0.018	(3 places)	0.22	(2 places)
× 1.7	+ (1 place)	× 0.16	+ (2 places)	× 1.5	+ (1 place)
224		108		110	
32		18		22	
5.44	(2 places)	0.00288	(5 places)	0.330	(3 places)
				0.330 = 0.33	

CLASS PRACTICE

Find the answers.

a. 1.5
   × 1.8

b. 3.75
   × 1.7

c. 5.05
   × 0.2

d. 0.62
   × 0.3

e. 3.241
   × 0.51

WRITTEN EXERCISES

A. *Multiply these decimals. Drop any final zeroes to the right of the decimal point.*

1. 2.3
   × 1.1

2. 4.58
   × 1.7

3. 3.11
   × 0.1

4. 7.79
   × 0.3

5. 5.62
   × 0.26

| 6. | 3.89
× 0.72 | 7. | 0.79
× 0.19 | 8. | 0.52
× 0.39 | 9. | 4.57
× 0.09 | 10. | 5.91
× 0.07 |

| 11. | 3.46
× 0.05 | 12. | 5.38
× 0.25 | 13. | 0.91
× 0.02 | 14. | 0.77
× 0.03 |

| 15. | 0.15
× 0.03 | 16. | 0.21
× 0.22 | 17. | 0.006
× 0.13 | 18. | 0.016
× 0.05 |

B. Solve these reading problems.

19. On Wednesday morning, David's temperature was 99.5°. By that evening, his temperature had risen 2.3°. But by the following morning, it had dropped 3.1°. What was David's temperature on Thursday morning?

20. A fever is serious if it goes above 104°, and definitely fatal by 113°. How much higher is 113° than a normal body temperature of 98.6°?

21. The diameter of the earth at the poles is 7,900 miles (to the nearest mile). The diameter of the sun is about 109.49 times as great. What is the diameter of the sun to the nearest hundred miles?

22. The diameter of the moon is about 0.2734 as great as the earth's diameter. What is the diameter of the moon to the nearest mile?

23. The largest planet, Jupiter has a polar diameter 10.381 times that of the earth. What is the polar diameter of Jupiter to the nearest ten miles?

24. The smallest planet, Mercury, has a diameter only 0.392 as great as that of the earth. What is the diameter of Mercury to the nearest ten miles?

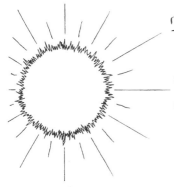
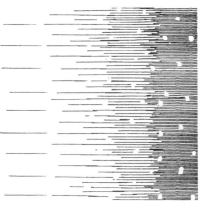

The heavens declare the glory of God; and the firmament sheweth his handywork. Day unto day uttereth speech, and night unto night sheweth knowledge.

Psalm 19: 1, 2

REVIEW EXERCISES

C. Solve by moving the decimal point. *(Lesson 59)*

25. 4.235 ÷ 100
26. 2.504 × 1,000
27. 0.717 × 100
28. 78.3 ÷ 1,000

D. Solve these addition and subtraction problems. *(Lessons 42, 58)*

29. $5\frac{1}{4}$
   $+\,3\frac{3}{5}$

30. $5\frac{3}{8}$
   $+\,2\frac{7}{12}$

31.   17.08
   $+\,4.2137$

32.   5
   $-\,2.0696$

E. Change these common fractions to decimals. Divide to the hundredths' place, and express the remainder as a fraction. *(Lesson 57)*

33. $\frac{6}{7}$ **34.** $\frac{1}{11}$ **35.** $\frac{11}{15}$ **36.** $\frac{11}{32}$

F. Change these linear measures. *(Lesson 25)*

37. 17 ft. = _____ in.
38. 19 yd. = _____ ft.
39. 200 in. = _____ ft.
40. 3 mi. = _____ ft.

61. Multiplying Mentally by Changing Decimals to Fractions

When one factor of a multiplication problem is a whole number and the other is a decimal, multiplication is sometimes much simpler if the decimal is changed to a common fraction. This is especially true if the whole number is divisible by the denominator of the equivalent common fraction. For example, finding $\frac{1}{8}$ of 16 is much simpler than multiplying 0.125×16.

Example A	**Example B**
Find 0.75 of 48.	Find 0.875 of $24.
Think: $0.75 = \frac{3}{4}$	Think: $0.875 = \frac{7}{8}$
$\frac{3}{4}$ of 48 = 48 ÷ 4 × 3 = 36	$\frac{7}{8}$ of $24 = $24 ÷ 8 × 7 = $21
0.75 of 48 = 36	0.875 of $24 = $21

CLASS PRACTICE

Find the answers mentally.

a. 0.5 of 36

b. 0.25 of 28

c. 0.75 of 32

d. 0.125 of $16

e. 0.625 × $32

f. 0.875 of $40

WRITTEN EXERCISES

A. *Change these decimals to common fractions. Work mentally if you can.*

1. $0.66\frac{2}{3}$

2. 0.6

3. 0.125

4. 0.625

5. 0.75

6. 0.8

7. 0.375

8. 0.875

B. *Solve these problems. See if you can do them mentally.*

9. 0.5 of 28

10. 0.5 of 64

11. 0.25 of 16

12. 0.25 of 44

13. 0.75 of 20

14. 0.75 of 24

15. $0.33\frac{1}{3}$ of $18

16. $0.33\frac{1}{3}$ of $27

17. $0.66\frac{2}{3}$ of $33

18. 0.2 of $25

19. 0.4 of $30

20. 0.6 of $45

21. 0.8 of $40

22. 0.125 of 40

23. 0.125 of $64

24. 0.875 of 48

25. 0.625 of $64

26. 0.375 of 32

C. Solve these reading problems. See if you can do numbers 27–30 mentally.

27. Of the 64 students at school, 0.375 are in grades 5 through 7. How many students are in grades 5 through 7?

28. Of the 15 students in grades 1 and 2, 0.6 are in first grade. How many first graders are there?

29. One day at school, 0.875 of the 24 students in grades 8 through 10 received a 100% score on their spelling test. How many students had a score of 100%?

30. Paint, with a regular price of $30.00 per gallon, was on sale at $0.33\frac{1}{3}$ off. How much did Father save on each gallon he bought?

31. Seven of the 24 students in grades 8 through 10 are in tenth grade. Write a decimal showing what part of the students in the room are in tenth grade. Use a bar to show the repeating digits.

32. One kilometer is equal to about 0.62 mile. How many miles are in 35.7 kilometers? Round your answer to the nearest tenth of a mile.

REVIEW EXERCISES

D. Solve these multiplication problems. Drop any final zeroes to the right of the decimal point. *(Lesson 60)*

33.	34.	35.	36.
7.14	1.08	0.65	0.07
× 1.03	× 0.29	× 0.08	× 0.017

E. Solve these problems by moving the decimal point. *(Lesson 59)*

37. 8.53×10

38. $4.53 \div 100$

39. 0.017×100

40. $2.0005 \times 1{,}000$

41. $2.02 \div 1{,}000$

42. $3.102 \div 100$

F. Change these common fractions to nonterminating decimals. Show the repeating digits by placing a bar above them. *(Lesson 57)*

43. $\frac{11}{12}$

44. $\frac{4}{9}$

45. $\frac{4}{15}$

46. $\frac{7}{18}$

G. Do these subtractions. *(Lesson 43)*

47.	48.	49.	50.
$4\frac{5}{6}$	$6\frac{3}{4}$	$7\frac{1}{3}$	$6\frac{3}{8}$
$-3\frac{1}{3}$	$-3\frac{7}{12}$	$-3\frac{3}{5}$	$-2\frac{7}{12}$

H. Change these measures as indicated. *(Lesson 26)*

51. 4 lb. = _____ oz.

52. 92 oz. = _____ lb.

53. 3.5 ton = _____ lb.

54. 4,400 lb. = _____ tons

62. Dividing Decimals by Whole Numbers

Division of decimals follows the same procedure as the division of whole numbers, with the added step of properly placing the decimal point in the quotient. If the divisor is a whole number, place the decimal point in the quotient directly above the one in the dividend.

If the division does not come out evenly, annex zeroes to the right of the dividend and continue dividing. All the division problems in this lesson come out evenly by the ten-thousandths' place.

Example A	Example B	Example C
$$\begin{array}{r} \$3.39 \\ 4\overline{)\$13.56} \\ \underline{12} \\ 15 \\ \underline{12} \\ 36 \\ \underline{36} \\ 0 \end{array}$$	$$\begin{array}{r} 1.725 \\ 8\overline{)13.800} \\ \underline{8} \\ 58 \\ \underline{56} \\ 20 \\ \underline{16} \\ 40 \\ \underline{40} \\ 0 \end{array}$$ (annex two zeroes)	$$\begin{array}{r} 0.045 \\ 6\overline{)0.270} \\ \underline{24} \\ 30 \\ \underline{30} \\ 0 \end{array}$$ (annex one zero)

CLASS PRACTICE

Divide these decimals.

a. $4\overline{)6.5}$

b. $17\overline{)236.64}$

c. $24\overline{)2.136}$

d. $32\overline{)2.64}$

WRITTEN EXERCISES

A. *Solve these problems. All answers divide evenly by the ten-thousandths' place.*

1. $7\overline{)\$18.20}$

2. $9\overline{)\$45.63}$

3. $12\overline{)\$47.52}$

4. $15\overline{)\$166.35}$

5. $18\overline{)36.09}$

6. $22\overline{)72.6}$

7. $38\overline{)574.75}$

8. $35\overline{)74.2}$

9. $25\overline{)83.26}$

10. $32\overline{)106.064}$

11. $32\overline{)34.128}$

12. $45\overline{)211.203}$

13. $16\overline{)47}$

14. $16\overline{)39}$

15. $28\overline{)29.6128}$

16. $34\overline{)43.435}$

B. Solve these reading problems.

17. The Miller family planted 75 acres of corn in 4 days. How many acres of corn did they average per day?

18. On Friday, David sprayed 30 of the 75 acres of corn. What decimal part of the 75 acres of corn did he spray?

19. The density of a material is determined by its weight for a given volume. Aluminum, a light metal, has a density of only 2.7 grams per cubic centimeter. Gold is 7.15 times as dense as aluminum. What is the density of gold per cubic centimeter? (Round to the nearest tenth of a gram.)

20. The lightest metal is lithium, which has a density of 0.5333 gram per cubic centimeter. The heaviest metal is osmium, with a density 42.16 times as great. What is the density of osmium? (Round to the nearest ten-thousandth gram.)

21. The liquid measures are measures of volume, containing a specific amount of space. A gallon contains 231 cubic inches. How many cubic inches does a quart contain?

22. A cup contains 0.25 quart. What part of a quart does a fluid ounce contain? For the number of ounces in a cup, see Lesson 27.

REVIEW EXERCISES

C. Solve these problems. Work mentally if you can. *(Lesson 61)*

23. 0.25 of 24

24. $0.33\frac{1}{3}$ of 33

25. 0.125 of 56

26. 0.625 of 32

D. Solve these multiplication problems. *(Lessons 45, 60)*

27.
$$\begin{array}{r} 2.17 \\ \times\ 3.05 \\ \hline \end{array}$$

28.
$$\begin{array}{r} 1.19 \\ \times\ 0.16 \\ \hline \end{array}$$

29. $\frac{4}{15} \times \frac{7}{8}$

30. $1\frac{1}{4} \times 3\frac{3}{5}$

E. Solve these addition problems. *(Lesson 58)*

31. $2.15 + 0.0786$

32. $0.4582 + 1.309$

F. Find the reciprocals of these numbers. *(Lesson 47)*

33. $\frac{3}{4}$

34. $\frac{5}{3}$

35. 3

36. $1\frac{3}{4}$

G. Change these measures as indicated. *(Lesson 27)*

37. 5 gal. = _____ qt.

38. 7 pk. = _____ bu.

39. $1\frac{1}{2}$ cups = _____ oz.

40. 9 qt. = _____ pk.

63. Dividing by Decimals

Dividing by decimals is the same as dividing by whole numbers except for the placing of the decimal point in the quotient. Study the problems below. What happens to the quotient when both the divisor and the dividend are multiplied by 10 or 100? The quotient remains the same.

$$
\begin{array}{r} 4 \\ 4\overline{)16} \\ \underline{16} \\ 0 \end{array}
\qquad
\begin{array}{r} 4 \\ 40\overline{)160} \\ \underline{160} \\ 0 \end{array}
\qquad
\begin{array}{r} 4 \\ 400\overline{)1{,}600} \\ \underline{1{,}600} \\ 0 \end{array}
$$

This same procedure is used when the divisor contains a decimal point. First the divisor is multiplied by moving the decimal point far enough to the right so that the divisor becomes a whole number. Then the decimal point in the dividend is moved the same number of places to the right. The decimal point in the quotient is placed directly above the new position of the decimal point in the dividend. Here are the steps to follow.

1. Move the decimal point in the divisor to the far right of the divisor, and mark its new position with a caret (˅).
2. Count the number of places that the decimal point in the divisor was moved, and move the decimal point in the dividend the same number of places. Annex zeroes if more places are needed. Mark this new position with a caret.
3. Place the decimal point for the quotient directly above the caret in the dividend.
4. Estimate and divide as usual.

Example A	Example B	Example C
$\begin{array}{r} 6.38 \\ 0.35\overline{)2.23{\scriptstyle\wedge}30} \\ \underline{210} \\ 133 \\ \underline{105} \\ 280 \\ \underline{280} \\ 0 \end{array}$	$\begin{array}{r} 87. \\ \$0.25\overline{)\$21.75} \\ \underline{200} \\ 175 \\ \underline{175} \\ 0 \end{array}$	$\begin{array}{r} 12.5 \\ 0.04\overline{)0.500} \\ \underline{4} \\ 10 \\ \underline{8} \\ 20 \\ \underline{20} \\ 0 \end{array}$

Notice in Example B that when money is divided by money, the quotient is not money. Rather, it is the number of *times* the amount of money in the divisor is contained in the dividend.

CLASS PRACTICE

Solve these problems. If the quotient does not come out evenly by the ten-thousandths' place, round it to the nearest thousandth.

a. $0.4\overline{)2.44}$ b. $0.15\overline{)0.155}$ c. $0.8\overline{)3.3}$ d. $\$0.55\overline{)\$17.59}$

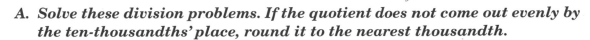

WRITTEN EXERCISES

A. Solve these division problems. If the quotient does not come out evenly by the ten-thousandths' place, round it to the nearest thousandth.

1. $0.5\overline{)3.65}$
2. $0.6\overline{)1.53}$
3. $0.8\overline{)2.44}$
4. $0.9\overline{)3.51}$

5. $1.1\overline{)3.355}$
6. $2.7\overline{)7.56}$
7. $6.4\overline{)1}$
8. $1.7\overline{)2.5}$

9. $\$0.45\overline{)\$1.71}$
10. $\$0.75\overline{)\$4.65}$
11. $\$1.10\overline{)\$5.28}$
12. $\$1.15\overline{)\$0.69}$

13. $0.04\overline{)0.0024}$
14. $0.05\overline{)0.0275}$
15. $0.12\overline{)4.4}$
16. $0.15\overline{)5.9}$

B. Solve these reading problems.

17. At the Beacon Hill Christian Bookstore, the clerks count the change every day after closing time. One afternoon they had $6.65 in nickels ($0.05). How many nickels did they have?

18. The clerks also counted $9.80 in dimes ($0.10). How many dimes did they have?

19. London, England, and Paris, France, are 214 air miles apart. On a certain map, London and Paris are 1.875 inches apart. How far is 1 inch on the map? Round your answer to the nearest mile.

20. Luke's home is 6 miles away from the post office. How far apart will the two locations be on a map with a scale of 2.3 miles per inch? Round your answer to the nearest thousandth of an inch.

21. The towns of Franklin and Millville are 3.875 inches apart on a map on which 1 inch equals 2.5 miles. How far apart are these two towns? Round your answer to the nearest tenth of a mile.

22. On the same map, two other towns are 8 miles apart. If each inch represents 2.5 miles, how far apart are the towns on the map?

REVIEW EXERCISES

C. Solve these problems. Work mentally if you can. *(Lessons 59, 61)*

23. 0.2 of 60
24. 0.125 of 32
25. 0.7 of 60
26. 0.75 of 36
27. 32.15 ÷ 100
28. 4.321 × 1,000
29. 0.1456 × 10
30. 1.231 ÷ 10

D. Write these decimals, using words. *(Lesson 54)*

31. 0.15
32. 0.609
33. 0.3005
34. 0.29001

E. Change these measures as indicated. *(Lesson 28)*

35. 4 sq. ft. = _____ sq. in.
36. 30 sq. ft. = _____ sq. yd.
37. 14 sq. yd. = _____ sq. ft.
38. 720 sq. in. = _____ sq. ft.

64. Reading Problems: Choosing the Reasonable Decimal Answer

The decimal point is a little mark that makes a great difference in the value of a number. For example, the numbers 345,000 and 0.00345 contain exactly the same digits, yet the first number is 100,000,000 times as large as the second one.

When writing decimals, be careful to place the decimal point correctly. Remember, writing no decimal point means that the decimal point is after the last digit in the number.

CLASS PRACTICE

Correct the number in each statement by moving the decimal point.

a. One group of hogs Father shipped to market weighed 2125 pounds each.

b. Jason is in the seventh grade. He is 1.25 years old.

c. The large book is three inches thick and has about 1.2 pages.

WRITTEN EXERCISES

A. *Some numbers in these statements are unreasonable because of missing or misplaced decimal points. Find those numbers and write them correctly, annexing zeroes if necessary. If all the numbers are reasonable, write* correct.

1. James is in the seventh grade and is 6075 inches tall.

2. The first European settlers in Lancaster County, Pennsylvania, came in 1710. The oldest building remaining in the county is the Christian Herr house, built by an original settler about 28 years ago.

3. The Masts traveled 125 miles to attend their aunt's wedding. Because there was little traffic on the road, they were able to travel the distance in 275 hours.

4. Brother Leinbach traveled by car to a distant location to serve in the new congregation being established there. He traveled a total of 3.5 miles in $7\frac{1}{2}$ hours.

5. Fuel oil is usually a bit less expensive per gallon than gasoline. When fuel oil was last delivered to the school, the price was $77.90 per gallon.

6. The freezing point of salt water is lower than that of fresh water. Because of its salt content, the ocean freezes at about 285°F, which is several degrees colder than the freezing point of fresh water.

7. The boiling point of water varies, depending on air pressure. The higher the elevation, the lower the boiling point of water. At an elevation of 10,000 feet, the boiling point of water is about 19.40° F, which is still scalding but not as hot as the boiling point of water at sea level. Because of this lower boiling point, the missionaries in the highlands of Guatemala must cook their food longer before it is ready to eat.

8. Father's copy of the *Martyrs Mirror* has 1,160 pages and is about 2.375 inches thick.

9. The Statue of Liberty in the New York harbor is a memorial to the millions of refugees from Europe who arrived on America's shores. Some of these refugees were fleeing persecution to a land that offered religious freedom. The Statue of Liberty is in the same height range as 20- to 25-story buildings. Its height from the base of the pedestal to the tip of the torch is 301,083 feet.

10. The Liberty Bell is found near Independence Hall in Philadelphia. It is called the Liberty Bell because on it is inscribed a phrase from Leviticus 25:10: "Proclaim liberty throughout all the land unto all the inhabitants thereof." The Liberty Bell is famous because it was rung when the Declaration of Independence was first read publicly in 1776. It is a large bell weighing more than a small automobile. Its weight is 20.8 pounds.

11. Brother Stauffer measured the length and the width of the classroom in order to calculate its area. The length of the room was 11.35 meters.

12. The Martin family traveled 275 miles to visit their relatives. On the trip, their van used 1.833 gallons of gasoline.

13. Jacob's older brother used the principles he had learned in his geometry lesson to measure the height of their house from the ground. He estimated their two-story house to be 285 feet high.

14. The Zimmerman family sold 20 acres of land to a business. Soon afterward, a large warehouse was built on the land. The warehouse measures 5.4 feet in length and 475 feet in width, and it covers several acres.

15. One ounce is equal to 1250 cups.

16. The walls in the Shirk residence are 985 inches high.

REVIEW EXERCISES

B. *Solve these multiplication and division problems. Drop any final zeroes to the right of the decimal point. If a division does not come out evenly by the ten-thousandths' place, round the quotient to the nearest thousandth. (Lessons 60, 62, 63)*

17. $\begin{array}{r} 1.45 \\ \times\, 2.07 \\ \hline \end{array}$ 18. $\begin{array}{r} 3.52 \\ \times\, 0.27 \\ \hline \end{array}$ 19. $\begin{array}{r} 0.28 \\ \times\, 0.16 \\ \hline \end{array}$ 20. $\begin{array}{r} 0.075 \\ \times\, 0.23 \\ \hline \end{array}$

21. $5\overline{)\$4.95}$ 22. $0.4\overline{)15.2}$ 23. $\$0.55\overline{)\$3.52}$ 24. $0.06\overline{)3.1}$

C. *Round these decimals as indicated. (Lesson 55)*

25. 0.8759 *(hundredth)*   26. 0.3995 *(thousandth)*

27. 0.7171 *(tenth)*   28. 0.4119 *(thousandth)*

D. *Find the unknown numbers. (Lesson 49)*

29. 12 is $\frac{2}{3}$ of _____   30. 15 is $\frac{3}{7}$ of _____

31. 8 is $\frac{4}{9}$ of _____   32. 6 is $\frac{4}{11}$ of _____

E. *Solve these multiplications mentally. (Lesson 44)*

33. $\frac{3}{4}$ of 20 = _____   34. $\frac{3}{5}$ of 25 = _____

35. $\frac{3}{8}$ of 40 = _____   36. $\frac{8}{9}$ of 27 = _____

F. *Change these measures as indicated. (Lesson 29)*

37. 5 hr. = _____ min.   38. 15 centuries = _____ yr.

39. 12 yr. = _____ mo.   40. 20 min. = _____ hr.

65. Chapter 5 Review

A. Express these decimals as common fractions. *(Lesson 54)*

1. 0.23
2. 0.209
3. 0.0179
4. 0.00354

B. Write these decimals, using words. *(Lesson 54)*

5. 0.07
6. 0.029
7. 0.10005
8. 0.000099

C. Express these common fractions as decimals. *(Lesson 54)*

9. $\frac{29}{100}$
10. $\frac{3}{100}$
11. $\frac{16}{1,000}$
12. $\frac{7\,07}{100,000}$

D. Copy each set of decimals, compare them, and write < or > between them. *(Lesson 55)*

13. 0.3087 _____ 0.31
14. 1.414 _____ 1.4

E. Round these numbers as indicated. *(Lesson 55)*

15. 6.588 *(tenth)*
16. 6.3999 *(hundredth)*

17. 5.5206 *(thousandth)*
18. $3.799 *(cent)*

F. Write these expressions as parts of a dollar. *(Lesson 55)*

19. 2.27\frac{9}{10}$
20. 0.79\frac{3}{10}$

G. Change these common fractions to decimals. They all divide evenly by the ten-thousandths' place. *(Lesson 56)*

21. $\frac{3}{20}$
22. $\frac{11}{40}$
23. $\frac{3}{16}$
24. $\frac{9}{16}$

H. Change these fractions to nonterminating decimals. Follow the instructions in working with the remainder. *(Lesson 57)*

Divide to the hundredths' place, and express the remainder as a fraction.

25. $\frac{1}{7}$
26. $\frac{1}{12}$

Round the decimal equivalent to the nearest thousandth.

27. $\frac{2}{9}$
28. $\frac{7}{15}$

Identify the repeating part of the decimal by drawing a bar above it.

29. $\frac{3}{11}$
30. $\frac{13}{22}$

I. **Solve these multiplication and division problems by moving the decimal points.** *(Lesson 59)*

31. 3.8×10

32. $0.09 \times 1,000$

33. 26.77×100

34. $56.0098 \div 10$

35. $0.021 \div 100$

36. $7.499 \div 1,000$

J. **Solve these problems. If a quotient does not divide evenly by the ten-thousandths' place, round it to the nearest thousandth.** *(Lessons 58–63)*

37.
```
   2.72
+ 3.0805
```

38.
```
   0.098
+ 5.01
```

39.
```
  13.07
- 5.875
```

40.
```
   28
- 13.54
```

41. $2.57 + 0.0065 + 7 + 21$

42. $3.1 + 2.908 + 17 + 0.009$

43. $4.5 - 2.209$

44. $2.51 - 0.0876$

45.
```
   3.6
× 0.79
```

46.
```
  0.707
× 0.05
```

47. $6)\overline{\$71.34}$

48. $9)\overline{2.713}$

49. 2.27×0.09

50. 3.55×0.6

51. $4.23 \div 0.4$

52. $5.71 \div 1.7$

K. **Solve these problems. See if you can do them mentally by first changing the decimal to a common fraction.** *(Lesson 61)*

53. 0.5 of 18

54. 0.25 of 44

55. 0.125 of 48

56. 0.75 of 28

57. 0.8 of 35

58. 0.625 of 32

59. $0.33\frac{1}{3}$ of \$27

60. $0.66\frac{2}{3}$ of \$36

L. **Some numbers in the following statements are unreasonable because of missing or misplaced decimal points. Find those numbers and write them correctly, annexing zeroes as needed. If all the numbers are reasonable, write** correct. *(Lesson 64)*

61. To bake a Busy Day Cake, Mother needs 167 cups of all-purpose flour.

62. The large meetinghouse was well filled for a bishop ordination. It was estimated that the attendance was 55.

63. Stanley took 5 grown rabbits to market. The total weight of the rabbits was 4.25 pounds.

64. Mother bought a 0.05-pound block of cheese. Because it would last her family a few weeks, she froze half of it.

M. *Solve these reading problems.*

65. Susan's baby sister, Mary Beth, weighed 3.5 kilograms at birth. When Mary Beth was a year old, she weighed 10 kilograms. How much weight did Mary Beth gain in her first year?

66. Sister Laura needs 20 pounds of ground beef to make meat-loaf for a family gathering. She had purchased on sale three packages weighing 6.21 pounds, 4.98 pounds, and 5.72 pounds. How many more pounds does she need to buy?

67. The Hollingers planted 10.55 acres of sweet corn at a rate of 12 pounds per acre. The cost of the seed was $2.75 per pound. What was the total cost of the seed?

68. The Hollingers also paid $382.90 to buy enough seeds to plant 8.9 acres of beets. To the nearest cent, what was the cost of the seed per acre?

69. The distance from the sun to the earth is 0.093003 billion miles. Round this decimal to the nearest hundredth.

70. The distance from the sun to Uranus is 1.7848 billion miles. Round this decimal to the nearest thousandth.

66. Chapter 5 Test

Chapter 6

Working With Ratios, Proportions, and Percents

[Elijah prayed,] "Lord, they have killed thy prophets, and digged down thine altars; and I am left alone, and they seek my life." But what saith the answer of God unto him? "I have reserved to myself seven thousand men, who have not bowed the knee to the image of Baal." Even so then at this present time also there is a remnant according to the election of grace.

(Romans 11:3–5)

67. Writing Ratios

In Lesson 40, you learned that fractions are used to compare numbers. You learned that if 3 out of 24 squares in a block are shaded, the number of shaded squares compared to all the squares can be expressed as the fraction $\frac{3}{24}$ and reduced to $\frac{1}{8}$. This means that there are $\frac{1}{8}$ as many shaded squares as there are total squares in the block.

Example A

$$\frac{3}{24} \quad \begin{array}{l} \text{antecedent} \\ \text{consequent} \end{array} \qquad \text{3 to 24} \qquad \text{3:24}$$

Reduced to lowest terms:

$$\frac{1}{8} \qquad \text{1 to 8} \qquad \text{1:8}$$

Ratios are another method of comparing numbers. Fractions are used to express one number as a part of another number. In the example above, 3 is $\frac{1}{8}$ of 24. Ratios are used to compare one number to another. The number of shaded squares in the block compared to the total number of blocks can be expressed with the ratio 3 to 24.

The first term of a ratio is called the **antecedent**, and the second term is called the **consequent**.

Ratios, like fractions, can be reduced. The ratio of 3 to 24 can be reduced to 1 to 8. *Three to twenty-four* and *one to eight* are examples of equivalent ratios.

Ratios can be written in the three different methods illustrated in Example A above. However, all the ratios in the first row are read, "Three to twenty-four," and all the ratios in the second row, "One to eight."

Ratios are written with the word *to* when it needs to be clearly understood that two numbers are being compared. The fractional form is common when ratios are used to solve problems. A colon is used when it is desirable to express the ratio concisely with whole numbers. This last form is often used to express the scale of miles on maps.

Ratios greater than one are written as improper fractions rather than mixed numbers. See the following examples.

Example B	**Example C**
$\frac{7}{3}$, 7 to 3, or 7:3; *not* $2\frac{1}{3}$	$\frac{5}{2}$, 5 to 2, or 5:2; *not* $2\frac{1}{2}$

CLASS PRACTICE

Use the blocks in Example A to answer questions a and b. Write a ratio to show each comparison.

a. The number of shaded blocks to the number of unshaded blocks.

b. The number of unshaded blocks in the first vertical row to the number of shaded blocks in that row.

c. To compare 8 cats to 2 dogs.

d. To compare 2 dogs to 8 cats.

e. To compare 7 acres of soybeans to 28 acres of corn.

WRITTEN EXERCISES

A. *Reduce these ratios to lowest terms. For problems 1 and 2, label each part of the ratios.*

1. $\frac{6}{15}$ _____   2. $\frac{9}{21}$ _____   3. $\frac{18}{12}$ 4. $\frac{60}{24}$

B. *Reduce these ratios to lowest terms. Write each answer in the same form as the form shown.*

5. 4 to 24   6. 28 to 12   7. 85 to 15   8. 33 to 55

9. 28:21   10. 24:40   11. 20:35   12. 81:45

C. *Write ratios in lowest terms to compare the lengths of the reigns indicated, using the table below.*

Length of the Reigns of the Kings of Israel		
Jeroboam I . . .22 yr.	Ahab . . . . .22 yr.	Jeroboam II . . .41 yr.
Nadab . . . . . . .2 yr.	Ahaziah . . . . . .2 yr.	Zachariah . . . .6 mo.
Baasha . . . . . .24 yr.	Jehoram . . . . .12 yr.	Shallum . . . . .1 mo.
Elah . . . . .2 yr.	Jehu . . . . .28 yr.	Pekah . . . . . . .20 yr.
Zimri . . . . . . .7 days	Jehoahaz . . . . .17 yr.	Pekahiah . . . . . .2 yr.
Omri . . . . .12 yr.	Jehoash . . . . . .16 yr.	Hoshea . . . . . . .9 yr.

13. The reign of Elah compared to the reign of Jeroboam I.

14. The reign of Omri compared to the reign of Baasha.

15. The reign of Jeroboam II compared to the reign of Jeroboam I.

16. The reign of Zechariah compared to the reign of Shallum.

17. The reigns of Omri and Jehoram together compared to the reign of Baasha.

18. The reign of Baasha compared to the reigns of Jehoram and Hoshea together.

19. The combined reigns of Jehu and Jehoahaz compared to the combined reigns of Jehoash and Jeroboam II.

20. The reign of Shallum compared to the reign of Pekah. (First express the length of Pekah's reign in months.)

21. Jeroboam and his son Nadab are known as Jeroboam's dynasty because they were of the same family. Because the three kings following Omri were his descendants, the period of the reigns of Omri, Ahab, Ahaziah, and Jehoram is known as the Omriac dynasty. Write a ratio comparing the length of the reign of Jeroboam's dynasty to that of Omri's dynasty.

22. God used Jehu to destroy the Omriac dynasty because of their wickedness. Jehu and his descendants ruled Israel longer than any other family. The last king who was a descendant of Jehu was Zachariah. Write a ratio comparing the length of the reign of Jehu's dynasty to the combined length of the reigns of the last three kings of Israel. (Count Zachariah's reign as a full year.)

REVIEW EXERCISES

D. Solve these multiplication and division problems. Drop any ending zeroes. *(Lessons 60, 62)*

23. $\begin{array}{r} 2.218 \\ \times\,0.15 \\ \hline \end{array}$
24. $\begin{array}{r} 4.105 \\ \times\,0.08 \\ \hline \end{array}$
25. $\begin{array}{r} 0.91 \\ \times\,0.07 \\ \hline \end{array}$
26. $\begin{array}{r} 0.035 \\ \times\,0.71 \\ \hline \end{array}$

27. $0.7\overline{)6.37}$ **28.** $0.3\overline{)3.36}$ **29.** $2.5\overline{)16}$ **30.** $0.015\overline{)3}$

E. Change these fractions to nonterminating decimals. Identify the repeating digits by placing a bar above them. *(Lesson 57)*

31. $\frac{5}{6}$ **32.** $\frac{4}{9}$ **33.** $\frac{7}{15}$ **34.** $\frac{7}{18}$

F. Write the value of the underlined digit in each number. *(Lesson 2)*

35. 4,5<u>6</u>2,663

36. 4<u>4</u>,006,783,000

37. 1<u>0</u>,000,000,000,000

38. <u>2</u>2,000,000,000,000

68. Writing and Using Proportions

A proportion is two equivalent ratios joined by an equal sign. The ratios in a proportion are usually written in fraction form because it is easier to compare and calculate with them in this form. Proportions are used to solve problems that involve ratios.

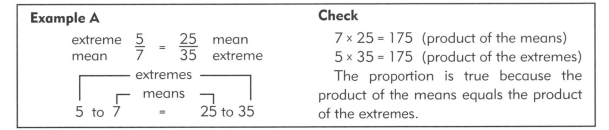

Example A	Check
extreme $\frac{5}{7}$ = $\frac{25}{35}$ mean mean extreme 5 to 7 = 25 to 35	$7 \times 25 = 175$ (product of the means) $5 \times 35 = 175$ (product of the extremes) The proportion is true because the product of the means equals the product of the extremes.

In a proportion, the first and last numbers are called the **extremes** because they are at the extreme ends of the proportion. The middle two numbers are called the **means** (one definition of *mean* is "middle"). If a proportion is true, the product of the means will equal the product of the extremes, as is shown in Example A. This is the method generally used to see if a proportion is true.

A proportion has four parts; three of the parts are known and are used to find the fourth part, the unknown number. Two of the numbers form a ratio showing how the third number is related to the unknown number (the answer).

To write a proportion to solve a problem, two ratios need to be set up. The first ratio, or primary ratio, shows how the numbers are related in the second ratio. Ratios are written and solved by using the steps below. Notice how the steps are used to solve the following problem.

Example B

One week Mark memorized 2 verses for every 3 verses that his older sister Ruth memorized. If Mark memorized 4 verses, how many verses did Ruth memorize?

Steps	Solution
1. Read the problem carefully. Pick out the three facts that are given and the question that needs to be answered.	The facts given are 2 verses, 3 verses, and 4 verses. We need to find the total number of verses Ruth memorized.
2. Write the two facts that form the primary ratio as the first ratio of the proportion.	Mark memorized 2 verses for every 3 verses that Ruth memorized. The ratio is $\frac{2}{3}$.
3. Label the facts in the primary ratio. Also write these labels at the same place in the second ratio.	Mark's verses $\frac{2}{3}$ = $\frac{}{}$ Mark's verses Ruth's verses Ruth's verses

4. Place the third fact given in the problem next to the label it relates to in the second proportion.	The third fact, 4 verses, is the verses Mark learned, so it belongs in the upper part of the second ratio. Mark's verses $\frac{2}{3} = \frac{4}{}$ Mark's verses Ruth's verses
5. Write n in the empty part of the second ratio to complete the proportion.	Mark's verses $\frac{2}{3} = \frac{4}{n}$ Mark's verses Ruth's verses
6. Cross multiply. Since one part of the proportion is a letter, there is only one pair of numbers to be cross multiplied.	The numbers to be cross multiplied are 3 and 4. $3 \times 4 = 12$
7. Divide the product of the cross multiplication by the remaining number in the proportion to find the answer (n).	$12 \div 2 = 6$ Answer: $n = 6$ Mark's verses $\frac{2}{3} = \frac{4}{6}$ Mark's verses Ruth's verses
8. Check the proportion by cross multiplying.	Check: means $3 \times 4 = 12$ ⌐ extremes $2 \times 6 = 12$ ⌐ The products are equal.

CLASS PRACTICE

Find the missing parts of these proportions. Express any remainders as fractions. Write n followed by an equal sign and a number for your answer.

a. $\frac{3}{4} = \frac{n}{28}$ b. $\frac{6}{15} = \frac{8}{n}$ c. $\frac{n}{6} = \frac{15}{25}$ d. $\frac{14}{n} = \frac{18}{25}$

Write a proportion for each set of facts. Label both parts of the primary ratio and the secondary ratio as shown in step 7 of Example B. Replace the phrase "a certain number" with the letter n, and then find the value of n.

e. Marcus has lived 3 years for every 11 years that his father has lived. Marcus is 9 years old, and his father is a certain number of years old. How old is Marcus's father?

f. King David was king 8 years for every 5 years that Jehoshaphat was king. David reigned for 40 years and Jehoshaphat for a certain number of years. How long did Jehoshaphat reign?

WRITTEN EXERCISES

A. *Check each proportion by cross multiplication, and write the two products. Then write* true *if the proportion is true, or* false *if it is false.*

1. $\frac{6}{9} = \frac{8}{12}$ 2. $\frac{7}{15} = \frac{5}{12}$ 3. $\frac{7}{12} = \frac{17}{30}$ 4. $\frac{2}{8} = \frac{3}{12}$

5. $\frac{3}{9} = \frac{7}{21}$ 6. $\frac{12}{8} = \frac{33}{22}$ 7. $\frac{25}{15} = \frac{60}{36}$ 8. $\frac{24}{33} = \frac{15}{22}$

B. *Find the missing parts of these proportions. Express any remainders as fractions.*

9. $\frac{10}{12} = \frac{n}{18}$ 10. $\frac{6}{14} = \frac{n}{21}$ 11. $\frac{6}{10} = \frac{15}{n}$ 12. $\frac{12}{16} = \frac{5}{n}$

13. $\frac{n}{21} = \frac{5}{15}$ 14. $\frac{n}{10} = \frac{12}{16}$ 15. $\frac{15}{n} = \frac{25}{35}$ 16. $\frac{16}{n} = \frac{7}{12}$

C. Write proportions for each set of facts. Label both the primary ratio and the secondary ratio as shown in step 7 of Example B.

17. The Zimmerman family's dairy herd produced 63 pounds of milk per cow, or 2,394 pounds for 38 cows.

18. The hogs that Brother Mark shipped weighed 230 pounds each, or 5,750 pounds for 25 hogs.

19. Matthew solved 3 math problems in 5 minutes, or 24 problems in 40 minutes.

20. Grades 5, 6, and 7 have 1 songbook for every 2 students, or 9 songbooks for the 18 students.

D. Write proportions for these problems as you did in Part C. Replace the phrase "a certain number" with the letter n, and then find the value of n.

21. For every 35 years that Abraham lived, Moses lived 24 years. Abraham lived a certain number of years, and Moses lived 120 years. How many years of life did God grant to Abraham?

22. There are 2 boys for every 3 girls at the Lisbon Mennonite School. The school has 14 boys and a certain number of girls.

23. One out of every four disciples were with Christ at His transfiguration. Three disciples, Peter, James, and John, out of a certain number accompanied Christ. How many disciples did Christ have?

24. David correctly completed 23 out of 25 math problems. He had a certain number out of every 100 problems done correctly.

REVIEW EXERCISES

E. Solve these division problems, taking special care to place the decimal points correctly. (Lesson 63)

25. $0.2\overline{)3.35}$ 26. $0.8\overline{)2.1}$ 27. $1.4\overline{)2.87}$ 28. $0.012\overline{)6}$

F. See if you can solve these problems mentally by first changing the decimals to common fractions. (Lesson 61)

29. 0.4 of 35   30. 0.75 of 28   31. 0.125 of 48   32. 0.875 of 32

G. Solve these addition and subtraction problems. (Lesson 58)

33. 2.7 + 2 + 1.5101 + 0.0321   34. 1.1202 + 0.02 + 151 + 0.00081

35. 5 − 1.215   36. 4.6 − 0.0077

H. Solve these problems relating to time, rate, and distance. (Lesson 32)

37. $t = 5$ hr.   38. $t = 4$ hr.   39. $d = 364$ mi.   40. $t = \frac{1}{3}$ hr.
    $r = 51$ m.p.h. $d = 140$ mi. $r = 52$ m.p.h. $r = 45$ m.p.h.
    $d =$ ____ $r =$ ____ $t =$ ____ $d =$ ____

I. Round these numbers as indicated. (Lesson 3)

41. 1,457 (hundred)   42. 379,833 (thousand)

43. 344,894,122 (ten million)   44. 17,899,932,000 (billion)

69. Reading Problems: Using Proportions

Proportions are useful in working with rates such as miles per hour or teaspoons per quart. They also provide an interesting way to find the heights of objects that are difficult to measure otherwise. Consider the following reading problem, and notice how the steps shown in Lesson 68 are used to find the solution.

> Ronald is 5 feet tall. One morning at 11:15, Ronald cast a 4-foot shadow. At the same time, the house Ronald lives in cast a 15-foot shadow. How high is the house?
>
> Step 1: The significant facts are Ronald's height (5 feet), the length of Ronald's shadow (4 feet), and the length of the house's shadow (15 feet). The fact needed is the height of the house.
>
> Steps 2–5: Ronald's height is related to the length of his shadow in the same way that the height of the house is related to the length of its shadow.
>
> Ronald's height $\dfrac{5}{4} = \dfrac{n}{15}$ Height of house
> Ronald's shadow   Shadow of house
>
> Step 6: Cross multiply. $5 \times 15 = 75$
>
> Step 7: Divide. $75 \div 4 = 18\frac{3}{4}$ $n = 18\frac{3}{4}$
>
> Ronald's height $\dfrac{5}{4} = \dfrac{18\frac{3}{4}}{15}$ Height of house
> Ronald's shadow   Shadow of house
>
> The house is $18\frac{3}{4}$ feet high.
>
> Step 8: Check. $5 \times 15 = 75$
> $4 \times 18\frac{3}{4} = 75$
> The proportion was solved correctly.

CLASS PRACTICE

Find the missing parts of these proportions.

  a. $\frac{6}{9} = \frac{n}{12}$ b. $\frac{12}{16} = \frac{27}{n}$ c. $\frac{14}{30} = \frac{n}{55}$

Write and solve proportions for these reading problems.

  d. Early one morning, Erma picked 22 quarts of strawberries in 2 hours. If she continues picking at that rate for a total of 5 hours, how many quarts will she pick?

  e. Brother Elmer is calculating how many songs he should be prepared to lead at the Thanksgiving assembly at school. If 3 songs can be sung in 10 minutes, how many songs should he have ready for a 35-minute singing period? (Round any fraction in your answer to the nearest whole number.)

WRITTEN EXERCISES

A. *Find the missing parts of these proportions. Express any remainders as fractions.*

1. $\frac{3}{4} = \frac{n}{20}$

2. $\frac{8}{12} = \frac{n}{21}$

3. $\frac{9}{15} = \frac{15}{n}$

4. $\frac{15}{18} = \frac{n}{24}$

5. $\frac{5}{10} = \frac{n}{18}$

6. $\frac{18}{24} = \frac{27}{n}$

B. *Complete these proportions, and use them to solve the problems.*

7. The Stoltzfus family plans to invite the visitors at church to their home for dinner. Mother is preparing a meat dish that requires 5 pounds of ground beef to serve 12 people. How much ground beef should she thaw to prepare enough for 15 people?

	Primary Ratio	*Secondary Ratio*	
pounds of beef	_____	_____	pounds of beef
people	_____	_____	people

8. One afternoon the Witmers' tractor used 22 gallons of fuel in 4 hours of plowing. At that rate, how much fuel will it take to use the tractor for 15 hours?

	Primary Ratio	*Secondary Ratio*	
gallons	_____	_____	gallons
hours	_____	_____	hours

9. The Myers' car traveled 120 miles on 5 gallons of gasoline. At that rate, how many miles will they be able to travel on the 16 gallons of gasoline that the fuel tank holds?

	Primary Ratio	*Secondary Ratio*	
miles	_____	_____	miles
gallons	_____	_____	gallons

10. The Brubakers are planning to use their van to take their minister to preach at a church 235 miles away. On an earlier trip, their van used 7 gallons of gasoline to travel 105 miles. At that rate, how many gallons will it take to travel to the church?

	Primary Ratio	*Secondary Ratio*	
miles	_____	_____	miles
gallons	_____	_____	gallons

Be not forgetful to entertain strangers.   *Hebrews 13:2*

C. *Write proportions to solve these reading problems. Label each part of the proportions as shown in Part B.*

11. The Martins' oil furnace can produce 125,000 Btu's of heat in an hour when it is running continuously. At that rate, how many Btu's of heat can the furnace produce in 3.5 hours?

12. A larger furnace burns 1.25 gallons of fuel oil to produce 145,000 Btu's of heat per hour. At that rate, how much fuel oil is needed to produce 377,000 Btu's of heat?

13. To put the first coat of paint on their basement floor, the Hostetters were instructed to mix paint thinner into paint at a ratio of 1:8. How much paint thinner will they need to mix with 6 gallons of paint?

14. The Sensenigs receive $13.50 for each 100 pounds of milk they ship. How much will they be paid for a milk shipment of 4,550 pounds?

15. Galen's father used 15 gallons of fungicide to spray 20 acres of corn. At that rate, how many gallons will he need to spray a 50-acre field?

16. The Wengers harvested 3,335 bushels of corn from their 23-acre corn field. If their 18-acre field produces equally well, how many bushels of corn will they harvest?

17. The Landis family is going to a family reunion. They traveled 75 miles during the first $1\frac{1}{2}$ hours of the trip. At that rate, how far will they travel in $5\frac{1}{2}$ hours?

18. The Landises traveled 120 miles in $2\frac{1}{2}$ hours. At that rate, how long will it take for them to travel 264 miles to their first stop?

19. Larry uses 425 pounds of soybean meal to mix a $2\frac{1}{2}$ ton batch of hog feed. At that rate, how much should he use for a $3\frac{1}{2}$ ton batch?

20. Larry's father bought 500 bushels of shelled corn for $1,150. How much would he have paid for 400 bushels?

REVIEW EXERCISES

D. *Solve these problems mentally by moving the decimal points.* *(Lesson 59)*

21. $35 \div 10$ 22. 4.77×100

23. $0.0078 \times 1,000$ 24. $57.9 \times 1,000$

25. $445.99 \div 1,000$ 26. $16.89 \div 100$

E. *Write these numbers with Arabic numerals.* *(Lesson 4)*

27. CDXLVII   28. MCMXCIV   29. $\overline{\text{X}}$CC   30. $\overline{\overline{\text{CC}}}$

F. *Write these numbers with Roman numerals.* *(Lesson 4)*

31. 177   32. 3,166   33. 15,000   34. 500,000

70. Problems With More Challenging Proportions

In the previous lessons, three of the four parts of the proportions were given in the problems. These could then be used to find the fourth part, the answer to the problem.

Sometimes not all three parts of a proportion are given as clearly as in the last two lessons. Consider the following example.

> There are three boys to every two girls at school. Out of the fifty-five students, how many are girls?

At first you might think that this problem is similar to the other proportion problems you have done so far. But notice what happens when you try to set up the proportion and label the parts. The third fact given, 55 students, does not fit anywhere in the proportion.

Incorrect

$$\frac{\text{boys}}{\text{girls}} \quad \frac{3}{2} = \frac{\rule{1cm}{0.4pt}}{\rule{1cm}{0.4pt}} \quad \frac{\text{boys}}{\text{girls}}$$

The reading problem does not give the number of boys or the number of girls. But it does give the number of students. So in order to solve this problem, we will need to form a ratio to calculate the number of girls in relation to the number of students.

To find the primary ratio, we must add to obtain one of the facts. Since there are 3 boys to 2 girls, there are 2 girls for every 5 students (3 boys + 2 girls). So the proportion can be written as shown below. Study the proportion until you are sure that you understand it.

Correct $\dfrac{\text{girls}}{\text{students}} \quad \dfrac{2}{5} = \dfrac{n}{55} \quad \dfrac{\text{girls}}{\text{students}}$

Solution: $2 \times 55 = 110; \quad 110 \div 5 = 22$ girls

Check: $\dfrac{\text{girls}}{\text{students}} \quad \dfrac{22}{55} = \dfrac{2}{5} \quad \dfrac{\text{girls}}{\text{students}} \qquad \begin{array}{l} 55 \times 2 = 110 \\ 22 \times 5 = 110 \end{array}$

55 students – 22 girls = 33 boys

33 to 22 = 3 to 2, the ratio in the original problem

In writing proportions, both ratios must be formed by the same logic. If the primary ratio compares the number of girls to the total number of students, the secondary ratio must also compare the number of girls to the total number of students.

CLASS PRACTICE

Express these facts as ratios.

a. The Weaver family has 2 acres of hay for every 5 acres of corn on their farm. Write a ratio comparing the acres of hay to the total acres of hay and corn.

b. There are 11 sixth graders and 13 seventh graders in school. Write a ratio comparing the number of sixth graders to the number of seventh graders.

c. During one year at Columbus, Ohio, there were 64 clear days and 301 cloudy or partly cloudy days. Write a ratio showing what part of the total days were clear.

d. During the same year, there were 208 clear days at Phoenix, Arizona, and 157 cloudy or partly cloudy days. Write a ratio comparing the number of clear days to the number of cloudy days that year.

Write proportions to solve these reading problems.

e. The Weaver family has 2 acres of hay for every 5 acres of corn on their farm. They have 24 acres of hay. How many acres of corn do they have?

f. The Weaver family has 2 acres of hay for every 5 acres of corn. They have 24 acres of hay. How many acres of corn and hay do they have in all?

WRITTEN EXERCISES

A. Read these facts carefully, and then express the ratios as directed. Give each ratio in lowest terms.

1. In Brother Galen's classroom there are 4 students in Grade 7 and 5 students in Grade 8. Write a ratio comparing the number of seventh graders to the number of eighth graders.

2. The seventh grade has 4 students and the eighth grade has 5 students. Write a ratio comparing the number of eighth graders to the total number of students in the seventh and eighth grades.

3. One morning in math class, Thomas had 31 answers correct and 2 answers incorrect. Write a ratio showing what part of his math lesson Thomas did correctly.

4. The Rudolphs have 3 boys and 6 girls. Write a ratio showing what part of the children in the Rudolph family are girls.

5. Write a ratio comparing the number of girls with the number of boys in the Rudolph family. (See problem 4)

6. Brother Reinford's farm consists of 15 acres of pasture, 65 acres of cropland, and 25 acres of woodland. Write a ratio showing what part of the Reinford farm is woodland.

7. Using the facts in problem 6, what part of the farm can the Reinfords use for farming (the pasture and the cropland)?

8. Using the facts in problem 6, write a ratio to compare the acres of woodland to the acres of pasture.

B. Write proportions to solve these reading problems. You will need to calculate parts of all these proportions.

9. Graybill's Cherry and Apple Orchard has 3 cherry trees for every 4 apple trees. There are 45 cherry trees in the orchard. How many trees are in the orchard in all?

10. Mother planted 2 rows of yellow sweet corn for every 3 rows of white sweet corn. She planted 15 rows of white sweet corn. How many rows of sweet corn did she plant in all?

11. The Burkholder family has three Holstein cows for each Jersey cow. How many of their 48 cows are Holsteins?

12. Of the Burkholders' 48 cows, 1 is dry for every 5 that they are milking. How many cows are the Burkholders milking?

C. Study these reading problems carefully, and solve them by writing proportions.

13. Father, who is 6 feet tall, cast a 14-foot shadow one evening. How tall is a tree that casts an 84-foot shadow at the same time?

14. Mother was helping to serve lunch at school. She poured 2 glasses of orange juice for every 3 glasses of fruit punch. If she filled 45 glasses in all, how many glasses of orange juice did she pour?

15. Sister Edna provided hot dogs for the lunch. For every 4 students who ate only one hot dog, 3 students took a second hot dog. How many of the 35 students ate two hot dogs?

16. Two out of every 5 students took a second serving of juice or punch. How many of the 35 students took a second serving of drink?

17. The new well on the Zook property produces 25 gallons of water per minute. At that rate, how many gallons does it produce per hour?

18. The Stover family has an orchard of apple and pear trees. One year they picked 2 bushels of pears for every 5 bushels of apples. If they picked 50 bushels of pears, how many bushels of fruit did they pick in all?

REVIEW EXERCISES

D. Solve these multiplication and division problems. *(Lessons 60, 62, 63)*

19.	20.	21.	22.
$5.80	0.75	3.5	0.077
× 1.6	× 2.5	× 0.06	× 0.53

23. 6)$45.54   24. 1.2)4.2   25. 0.4)3.99   26. 0.016)0.712

E. Solve these addition problems. Label each part of numbers 27 and 28. *(Lesson 5)*

27.	28.	29.	30.
4,561 ____	23,401 ____	$2,310.89	3,158,278
3,201 ____	314,151 ____	5,172.70	5,614,812
12,908 ____	413 ____	3,215.00	+ 2,002,512
+ 3,917 ____	+ 77,621 ____	+ 2,231.89	

71. Introduction to Percents

The denominator most commonly used in comparisons is 100. Because it is so common, the denominator 100 has been replaced with the percent sign (%) to make writing of the comparison shorter. The word **percent** means "per hundred." Following is an example of using percents.

Example A

Sarah was comparing the scores she received on two history lessons. She had 2 answers wrong in each lesson. Her score on one assignment was 92%, but on the other it was 90%.

points correct $\frac{23}{25} = \frac{92}{100}$ or 92% total points	points correct $\frac{18}{20} = \frac{90}{100}$ or 90% total points
Check: $25 \times 92 = 2{,}300$ $23 \times 100 = 2{,}300$	Check: $20 \times 90 = 1{,}800$ $18 \times 100 = 1{,}800$

The 92% that Sarah received on one assignment means that Sarah had completed the equivalent of 92 out of every 100 exercises correctly. The 90% means that she had done the equivalent of 90 out of every 100 exercises correctly.

Percents are changed to fractions by the following steps: (1) remove the % sign, (2) write the number as the numerator of a fraction with a denominator of 100, and (3) reduce the fraction to lowest terms. See Example B below.

If a common fraction has a denominator that is a factor of 100, it can easily be changed to a percent. First change the fraction to an equivalent fraction with 100 as the denominator, and then write the numerator followed by the percent sign (%). See Example C below.

To express a percent as a decimal, move the decimal point two places to the left and drop the percent sign. See Example D below.

To express a decimal as a percent, move the decimal point two places to the right and place a percent sign after the number. See Example E below.

Example B	**Example C**	**Example D**	**Example E**
$50\% = \frac{50}{100} = \frac{1}{2}$	$\frac{3}{50} = \frac{6}{100} = 6\%$	$45\% = 0.45$	$0.54 = 54\%$

CLASS PRACTICE

Write these decimals and common fractions as percents.

a. 0.70   b. 0.04   c. $\frac{59}{100}$ d. $\frac{8}{100}$

Write these percents as decimals.

e. 63%   f. 31%   g. 14%   h. 6%

Write these percents as common fractions in lowest terms.

i. 27%   j. 38%   k. 50%   l. 24%

WRITTEN EXERCISES

A. Write these decimals and common fractions as percents.

1. 0.85   2. 0.21   3. 0.62   4. 0.90   5. 0.09   6. 0.03

7. $\frac{17}{100}$ 8. $\frac{39}{100}$ 9. $\frac{26}{100}$ 10. $\frac{42}{100}$ 11. $\frac{7}{100}$ 12. $\frac{5}{100}$

B. Write these percents as decimals.

13. 29%   14. 17%   15. 68%   16. 75%

17. 90%   18. 60%   19. 4%   20. 6%

C. Write these percents as common fractions in lowest terms.

21. 41%   22. 53%   23. 49%   24. 99%

25. 22%   26. 62%   27. 1%   28. 7%

D. Solve these reading problems. Use proportions for numbers 33 and 34.

29. Exodus 16 records that Aaron gathered an omer of manna and laid it up before the Testimony as a memorial. An omer is one-tenth of an ephah, another Bible measure. Write as a percent the part of an ephah that an omer is.

30. Genesis 41:34 states that Joseph advised Pharaoh to gather one-fifth of the crops during the seven good years to prepare for the seven years of famine. Write the percent of the crops that this was.

31. A certain vitamin tablet provides 60% of the daily need of vitamin A for children over 4 years old. What fraction of their daily need is provided? (Express your answer in lowest terms.)

32. A pain relief spray has 20% active ingredient. Write 20% as a fraction in lowest terms.

33. Sarah and her younger sister picked all the raspberries one morning. Sarah picked 5 quarts of berries for every 2 quarts her sister picked. They picked 21 quarts in all. How many quarts did Sarah pick?

34. One morning in Bible class, Daniel had two test questions incorrect for every 15 questions he had correct. There were 51 questions in all. How many did Daniel do correctly?

REVIEW EXERCISES

E. See if you can solve these problems mentally by first changing the decimal to a common fraction. *(Lesson 61)*

35. 0.2 of 45   36. 0.125 of 32   37. 0.75 of 24

38. $0.66\frac{2}{3}$ of 27   39. 0.375 of 24   40. 0.875 of 16

F. Add these numbers mentally by finding pairs that make 10. *(Lesson 6)*

41. 6 + 4 + 7 + 2 + 3   42. 5 + 3 + 5 + 6 + 4

43. 3 + 7 + 7 + 4 + 6   44. 6 + 3 + 7 + 2 + 2 + 8

G. Add these numbers mentally. *(Lesson 6)*

45. 35 + 46   46. 43 + 39   47. 26 + 83   48. 57 + 79

72. Fractions, Decimals, and Percents

Fractions, decimals, and percents are three different ways to express fractional parts. Fractions and decimals have the more specific names of common fractions and decimal fractions. Although percents are not called "percent fractions," they are a convenient way to express fractions that have denominators of 100. It is possible to express the same value as a fraction, a decimal, and a percent. Some of the decimals and percents, however, are nonterminating.

Changing Fractions to Percents

To change fractions to percents, the simplest way is usually to first change them to decimals. Because of this, changing fractions to percents is much the same as changing fractions to decimals. The only extra step is that of changing the decimal to a percent. This method is described below.

Step 1: Divide the numerator by the denominator to obtain a decimal. If the answer does not divide evenly to the hundredths' place, write the remainder as a fraction in lowest terms.

Step 2: Change the decimal to a percent.

Example A	Example B
Express $\frac{1}{7}$ as a percent.	Express $\frac{7}{15}$ as a percent.
Step 1: Change $\frac{1}{7}$ to a decimal.	Step 1: Change $\frac{7}{15}$ to a decimal.
$\begin{array}{r} 0.14\frac{2}{7} \\ 7\overline{)1.00} \\ \underline{7} \\ 30 \\ \underline{28} \\ 2 \end{array}$	$\begin{array}{r} 0.46\frac{10}{15} = 0.46\frac{2}{3} \\ 15\overline{)7.00} \\ \underline{60} \\ 100 \\ \underline{90} \\ 10 \end{array}$
Step 2: Express the decimal from Step 1 as a percent. $0.14\frac{2}{7} = 14\frac{2}{7}\%$	Step 2: Express the decimal from Step 1 as a percent. $0.46\frac{2}{3} = 46\frac{2}{3}\%$

Just as it is beneficial to know by memory the decimal equivalents of frequently used common fractions, so it is also helpful to know their percent equivalents. Memorize the following percent equivalents of common fractions.

$\frac{1}{2} = 50\%$	$\frac{1}{3} = 33\frac{1}{3}\%$	$\frac{2}{3} = 66\frac{2}{3}\%$	$\frac{1}{4} = 25\%$	$\frac{3}{4} = 75\%$
$\frac{1}{5} = 20\%$	$\frac{2}{5} = 40\%$		$\frac{3}{5} = 60\%$	$\frac{4}{5} = 80\%$
$\frac{1}{8} = 12\frac{1}{2}\%$	$\frac{3}{8} = 37\frac{1}{2}\%$		$\frac{5}{8} = 62\frac{1}{2}\%$	$\frac{7}{8} = 87\frac{1}{2}\%$

CLASS PRACTICE

Express these fractions as percents.

a. $\frac{9}{25}$ = _____   b. $\frac{3}{50}$ = _____   c. $\frac{9}{16}$ = _____   d. $\frac{17}{30}$ = _____

WRITTEN EXERCISES

A. *Express these fractions as percents.*

1. $\frac{13}{25}$ = _____   2. $\frac{17}{25}$ = _____   3. $\frac{11}{50}$ = _____   4. $\frac{49}{50}$ = _____

5. $\frac{1}{25}$ = _____   6. $\frac{7}{50}$ = _____   7. $\frac{7}{16}$ = _____   8. $\frac{11}{16}$ = _____

9. $\frac{23}{40}$ = _____   10. $\frac{11}{15}$ = _____   11. $\frac{1}{11}$ = _____   12. $\frac{1}{18}$ = _____

B. *Complete the following chart.*

	Fraction	Decimal	Percent
13.	$\frac{14}{25}$		
15.		0.45	
17.			7%

	Fraction	Decimal	Percent
14.	$\frac{17}{50}$		
16.		0.02	
18.			37%

C. *Solve these reading problems. Use proportions for numbers 23 and 24.*

19. Exodus 29:40 gives the things to be sacrificed with the lamb that was offered every morning. Those things included one-fourth hin of beaten oil. What percent of a hin of beaten oil was used?

20. In Numbers 15:6, the Lord commanded that one-third hin of oil be used when offering a ram for a burnt offering. What percent of a hin of oil was that?

21. Marcus correctly did 32 out of 35 math problems in one assignment. What was his score as a percent, to the nearest whole number?

22. The 12 members of the Brubaker family moved to Paraguay for a term of service at the mission there. The congregation they were a part of in North America had a regular attendance of 56. What percent of the congregation moved to Paraguay?

23. In a certain silo, the ratio of the depth of footer to the height of the silo is 1:40. The total depth of the footer is 2 feet. What is the combined measure of the footer and silo?

24. During a two-week period of heavy snowfall in one area, it snowed a total of 45 inches. Two inches of snow fell in the first week for every 7 inches that fell the second. How many inches fell the second week?

REVIEW EXERCISES

D. *Solve these division problems.* (Lesson 63)

25. $1.3\overline{)4.875}$ 26. $0.4\overline{)2.7}$ 27. $0.72\overline{)1.8}$ 28. $0.055\overline{)0.2332}$

E. *Round these decimals as indicated.* (Lesson 55)

29. 0.0179 *(hundredth)*   30. 0.27299 *(ten-thousandth)*

31. 0.99999 *(thousandth)*   32. 0.5169 *(tenth)*

73. Finding a Percentage of a Number

One of the most frequent uses of percents is to find a percentage of a number. Finding a percentage of a number is the same as finding a decimal part of a number. In fact, to find a percentage of a number, the rate or percent is changed to a decimal before multiplying.

Example A	**Example B**
Find 24% of 75.	Find 6% of 46.
Step 1: Change 24% to 0.24.	Step 1: Change 6% to 0.06.
Step 2: Multiply.	Step 2: Multiply.
$\begin{array}{r} 75 \\ \times\,0.24 \\ \hline 300 \\ 150 \\ \hline 18.00 \end{array}$	$\begin{array}{r} 46 \\ \times\,0.06 \\ \hline 2.76 \end{array}$
24% of 75 = 18	6% of 46 = 2.76

> **To find a percentage of a number, change the percent to a decimal and multiply the number by the decimal.**

In working with percentages, three terms are applied to the three parts of percent problems. Learn these terms; they will be used in later lessons as percents are used in different ways.

Base—The whole amount.

Rate—The percent figure, such as 5%, 6%, 15%.

Percentage—The amount that is part of the whole. The answer to each problem in this lesson is a percentage of the whole.

Rate	Base		Percentage		Percentage		Rate	Base	
75%	of	36	=	27	27	is	75%	of	36

CLASS PRACTICE

Find the percentages of the bases given.

a. 55% of 16   b. 13% × 61   c. 4% of 78   d. 7% of 89

Find 5% of each base given.

e. 40   f. 50   g. 34   h. 61

WRITTEN EXERCISES

A. *Find the percentages.*

1. 35% of 40
2. 55% of 60
3. 26% of 43
4. 43% of 75
5. 49% of 37
6. 22% of 15
7. 48% of 61
8. 34% of 66
9. 34 × 92%
10. 39 × 88%
11. 27 × 82%
12. 41 × 97%
13. 7% × 40
14. 9% × 91
15. 45 × 7%
16. 51 × 2%

B. *Find 8% of each base given.*

17. 50
18. 60
19. 41
20. 36

C. *Finish these statements.*

21. In the equation *15% of 80 = 12*, 12 is the ____.
22. In the equation *8 = 20% of 40*, 40 is the ____.

D. *Solve these reading problems. Use the facts in the italicized paragraph to do numbers 25–30, and use proportions to do numbers 31 and 32.*

23. Mr. Martin's annual income is about $20,400. He spends 25% of that for rent. How much does he spend annually for rent?

24. Brother Harold planted 40% of his 160 acres in corn. How many acres of corn did he plant?

   Dairy farmers use different formulas for determining the grain mixture needed by their cows, depending on the quality of the roughage being fed. One formula designed for cows receiving a good supply of alfalfa is given below. Find how many pounds of each ingredient is needed to make a 2,000-pound mix. Hint: To check numbers 25–30, add the answers together. The sum will be 2,000 if they are all correct.

25. Corn—38%
26. Oats—30%
27. Wheat bran—25%
28. Linseed meal—5%
29. Bone meal—1%
30. Salt—1%

31. An adult may spend 5 hours sleeping for every 11 hours that he is awake. How many hours of sleep is that in a day (24 hours)?

*32. If an adult spends 5 hours sleeping for every 11 hours that he is awake, how many years does it take for him to have slept a period of 12 years?

REVIEW EXERCISES

E. *Complete the following chart.* (Lesson 72)

	Fraction	*Decimal*	*Percent*
33.	$\frac{13}{25}$		
35.			49%

	Fraction	*Decimal*	*Percent*
34.	$\frac{21}{40}$		
36.		0.07	

F. *Solve these subtraction problems mentally.* (Lesson 8)

37. 48 − 29
38. 71 − 27
39. 156 − 37
40. 171 − 47

74. Finding a Percent More or Less Than a Number

The rate of a price increase or decrease is often given as a percent. When a retail store advertises "Inventory Clearance Sale—All Items Reduced 15%," all prices in the store are reduced by a rate of 15%. Another term for a decrease in price is a discount.

The rate of price increases are also given in percents for the sake of comparison. The rate of inflation (price increases), for example, may be 4% for a certain year.

To find both the amount of increase or decrease and the new amount, use the following steps.

Step 1: Change the percent of increase or decrease to a decimal by moving the decimal point two places to the left.

Step 2: Multiply the original price by the decimal.

Step 3: If the product has more than two decimal places, round the answer to the nearest cent (hundredth of a dollar). This answer is the amount of the increase or decrease.

Step 4: To find the new price, add the increase to, or subtract the decrease from, the original amount.

Example A	**Example B**
Find the new price of an item priced at $13.50 after an increase of 7%.	Find the sale price of an item that normally sells for $12.95, but is on sale at a 15% discount.
Step 1: 7% = 0.07	Step 1: 15% = 0.15
Step 2: $13.50 × 0.07 = $0.945	Step 2: $12.95 × 0.15 = $1.9425
Step 3: $0.945 rounds to $0.95	Step 3: $1.9425 rounds to $1.94

Step 4: $13.50
       + 0.95
       $14.45
	Step 4: $12.95
	       − 1.94
	       $11.01

CLASS PRACTICE

Find the new prices, rounding to the nearest cent if needed. Include both the
amount of increase or decrease and the new price in each answer.

a. $12.00 increased by 10%   b. $6.95 decreased by 20%

c. $14.25 increased by 35%   d. $9.50 decreased by 30%

WRITTEN EXERCISES

A. *Find the new prices, rounding to the nearest cent if needed. Include both*
   the amount of increase and the new price in each answer.

1. $15.00 increased by 5%   2. $30.00 increased by 8%

3. $25.00 increased by 20%   4. $18.00 increased by 15%

5. $9.95 increased by 15%   6. $8.99 increased by 12%

7. $12.95 increased by 25%   8. $8.95 increased by 18%

B. *Find the new prices, rounding to the nearest cent if needed. Include both*
   the amount of decrease and the new price in each answer.

9. $20.00 decreased by 8%   10. $25.00 decreased by 10%

11. $16.00 decreased by 14%   12. $17.50 decreased by 30%

13. $16.95 decreased by 12%   14. $18.98 decreased by 18%

15. $4.99 decreased by 25%   16. $9.95 decreased by 35%

C. *Find the new prices, rounding to the nearest cent if needed. Include both*
   the amount of increase or decrease and the new price in each answer.

17. $18.00 decreased by 10%   18. $20.00 increased by 15%

19. $28.00 increased by 12%   20. $18.75 increased by 22%

21. $19.69 increased by 35%   22. $12.95 decreased by 20%

23. $25.75 decreased by 40%   24. $9.49 increased by 18%

D. *Solve these reading problems. Write proportions for numbers 29 and 30.*

25. The price of heating fuel one fall was $0.78 per gallon. During the extremely cold
    winter that followed, the price increased 25%. What was the price after the increase?
    (Do not round your answer.)

26. If gasoline prices decrease 10% from $1.179, what is the price of gasoline? Round your
    answer to the nearest tenth of a cent.

27. Dairy farmers often notice a drop in milk production during very warm weather. A
    normal shipment of milk for the Wises is 4,800 pounds, but there was a decrease of
    12% during a heat wave. How many pounds of milk did the Wises ship then?

28. The market price of hogs often varies considerably. For example, the average price received by hog farmers per 100 pounds of weight dropped about 17% from 1987 to 1988. In 1987 the average price per 100 pounds was $51.20. What was it in 1988?

29. One day the Zooks shipped hogs weighing 3,250 pounds, which sold for $48.95 per hundred pounds. How much did the hogs sell for?

30. One hog sold for $114.57, or $50.25 per hundred pounds of live weight. How many pounds did the hog weigh?

REVIEW EXERCISES

E. Complete the following chart. *(Lesson 72)*

	Fraction	Decimal	Percent
31.	$\frac{22}{25}$		
33.			58%

	Fraction	Decimal	Percent
32.	$\frac{29}{60}$		
34.		0.01	

F. Find the greatest common factor of each set. *(Lesson 38)*

35. 36, 63   **36.** 34, 85   **37.** 24, 40   **38.** 36, 60

75. Using the Scale of Miles on a Map

Maps contain a wealth of information if they are understood. Among the many things that they show us, maps give information about roads to take when traveling, the sizes of cities, the heights of mountains, political boundaries, and distances between locations.

Maps can show distances because they are drawn to a certain scale, which is usually given on the map. By measuring the distances between two locations on a map and using the scale of miles, the straight-line distance can be determined between the two locations. Remember, though, that the road distance between two locations is usually longer than the straight-line distance because roads are not altogether direct.

Since a small distance on a map represents a much longer actual distance, a scale of miles is really a ratio. For example, if the scale is 1 inch = 50 miles, the ratio can be set up as follows:

$$\frac{1 \text{ inch}}{50 \text{ miles}}$$

Such a ratio can be written as part of a proportion, and then the actual distance can be found in the usual way of solving proportion problems. The following steps explain how this is done.

Step 1: Write the scale as the first ratio of a proportion, with each part correctly labeled. Also write those labels at the same place in the second ratio of the proportion.

Step 2: Measure carefully the distance on the map, and write the measurement beside the correct label in the second ratio. Write n in the empty part of the second ratio to complete the proportion.

Step 3: Cross multiply, and then divide the product by the third fact in the proportion to find the answer (n).

Step 4: Check the proportion by cross multiplying.

Example A	**Example B**
From the map on page 204, find the distance between Millstream and Great Bend.	What is the distance represented by $3\frac{1}{2}$ inches on a map with a scale of $\frac{3}{8}$ inch = 1 mile?
Step 1: $\dfrac{\text{inches}}{\text{miles}} \dfrac{1}{16} = \dfrac{\text{inches}}{\text{miles}}$	Step 1: $\dfrac{\text{inches}}{\text{miles}} \dfrac{\frac{3}{8}}{1} = \dfrac{\text{inches}}{\text{miles}}$
Step 2: $\dfrac{\text{inches}}{\text{miles}} \dfrac{1}{16} = \dfrac{2}{n} \dfrac{\text{inches}}{\text{miles}}$	Step 2: $\dfrac{\text{inches}}{\text{miles}} \dfrac{\frac{3}{8}}{1} = \dfrac{3\frac{1}{2}}{n} \dfrac{\text{inches}}{\text{miles}}$
Step 3: $16 \times 2 = 32$ $32 \div 1 = 32$ Answer: 32 miles	Step 3: $1 \times 3\frac{1}{2} = 3\frac{1}{2}$ $3\frac{1}{2} \div \frac{3}{8} = 9\frac{1}{3}$ Answer: $9\frac{1}{3}$ miles
Step 4: $\dfrac{\text{inches}}{\text{miles}} \dfrac{1}{16} = \dfrac{2}{32} \dfrac{\text{inches}}{\text{miles}}$ $1 \times 32 = 32$ $16 \times 2 = 32$	Step 4: $\dfrac{\text{inches}}{\text{miles}} \dfrac{\frac{3}{8}}{1} = \dfrac{3\frac{1}{2}}{9\frac{1}{3}} \dfrac{\text{inches}}{\text{miles}}$ $\frac{3}{8} \times 9\frac{1}{3} = 3\frac{1}{2}$ $1 \times 3\frac{1}{2} = 3\frac{1}{2}$

Example C

What is the distance represented by $3\frac{1}{4}$ inches on a map with a scale of $\frac{5}{8}$ inch = 10 miles?

Step 1:   inches $\dfrac{\frac{5}{8}}{10} = \dfrac{\underline{\quad}}{\underline{\quad}}$ inches
          miles   miles

Step 2:   inches $\dfrac{\frac{5}{8}}{10} = \dfrac{3\frac{1}{4}}{n}$ inches
          miles   miles

Step 3: $10 \times 3\frac{1}{4} = 32\frac{1}{2}$

          $32\frac{1}{2} \div \frac{5}{8} = 52$

          Answer: 52 miles

Step 4:   inches $\dfrac{\frac{5}{8}}{10} = \dfrac{3\frac{1}{4}}{52}$ inches
          miles   miles

          $\frac{5}{8} \times 52 = 32\frac{1}{2}$

          $10 \times 3\frac{1}{4} = 32\frac{1}{2}$

The same steps can be used to draw a map to scale. The only difference in solving the proportion is that a different number must be found.

Example D

The distance between two cities is 25 miles. How far apart should the cities be on a map with a scale of $\frac{1}{4}$ inch = 2 miles?

Step 1:   inches $\dfrac{\frac{1}{4}}{2} = \dfrac{\underline{\quad}}{\underline{\quad}}$ inches
          miles   miles

Step 2:   inches $\dfrac{\frac{1}{4}}{2} = \dfrac{n}{25}$ inches
          miles   miles

Step 3: $\frac{1}{4} \times 25 = 6\frac{1}{4}$

          $6\frac{1}{4} \div 2 = 3\frac{1}{8}$

          Answer: $3\frac{1}{8}$ inches

Step 4:   inches $\dfrac{\frac{1}{4}}{2} = \dfrac{3\frac{1}{8}}{25}$ inches
          miles   miles

          $\frac{1}{4} \times 25 = 6\frac{1}{4}$

          $2 \times 3\frac{1}{8} = 6\frac{1}{4}$

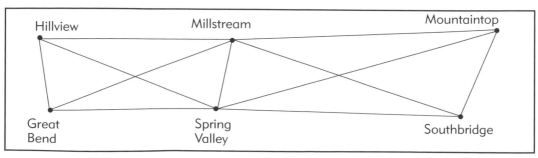

Scale: 1 inch = 16 miles

CLASS PRACTICE

Use the map on page 204 to answer questions a–e. Write both the actual measurement and the distance it represents as your answer. Do all measuring to the nearest $\frac{1}{4}$ inch.

a. What distance is represented horizontally across the map, from one edge to the other?

b. What distance is represented vertically across the map, from the top edge to the bottom?

c. What is the distance between Southbridge and Mountaintop?

d. What is the shortest road distance between Southbridge and Millstream?

e. With the scale above, how long a line is needed on the map to show a distance of 10 miles?

f. With a scale of $\frac{3}{8}$ inch = 2 miles, how long a line is needed on a map to show a distance of 9 miles?

WRITTEN EXERCISES

A. *Use the map on page 204 to answer these questions. Write both the actual measurement and the distance it represents as your answer. Do all measuring to the nearest $\frac{1}{4}$ inch.*

1. What is the distance between Great Bend and Southbridge?

2. What is the distance between Millstream and Mountaintop?

3. What is the distance between Hillview and Great Bend?

4. What is the distance between Hillview and Spring Valley?

5. What is the distance from Great Bend to Mountaintop if you travel through Spring Valley?

6. What is the distance from Mountaintop to Hillview if you travel through Millstream?

7. The Zimmermans live in Spring Valley and attend church in Millstream. One Sunday morning they drove to Millstream for the worship service. They ate dinner in that area and then traveled to Mountaintop to distribute the *Star of Hope*. From there they returned home to Spring Valley by the shortest route possible. How far did they travel?

8. How much closer is it to go directly from Great Bend to Southbridge than to travel from Great Bend to Southbridge by way of Millstream?

B. *Find the distances represented by these measurements on a map with a scale of $\frac{3}{8}$ inch = 1 mile.*

9. 3″   10. 5″   11. $5\frac{1}{2}$″   12. $3\frac{3}{4}$″

C. *Find the distances represented by these measurements on a map with a scale of $\frac{5}{16}$ inch = 10 miles.*

13. 4″   14. 2″   15. $4\frac{1}{2}$″   16. $16\frac{1}{4}$″

D. Draw a line of the proper length to represent each distance on a map with a scale of $\frac{5}{8}$ inch = 4 miles. Label your lines with the correct number of inches.

17. 10 mi.   **18.** 18 mi.   **19.** 26 mi.   **20.** 38 mi.

E. Solve these reading problems.

21. Union House and Cedar Lane are $5\frac{7}{8}$ inches apart on a local map. What is the actual distance between the two places if the scale of miles is 1 inch = 2.3 miles? Change $5\frac{7}{8}$ to a decimal to calculate, and round your answer to the nearest tenth of a mile.

22. The distance between the Union Station Meetinghouse and the Bern Meetinghouse is $5\frac{3}{4}$ inches. How far apart are the two meetinghouses if the scale of miles is $\frac{7}{16}$ inch = 1 mile?

23. Father used a road atlas to find the distance from his home to the Granville Mennonite Church, which the Miller family was planning to visit. The distance on the map was 5 inches, and the scale was 1 inch = 15 miles. Father decided to increase the distance by 15% to make allowance for several mountains they would need to cross. What is the distance according to Father's calculations?

24. On a map, the distance between Blue Lake and Woodvale is 10 inches. The scale of miles is 1 inch = $11\frac{1}{2}$ miles. Because the main roads are not direct, the road distance is 26% farther than the direct distance. To the nearest mile, what is the road distance between Blue Lake and Woodvale?

25. The Leinbach family bought a van to use for school transportation. Father calculated that the gas mileage of the van is 35% less than that of their car, which has an average of 26 miles per gallon. To the nearest whole number, what is the fuel mileage of the van?

26. The van does not require as high a grade of gasoline as the car does. The lower grade of gasoline is 13% less expensive than the higher grade, which sells for $1.26 per gallon. To the nearest cent, what is the price of the lower grade?

REVIEW EXERCISES

F. Find the new prices, rounding to the nearest cent if needed. Include both the amount of increase or decrease and the new price in each answer. (Lesson 74)

27. $14.52 decreased by 15%   **28.** $25.75 increased by 18%

29. $14.99 increased by 12%   **30.** $3.99 decreased by 24%

G. Find 5% of each base given. (Lesson 73)

31. 46   **32.** 78   **33.** 139   **34.** 899

H. Find the nonterminating decimal equivalent of each fraction. Round the answers to the nearest thousandth. (Lesson 57)

35. $\frac{5}{14}$ **36.** $\frac{7}{12}$ **37.** $\frac{1}{7}$ **38.** $\frac{10}{71}$

I. Find the lowest common multiple of each set. (Lesson 39)

39. 4, 6   **40.** 8, 14   **41.** 12, 15   **42.** 10, 16

76. Using the Scale on a Blueprint

A blueprint is a kind of map. However, instead of being a map that represents miles of land and sea, it represents something constructed by man such as a building.

Neither is a blueprint designed to help you find your way in a building. Rather, it is made by an architect to show on paper the layout of a building that is planned. The builder then uses the blueprint as his guide in putting up the building. He makes the building of the size shown, and he places partitions and other features of the building as indicated on the blueprint.

Calculating distances on a blueprint is done by using proportions, the same as for calculating distances on a map. The scale of the blueprint is one ratio in the proportion.

Step 1: Write the scale as the first ratio of a proportion, with each part correctly labeled. Also write those labels at the same place in the second ratio of the proportion.

Step 2: Measure carefully the distance on the blueprint, and write the measurement beside the correct label in the second ratio. Write n in the empty part of the second ratio to complete the proportion.

Step 3: Cross multiply, and then divide the product by the third fact in the proportion to find the answer (n).

Step 4: Check the proportion by cross multiplying.

The same steps are used to calculate distances to place on a blueprint. You simply find a different number in the proportion.

Example A	Example B
Find the distance represented by a $3\frac{3}{4}$-inch line on a blueprint with a scale of $\frac{3}{4}$ inch = 1 foot.	Robert wants to show a 12-foot wall on a blueprint with a scale of $\frac{3}{8}$ inch = 1 foot. How long should the wall be on the blueprint?
Step 1: $\dfrac{\text{inches}}{\text{feet}} \dfrac{\frac{3}{4}}{1} = \dfrac{\text{---}}{\text{---}} \dfrac{\text{inches}}{\text{feet}}$	Step 1: $\dfrac{\text{inches}}{\text{feet}} \dfrac{\frac{3}{8}}{1} = \dfrac{\text{---}}{\text{---}} \dfrac{\text{inches}}{\text{feet}}$
Step 2: $\dfrac{\text{inches}}{\text{feet}} \dfrac{\frac{3}{4}}{1} = \dfrac{3\frac{3}{4}}{n} \dfrac{\text{inches}}{\text{feet}}$	Step 2: $\dfrac{\text{inches}}{\text{feet}} \dfrac{\frac{3}{8}}{1} = \dfrac{n}{12} \dfrac{\text{inches}}{\text{feet}}$
Step 3: $1 \times 3\frac{3}{4} = 3\frac{3}{4}$ $3\frac{3}{4} \div \frac{3}{4} = 5$ Answer: 5 feet	Step 3: $\frac{3}{8} \times 12 = 4\frac{1}{2}$ $4\frac{1}{2} \div 1 = 4\frac{1}{2}$ Answer: $4\frac{1}{2}$ inches
Step 4: $\dfrac{\text{inches}}{\text{feet}} \dfrac{\frac{3}{4}}{1} = \dfrac{3\frac{3}{4}}{5} \dfrac{\text{inches}}{\text{feet}}$ $\frac{3}{4} \times 5 = 3\frac{3}{4}$ $1 \times 3\frac{3}{4} = 3\frac{3}{4}$	Step 4: $\dfrac{\text{inches}}{\text{feet}} \dfrac{\frac{3}{8}}{1} = \dfrac{4\frac{1}{2}}{12} \dfrac{\text{inches}}{\text{feet}}$ $\frac{3}{8} \times 12 = 4\frac{1}{2}$ $1 \times 4\frac{1}{2} = 4\frac{1}{2}$

1 inch = 8 feet

CLASS PRACTICE

Solve these problems. Refer to the blueprint above for a and b.

a. What is the overall length of the house?

b. What is the width of the front door?

c. What distance on a blueprint represents 15 feet if the scale is $\frac{1}{4}$ inch = 1 foot?

d. What distance on a blueprint represents 18 feet if the scale is $\frac{3}{8}$ inch = 1 foot?

Use a scale of $\frac{1}{2}$ inch = 1 foot to find the distances represented by these measurements on a blueprint.

e. 5 in.   f. 7 in.   g. $6\frac{1}{2}$ in.   h. $15\frac{3}{8}$ in.   i. $14\frac{1}{4}$ in.

WRITTEN EXERCISES

A. *Refer to the blueprint above to answer the following questions. Write both the scale measurement and the actual measurement it represents. Remember, the longer side of a rectangle is the length and the shorter dimension is the width. Generally use inside measurements, without including the thickness of the walls.*

1. How long is the laundry?

2. What is the width of the kitchen/living room area?

3. How wide are the stairs?

4. What is the length of bedroom #1?

5. What is the width of bedroom #2?

6. What is the perimeter of the master bedroom?

7. What is the outside width of the house?

8. What is the perimeter of the outside of the house?

B. Give the actual length represented by each measurement on a blueprint if the scale is $\frac{1}{4}$ inch = 1 foot.

9. 6 in.

10. $4\frac{3}{4}$ in.

11. $12\frac{1}{2}$ in.

C. Give the actual length represented by each measurement on a blueprint if the scale is $\frac{1}{8}$ inch = 1 foot.

12. 5 in.

13. 7 in.

14. $9\frac{5}{8}$ in.

D. If the scale of a blueprint is $\frac{1}{4}$ inch = 1 foot, how long a line would be needed to represent each distance?

15. 10 ft.

16. 18 ft.

17. 23 ft.

E. If the scale of a blueprint is $\frac{1}{8}$ inch = 1 foot, how long a line would be needed to represent each distance?

18. 36 ft.

19. 39 ft.

20. 47 ft.

Except the Lord build the house, they labour in vain that build it.

Psalm 127:1

F. Solve these reading problems.

21. Dale was studying the blueprint that had been used to build the house his family lived in. The scale of the blueprint was $\frac{3}{4}$ inch = 1 foot. On the blueprint, the length of the living room was $14\frac{1}{4}$ inches. How long is the living room?

22. The width of the hall on the blueprint was $2\frac{1}{4}$ inches. How wide should the hall be if the scale is $\frac{3}{4}$ inch = 1 foot?

23. Dale's father told him that their house is 48 feet long. How long should the house be on the blueprint if the scale is $\frac{3}{4}$ inch = 1 foot?

24. The lot on which the house is located is 279 feet long. If the lot were drawn to the same scale as the house ($\frac{3}{4}$ inch = 1 foot), how long would the lot be drawn?

25. The greatest east–west distance across the conterminous United States is 2,807 miles. To the nearest inch, how long a distance would that be on a map with a scale of 1 inch = 50 miles?

26. On a large map of Canada, the greatest distance from east to west measures $37\frac{1}{2}$ inches. If the scale is $\frac{3}{4}$ inch = 70 miles, what is the greatest east–west distance across Canada?

REVIEW EXERCISES

G. *Find the distance represented by each measurement on a map if the scale is $\frac{7}{8}$ inch = 2 miles. (Lesson 75)*

27. $4\frac{3}{4}$ in.

28. $2\frac{7}{8}$ in.

H. *Find the new prices, rounding to the nearest cent if needed. Include both the amount of increase or decrease and the new price in each answer. (Lesson 74)*

29. $17.00 decreased by 14%

30. $24.00 increased by 8%

31. $17.89 increased by 15%

32. $14.55 decreased by 18%

I. *Complete the following chart. (Lesson 72)*

	Fraction	Decimal	Percent
33.	$\frac{21}{25}$		

	Fraction	Decimal	Percent
34.		0.28	

J. *Solve these addition and subtraction problems. (Lesson 58)*

35. 4.5 + 3.56 + 10 + 0.056

36. 0.007 + 0.3 + 1.0002 + 3.6

37. 6.3 – 3.2643

38. 15 – 0.9704

77. Reading Problems: Estimating a Logical Solution

The Groff family is traveling to attend a Bible conference. During the first $3\frac{1}{2}$ hours of travel, the Groffs' average speed was 50 miles per hour. During the first $3\frac{1}{2}$ hours, they traveled (220, 210, 175, 145) miles.

Perhaps if you concentrate, you can mentally calculate the answer to the problem above ($3 \times 50 = 150$; $\frac{1}{2} \times 50 = 25$; $150 + 25 = 175$ miles). Without using pencil and paper, though, you should be able to choose the most logical answer. This can be done by using the following steps.

Step 1: Multiply $3 \times 50 = 150$. The answer is more than 150.

Step 2: Multiply $4 \times 50 = 200$. The answer is less than 200.

Step 3: The correct answer is more than 150 miles and less than 200 miles. The most logical answer is 175 miles.

Estimating shows quickly whether an answer is reasonable. In the example above, only the choice 175 falls within the boundaries established by the estimates. Any answer less than 150 or greater than 200 is ruled out.

To estimate a product when one or both factors are mixed numbers, use the steps given below.

Step 1: Round each mixed number to the next lower whole number and solve.

Step 2: Round each mixed number to the next higher whole number and solve.

Step 3: Check the exact answer with these estimates. It should be higher than the lower estimate and lower than the higher estimate.

This form of estimating is practical not only for checking problems for correctness but also for finding the range in which the correct answer falls.

$$4\frac{1}{4} \times 5\frac{3}{4} = (16\frac{7}{16},\quad 19\frac{7}{16},\quad 24\frac{7}{16},\quad 31\frac{7}{16})$$

Step 1: Lower estimate: $4 \times 5 = 20$

Step 2: Higher estimate: $5 \times 6 = 30$

Step 3: The correct answer is more than 20 and less than 30.
The most logical choice above is $24\frac{7}{16}$.

CLASS PRACTICE

Find the correct answers. Then check each one by using the steps above to determine the lower estimate and the higher estimate.

a. $5\frac{1}{2} \times 7$ b. $11\frac{3}{4} \times 7$ c. 10.5×6.75

d. $5\frac{5}{8} \times 8\frac{5}{8}$ e. 8×3.6 f. $5 \times 7\frac{1}{8}$

g. $8\frac{1}{2} \times 9\frac{3}{4}$ h. 8.2×9.2 i. 3.6×9.7

WRITTEN EXERCISES

A. Use estimation to choose the most logical answers. After each choice, write both a lower and a higher estimate as shown in the lesson.

Example: $6\frac{1}{4} \times 3\frac{1}{2} = (9\frac{7}{8},\ 17\frac{7}{8},\ 21\frac{7}{8},\ 28\frac{7}{8},\ 33\frac{7}{8})$

Answers: $21\frac{7}{8}$; 18, 28

1. $4\frac{1}{2} \times 12 =$ (34, 44, 54, 64, 74)

2. $6\frac{3}{4} \times 11 =$ ($74\frac{1}{4}$, $84\frac{1}{4}$, $94\frac{1}{4}$, $104\frac{1}{4}$, $114\frac{1}{4}$)

3. $11\frac{1}{9} \times 9 =$ (70, 80, 90, 100, 110)

4. $11\frac{5}{7} \times 11 =$ ($118\frac{6}{7}$, $128\frac{6}{7}$, $138\frac{6}{7}$, $148\frac{6}{7}$, $158\frac{6}{7}$)

5. $7\frac{1}{2} \times 8\frac{5}{6} =$ ($22\frac{1}{4}$, $33\frac{1}{4}$, $44\frac{1}{4}$, $55\frac{1}{4}$, $66\frac{1}{4}$)

6. $3\frac{3}{4} \times 7\frac{2}{3} =$ ($18\frac{3}{4}$, $28\frac{3}{4}$, $38\frac{3}{4}$, $48\frac{3}{4}$, $58\frac{3}{4}$)

7. $6 \times 3\frac{1}{2} =$ (16, 17, 21, 25)

8. $7 \times 9\frac{1}{2} =$ (36.5, 46.5, 56.5, 66.5)

9. $9.5 \times 10.5 =$ (99.75, 111.75, 123.75, 135.75)

10. $8.8 \times 6.9 =$ (30.72, 45.72, 60.72, 75.72)

11. $20.25 \times 4.25 =$ (56.0625, 66.0625, 76.0625, 86.0625)

12. $5.2 \times 3.6 =$ (14.72, 18.72, 24.72, 27.72)

B. Solve these reading problems. Check each answer by writing both a lower and a higher estimate as in Part A.

13. Thomas disked a large field at the rate of $4\frac{1}{2}$ acres per hour. How much disking did he do in 6 hours?

14. Marcus planted corn at the rate of $5\frac{3}{8}$ acres per hour. How much corn did he plant in 7 hours?

15. The Horsts bought 6 bushels of peaches for $8.25 per bushel. How much did they pay for the peaches?

16. Father bought eight 100-pound bags of duck feed at a price of $10.25 per bag. How much did he pay for the feed?

REVIEW EXERCISES

C. If the scale of a blueprint is $\frac{1}{4}$ inch = 1 foot, how much length on the blueprint is needed to represent each distance? *(Lesson 76)*

17. 7 ft.   18. 9 ft.   19. 13 ft.   20. 18 ft.

D. If the scale of a map is $\frac{5}{8}$ inch = 5 miles, how much length on the map is needed to represent each distance? *(Lesson 75)*

21. 16 mi.   22. 12 mi.   23. 71 mi.   24. 103 mi.

E. Use proportions to solve these reading problems. *(Lessons 68–70)*

25. The number of pounds of feed an animal eats for each pound of weight it gains is known as feed conversion. This feed conversion is expressed as a ratio. For example, a batch of hogs may have a feed conversion of 3.7 to 1. This means that the hogs eat 3.7 pounds of feed for every pound of weight they gain. The Kreiders' hogs ate 2,000 pounds of feed in several days. At a feed-conversion ratio of 3.7:1, how many pounds of weight should they have gained? (Answer to the nearest whole pound.)

26. For various reasons such as the type of feed and the presence of disease, hogs sometimes do not gain weight as rapidly as they should. If a batch of hogs has a feed-conversion ratio of 4.3:1, how much weight will they gain from eating 100 pounds of feed? (Answer to the nearest pound.)

27. A typical feed-conversion ratio for steers is 7.5:1. This means that for every 7.5 pounds a steer eats, it gains 1 pound. The Myers' steers are gaining an average of 2.7 pounds of weight per day. At a feed-conversion ratio of 7.5:1, how much is an average steer eating per day?

28. The typical feed-conversion ratio for chickens is much higher than that for steers or hogs. Chickens eat about 2 pounds of feed for every pound of weight they gain. One day the Nolts received a delivery of 20 tons of feed. At a feed-conversion ratio of 2.1:1, find how much weight their flock of chickens should gain from that load of feed (to the nearest pound).

Every moving thing that liveth shall be meat for you; even as the green herb have I given you all things.

Genesis 9:3

F. Solve these problems mentally by moving the decimal points. *(Lesson 59)*

29. 95.6 × 10

30. 4.855 × 1,000

31. 490.8 ÷ 100

32. 35.76 ÷ 1,000

G. Write each fraction in simplest form. *(Lesson 41)*

33. $\frac{12}{30}$

34. $\frac{25}{40}$

35. $\frac{12}{8}$

36. $\frac{28}{6}$

H. Solve these multiplication problems. In problems 37 and 38, label each part with the correct term, including answers. *(Lesson 12)*

37. 574 _____
　　× 600 _____

38. 675 _____
　　× 500 _____

39. 715
　　× 245

40. 846
　　× 317

78. Chapter 6 Review

A. Reduce these ratios to lowest terms, using the same form as the one shown. Label each part of the first two ratios. *(Lesson 67)*

1. $\frac{8}{36}$
2. 15 to 45
3. 24:39
4. 21:49

B. Write ratios in lowest terms to make the comparisons indicated, using the chart below.

5. First graders compared to second graders.

6. Second graders compared to third graders.

7. Total of grades 1, 2, and 3 compared to the total number of students in the school.

8. Total of grades 1, 2, and 3 compared to the total number of students in grades 4, 5, and 6.

Students in the Sandville Christian School	
Grade 1	5
Grade 2	4
Grade 3	6
Grade 4	2
Grade 5	5
Grade 6	5
Grade 7	4
Grade 8	3
Grade 9	4
Grade 10	2
	40

C. Check each proportion by cross multiplication, and write the two products that you obtain. Then write *true* if the proportion is true or *false* if it is false. *(Lesson 68)*

9. $\frac{4}{6} = \frac{14}{21}$
10. $\frac{9}{15} = \frac{21}{35}$
11. $\frac{20}{12} = \frac{24}{15}$
12. $\frac{18}{24} = \frac{33}{44}$

D. Find the missing parts of these proportions. Express any remainders as fractions. *(Lesson 68)*

13. $\frac{5}{8} = \frac{n}{40}$
14. $\frac{9}{21} = \frac{n}{28}$
15. $\frac{27}{18} = \frac{40}{n}$
16. $\frac{24}{18} = \frac{40}{n}$

E. Complete the following chart. *(Lesson 72)*

	Fraction	Decimal	Percent
17.	$\frac{17}{25}$		
19.		0.38	

	Fraction	Decimal	Percent
18.	$\frac{7}{12}$		
20.			5%

F. Express these common fractions as percents. *(Lesson 72)*

21. $\frac{27}{40}$ = _____   **22.** $\frac{8}{15}$ = _____   **23.** $\frac{7}{11}$ = _____   **24.** $\frac{1}{21}$ = _____

G. Find these percentages. *(Lesson 73)*

25. 45% of 30   **26.** 61% of 79   **27.** 24% of 29   **28.** 73% of 59

H. Find 5% of each base. *(Lesson 73)*

29. 60   **30.** 75   **31.** 89   **32.** 116

I. Find 14% of each base. *(Lesson 73)*

33. 70   **34.** 45   **35.** 91   **36.** 123

J. Finish these statements. *(Lesson 73)*

37. In the equation $5 = 30\%$ of $16\frac{2}{3}$, 30% is the _____.

38. In the equation $9 = 20\%$ of 45, 45 is the _____.

39. In the equation 15% of $80 = 12$, 12 is the _____.

K. Find the new prices, showing both the increase or decrease and the new price in each answer. Round to the nearest cent. *(Lesson 74)*

40. $30.00 increased by 8%   **41.** $35.00 increased by 4%

42. $49.95 increased by 20%   **43.** $48.50 increased by 15%

44. $20.00 decreased by 9%   **45.** $15.00 decreased by 15%

46. $38.00 decreased by 12%   **47.** $14.95 decreased by 32%

48. $27.50 decreased by 2%   **49.** $19.50 increased by 3%

L. Find the distance represented by each measurement on a map if the scale is $\frac{5}{8}$ inch = 15 miles. *(Lesson 75)*

50. 3″   **51.** 5″   **52.** $5\frac{1}{2}$″   **53.** $3\frac{3}{4}$″

M. If the scale of a map is $\frac{3}{8}$ inch = 4 miles, how much length on the map is needed to represent each distance? *(Lesson 75)*

54. 20 mi.   **55.** 16 mi.   **56.** 34 mi.   **57.** 50 mi.

N. Give the actual length represented by each measurement on a blueprint if the scale is $\frac{3}{4}$ inch = 1 foot. *(Lesson 76)*

58. 9 in.   **59.** 12 in.   **60.** $13\frac{1}{2}$ in.   **61.** $15\frac{3}{8}$ in.

O. If the scale of a blueprint is $\frac{3}{8}$ inch = 1 foot, how much length on the blueprint is needed to represent each distance? *(Lesson 76)*

62. 12 ft.   **63.** 15 ft.   **64.** 20 ft.   **65.** 25 ft.

P. Use estimation to choose the most logical answer to each problem. After your choice, write both a lower and a higher estimate. *(Lesson 77)*

66. $5\frac{1}{2} \times 9\frac{3}{4} = (43\frac{5}{8},\ 53\frac{5}{8},\ 63\frac{5}{8},\ 73\frac{5}{8},\ 79\frac{5}{8})$

67. $6.5 \times 8.5 = (25.25,\ 35.25,\ 45.25,\ 55.25,\ 65.25)$

68. $4.5 \times 7.5 = (7.75,\ 13.75,\ 23.75,\ 33.75,\ 43.75)$

69. $7.5 \times 9.5 = (61.25,\ 71.25,\ 81.25,\ 91.25,\ 101.25)$

Q. Use proportions to solve these reading problems. *(Lessons 68–70)*

70. The feed-conversion ratio for one batch of 100 hogs was 3.8:1, or 3.8 pounds of feed for each pound of weight the hogs gained. If the total weight gain was 18,000 pounds, how much feed did the hogs eat?

71. The Sauders sold five beef cattle that had gained a total of 6,000 pounds since they were bought as calves. If the feed-conversion ratio was 7.5:1, what was the weight of feed that the beef cattle ate?

72. To mix mortar, John used 2 parts of sand for each part of cement. One day John mixed 12 cubic feet of mortar. How many cubic feet of sand did he use?

73. Before painting the concrete floor of their basement, the Snaders etched the concrete to make it porous so that it would absorb the paint. The etching was made by mixing 1 part muriatic acid with 3 parts water. If Father used $1\frac{3}{4}$ gallons of muriatic acid, how many gallons of etching did he mix?

74. The Snaders plan to use paint that covers 400 square feet per gallon. If the basement floor contains 1,400 square feet and they apply two coats, how many gallons of paint will they need?

75. The Snaders used a kerosene heater to dry the basement before painting it. If the heater produced 300,000 Btu's of heat on 1.9 gallons of kerosene, how many Btu's per gallon did it produce? Round your answer to the nearest thousand.

79. Semester Review I: Chapters 1 and 2

A. Write out these numbers in words. Use commas with the words just as they are used with digits. *(Lesson 1)*

1. 7,166,000,000

2. 5,000,055,000,000

B. Write numerals for these number words. *(Lesson 1)*

3. Forty-five million, six thousand, four hundred seventy-seven

4. Six trillion, 50 billion, fourteen

C. Write the value of each underlined digit. *(Lesson 2)*

5. 772,200,000

6. 491,912,000,000,000

D. Round these numbers as indicated. *(Lesson 3)*

7. 596 *(ten)*

8. 749 *(hundred)*

9. 4,679,717 *(million)*

10. 4,553,800,000 *(hundred million)*

E. Express these Roman numerals as Arabic numerals. *(Lesson 4)*

11. DCCXIII
12. CMXCIX
13. $\overline{\text{LXV}}$
14. $\overline{\text{CIVDCC}}$

F. Express these Arabic numerals as Roman numerals. *(Lesson 4)*

15. 79
16. 495
17. 2,354
18. 10,421

G. Copy each problem, find the answer, and check your work in the ways indicated below. (Show your check.) Label each part in problems 21, 25, and 28, including answers. *(Lessons 5–17)*

Addition: Add upward. (Lesson 5)

Subtraction: Add the subtrahend to the difference. (Lesson 7)

Multiplication and division: Cast out nines, and write the check numbers. (Lesson 13, 17)

19.	20.	21.	22.
4,512	15,728	122,815 ____	141,714
6,512	35,721	451,711 ____	727,996
2,781	71,232	+ 900,022 ____	361,781
4,512	12,712		+ 825,284
7,213	15,672		
+ 7,825	+ 56,462		

23.	24.	25.	26.
56,311	2,621,233	79,433,277 ____	$74,381.87
− 26,517	− 1,732,566	− 19,911,132 ____	− 46,272.81

27. $4.99
         × 42

28. $7.36 _____
         × 53 _____

29.   4,721
         × 415

30.   4,271
         ×2,314

31. 57)$43.32

32. 71)$77.39

33. 600)43,800

34. 1,500)535,500

35. 312)6,177

36. 1,123)42,524

H. Solve these horizontal problems. Write each answer one digit at a time.
(Lessons 5, 7, 12, 17)

37. 372 + 658

38. 749 + 583

39. 735 – 587

40. 61,115 – 27,262

41. 9 × 73

42. 7 × 638

43. 5 × 915

44. 3)5,772

45. 5)7,543

46. 7)9,482

I. Solve these problems mentally. Write only the answers. *(Lessons 6, 8, 14, 15, 20)*

47. 3 + 7 + 2 + 5 + 8 + 6 + 4

48. 5 + 7 + 5 + 1 + 9 + 4 + 6

49. 39 + 54

50. 65 + 79

51. 63 – 19

52. 265 – 76

53. 24 × 15

54. 5 × 88

55. 46 × 50

56. 32 × 25

57. 6 × 9 × 5

58. 4 × 80 × 5 × 3

59. 168 ÷ 24

60. 132 ÷ 22

61. 650 ÷ 50

62. 450 ÷ 25

J. Estimate the products. You do not need to find exact answers. *(Lesson 14)*

63.   8,171
         × 4,421

64.   2,977
         × 3,155

K. Find the average of each set of numbers. Express remainders as fractions. *(Lesson 19)*

65. 53, 55, 46, 59, 60

66. 477, 512, 455, 490

L. Copy the numbers below. After each number, write the divisors 2, 3, 4, 5, 6, 9, and 10 by which the number is divisible. *(Lesson 20)*

67. 480

68. 585

M. Use the graph to answer the question below. *(Lesson 21)*

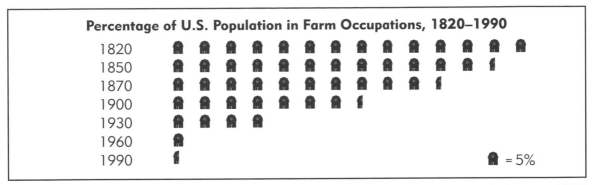

Source: *World Almanac, 1992*

What percent of United States workers were working on farms in the following years?

69. 1820   **70.** 1870   **71.** 1900   **72.** 1960

N. Read each problem carefully, and write what information you would need in order to solve it. *(Lesson 9)*

73. Leonard milked 20 cows one morning. On the average, how many minutes did it take him to milk one cow?

74. The Stauffers' dairy herd produces an average of 63 pounds per cow each day. How many pounds of milk does the herd produce in a week?

75. Marlin helped load egg crates on the egg truck. He carried 34 crates in all. How much weight did he carry?

76. Sandra is baking a triple batch of cookies. How much flour should she measure?

O. Solve these reading problems, being careful to use the right operation or operations. *(Lesson 22)*

77. A greenhouse covered with a single layer of plastic required the use of 1,956 gallons of fuel for heating. When the greenhouse was covered with a double layer of plastic with an air space between the two layers, only 1,174 gallons of fuel were used. How much fuel was saved?

78. One business became concerned about the amount of paper used each year. They decided to start using both sides of all paper, to use scrap paper and old envelopes for in-office memos, and to take other similar measures. By this effort the business reduced the annual consumption of paper by 24,500 sheets. They now use 37,500 sheets per year. How many sheets of paper had they used annually before they began conserving it?

79. A school with 5 classrooms is buying enough desks to have 18 in each room. The price of the desks is $142.65 each. What is the total cost of the new desks?

80. Mr. Willis' store received an invoice for 250 cans of paint at a total cost of $2,040 including tax. What was the cost per can of paint?

80. Semester Review II: Chapters 3 and 4

A. Measure each line and write the measurement on your paper. *(Lesson 25)*

1. _____   2. _____

B. Write the abbreviation for each of these English measures. *(Lessons 26–29)*

3. peck   4. square foot   5. fluid ounce   6. year

C. Change these measures as indicated. *(Lessons 25–29)*

7. 25 ft. = _____ in.   8. 78 ft. = _____ yd.

9. 9 lb. = _____ oz.   10. 31,000 lb. = _____ tons

11. 9 pk. = _____ bu.   12. 55 mo. = _____ yr.

13. 24 fl. oz. = _____ cups   14. 4 millennia = _____ yr.

15. 90 sq. ft. = _____ sq. yd.   16. 20 sq. mi. = _____ a.

17. 4 sq. mi. 100 a. = _____ a.   18. 4 cups 3 fl. oz. = _____ fl. oz.

D. Write what time it is in the time zones indicated if it is 12:00 midnight in the Pacific Time Zone. *(Lesson 30)*

19. Hawaii–Aleutian Time Zone   20. Atlantic Time Zone

E. Find the missing numbers. Write any remainder as a fraction. *(Lesson 33)*

21. $d = 735$ mi.   22. $t = 7.2$ hr.   23. $t = 5$ hr.   24. $d = 275$ mi.
    $t = 15$ hr. $r = 47$ m.p.h. $r = 313$ m.p.h $r = 45$ m.p.h.
    $r = $ _____ $d = $ _____ $d = $ _____ $t = $ _____

F. Identify each number as being prime or composite. *(Lesson 37)*

25. 23   26. 25   27. 27   28. 29

G. Divide by primes to find the prime factors of these composite numbers. *(Lesson 37)*

29. 16   30. 18   31. 20   32. 21

H. Find the greatest common factor (g.c.f.) of each pair. *(Lesson 38)*

33. 12, 16   34. 20, 50   35. 32, 56   36. 42, 70

I. Find the lowest common multiple of each pair by using Method 1 and then Method 2 if necessary. *(Lesson 39)*

37. 15, 20   38. 12, 16   39. 8, 10   40. 12, 15

J. Study the line graph below, and answer the question that follows. *(Lesson 34)*

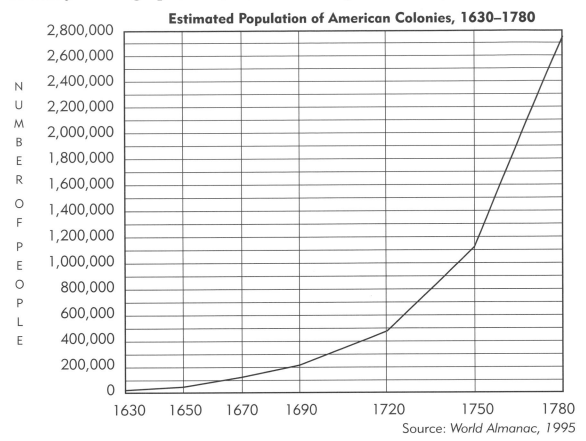

Estimated Population of American Colonies, 1630–1780

Source: *World Almanac, 1995*

About how many people were living in the American colonies in the years given?

41. 1650

42. 1720

K. Answer these questions about the terms used with fractions. *(Lesson 40)*

43. Which of these is a mixed number? $\frac{5}{6}$ $\frac{6}{5}$ $\frac{7}{7}$ $4\frac{1}{2}$

44. Which of these is an improper fraction? $\frac{7}{2}$ 8 $\frac{4}{7}$ $1\frac{3}{7}$

L. Reduce these fractions to lowest terms. *(Lesson 41)*

45. $\frac{18}{45}$

46. $\frac{24}{42}$

M. Copy these fractions, compare them, and write < or > between them. *(Lesson 41)*

47. $\frac{7}{9}$ _____ $\frac{9}{12}$

48. $\frac{4}{9}$ _____ $\frac{3}{8}$

N. Write the reciprocals of these numbers. *(Lesson 47)*

49. $\frac{7}{9}$

50. $6\frac{1}{6}$

O. *Solve these problems mentally.* *(Lessons 44, 47)*

51. $\frac{1}{5}$ of 55   **52.** $66 \times \frac{7}{11}$ **53.** $54 \times \frac{5}{9}$

54. $7 \div \frac{1}{8}$ **55.** $9 \div \frac{1}{6}$ **56.** $4 \div \frac{1}{12}$

P. *Solve these problems involving fractions.* *(Lessons 42–48)*

57. $\begin{array}{r} \frac{5}{6} \\ + \frac{3}{4} \\ \hline \end{array}$ **58.** $\begin{array}{r} 2\frac{4}{5} \\ + 3\frac{1}{2} \\ \hline \end{array}$ **59.** $\begin{array}{r} 9 \\ - 4\frac{5}{7} \\ \hline \end{array}$ **60.** $\begin{array}{r} 14 \\ - 7\frac{7}{12} \\ \hline \end{array}$

61. $\frac{5}{7} \times \frac{7}{8}$ **62.** $\frac{3}{8} \times 2\frac{1}{6}$ **63.** $3\frac{1}{7} \times 2\frac{1}{11}$ **64.** $5\frac{3}{4} \times 1\frac{1}{2}$

65. $\frac{2}{3} \div \frac{2}{9}$ **66.** $\frac{9}{10} \div \frac{3}{4}$ **67.** $3\frac{1}{3} \div 2\frac{1}{4}$ **68.** $4\frac{1}{3} \div 1\frac{1}{9}$

Q. *Copy and solve these problems by the vertical method.* *(Lesson 46)*

69. $\begin{array}{r} 9 \\ \times 5\frac{1}{3} \\ \hline \end{array}$ **70.** $\begin{array}{r} 12 \\ \times 7\frac{1}{4} \\ \hline \end{array}$

R. *Find the unknown numbers.* *(Lesson 49)*

71. 9 is $\frac{1}{3}$ of _____   **72.** 12 is $\frac{3}{4}$ of _____

73. 16 is $\frac{4}{9}$ of _____   **74.** 15 is $\frac{3}{7}$ of _____

S. *Use the following bar graph to answer the questions below.* *(Lesson 51)*

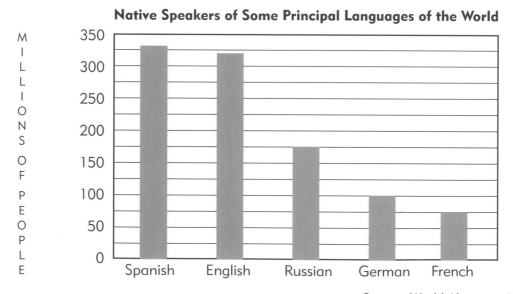

Native Speakers of Some Principal Languages of the World

Source: *World Almanac, 1995*

75. About how many people speak French as their native language?

76. Mandarin, the official language of China, is the native language for as many people as Spanish, English, and Russian combined. About how many people speak Mandarin as their native language?

T. **Study each reading problem carefully, and decide what facts are needed to find the solution. Write the unneeded numbers on your paper, and then solve the problem.** *(Lesson 50)*

77. Samuel is $3\frac{3}{4}$ times as old as his younger brother. His younger brother is 2 years old and 33 inches tall. How old is Samuel?

78. In comparison with New York, Pennsylvania has about $\frac{2}{3}$ as many people and is $\frac{49}{50}$ as large. Pennsylvania has about 12 million people and 45,000 square miles. How many people live in New York?

79. One week it rained $1\frac{2}{10}$ inches, $\frac{7}{10}$ of it coming on Tuesday. The next week it rained $\frac{3}{4}$ as much as it had the week before. That week, $\frac{6}{10}$ inch of rain fell on Friday. How much did it rain the second week?

80. After supper Monday evening, Brian had $1\frac{1}{2}$ hours before bedtime. He spent $\frac{2}{3}$ of that time helping his younger brother make a bird feeder and $\frac{2}{9}$ of it reviewing his Bible memory. How much time did he spend helping his brother with the bird feeder?

Thy word have I hid in mine heart, that I might not sin against thee.
Psalms 119:11

81. Kathryn helped her mother for 3 hours after school. She spent $\frac{2}{3}$ of that time peeling and canning sweet potatoes, $\frac{1}{4}$ of the time doing dishes, and $\frac{1}{12}$ of the time sweeping. How much time did she spend doing dishes?

82. Sarah and Susan helped serve the trays at a fellowship dinner. Part of Sarah's job was to place two cookies on each tray. After dinner $\frac{1}{8}$ of the 36 dozen cookies were left. How many cookies were left?

81. Semester Review III: Chapters 5 and 6

A. Write these decimals, using words. *(Lesson 54)*

1. 0.056

2. 0.00325

B. Complete the following chart. *(Lessons 54, 71, 72)*

	Fraction	*Decimal*	*Percent*
3.	$\frac{3}{25}$		
5.		0.58	
7.			18%

	Fraction	*Decimal*	*Percent*
4.	$\frac{9}{14}$		
6.		0.06	
8.			55%

C. Copy each set of decimals, compare them, and write > or < between them. *(Lesson 55)*

9. 0.4209 _____ 0.42

10. 2.077 _____ 2.1

D. Round these numbers as indicated. *(Lesson 55)*

11. 4.0799 *(tenth)*

12. 3.75573 *(thousandth)*

E. Express these fractions of cents as parts of a dollar. *(Lesson 55)*

13. $4.15 $\frac{7}{10}$

14. $0.86 $\frac{9}{10}$

F. Change these fractions to nonterminating decimals. Follow the instructions in working with the remainder. *(Lessons 57)*

Divide to the hundredths' place, and express the remainder as a fraction.

15. $\frac{11}{15}$

16. $\frac{7}{18}$

Round to the nearest thousandth.

17. $\frac{5}{7}$

18. $\frac{6}{13}$

Identify the repeating digits by drawing a bar above them.

19. $\frac{1}{15}$

20. $\frac{17}{18}$

G. Solve these multiplication and division problems by moving the decimal points. *(Lesson 59)*

21. 2.01 × 10

22. 30.045 × 100

23. 2.3712 ÷ 100

24. 15.98 ÷ 1,000

H. Solve these problems involving decimals. If a quotient does not come out evenly by the ten-thousandths' place, round it to the nearest thousandth. Drop any ending zeroes. *(Lessons 58, 60, 62, 63)*

25. $4.1 + 0.0305 + 7 + 0.7$　　　**26.** $5.2 + 2.059 + 6 + 0.301$

27. $5.3 - 1.795$　　　　　　　　**28.** $3 - 0.09067$

29. 5.18×0.07　　　　　　　　**30.** 5.73×0.4

31. $2.66 \div 0.7$　　　　　　　　　**32.** $3.98 \div 1.2$

I. Solve these problems. Try to do them mentally by first changing the decimal to a common fraction. *(Lesson 61)*

33. 0.5 of 80　　　　　　　　　　**34.** 0.375 of 48

35. $0.33\frac{1}{3}$ of $45　　　　　　　**36** 0.6 of $35

J. Reduce these ratios to lowest terms, using the same form as the one shown. Label each part of the ratios. *(Lesson 67)*

37. $\frac{28}{35}$　　　　　　　　　　　**38.** 18:42

K. Write a ratio for each statement. *(Lesson 67)*

39. 25 pounds of cherries compared to 20 quarts.

40. 2,240 pounds of hog feed compared to 800 pounds gained.

41. 9 gallons of herbicide compared to a 12 acre corn field.

42. 2 pounds of seed corn compared to 2,400 ears of corn.

L. Find the missing parts of these proportions. Express any remainders as fractions. *(Lesson 68)*

43. $\frac{6}{15} = \frac{n}{40}$　　　　　　　　　**44.** $\frac{35}{18} = \frac{40}{n}$

M. Use proportions to solve these reading problems. *(Lessons 68–70)*

45. Mother calculates that each bushel of raw pears yields 18 quarts of canned pears. Father bought $4\frac{1}{2}$ bushels of pears at the market. How many quarts of canned pears can Mother expect to get from them?

46. When hogs are butchered, the ratio of the carcass weight to the live weight is about 2:3. The Ebersoles butchered a hog that weighed 225 pounds. How much meat can they expect to have?

47. For beef cattle, the ratio of the carcass weight to the live weight is about 3:5. The Weavers had a 1,300-pound steer butchered for their own use. How much meat can they expect to get?

48. Brother Amos is planning to harvest some of his corn as corn silage. If he gets 18 tons of corn silage per acre and his silo holds 180 tons of silage, how many acres of corn must he harvest to fill his silo?

N. Express these common fractions as percents. *(Lesson 72)*

49. $\frac{13}{40}$ 50. $\frac{1}{12}$ 51. $\frac{9}{11}$ 52. $\frac{4}{21}$

O. Find 8% of each base. *(Lesson 73)*

53. 70   54. 65   55. 49   56. 52

P. Find 11% of each base. *(Lesson 73)*

57. 35   58. 46   59. 79   60. 113

Q. Find the new price. In your answer show both the increase or decrease and the new price. Round to the nearest cent. *(Lesson 74)*

61. $25.00 increased by 6%   62. $32.00 increased by 9%

63. $28.95 decreased by 12%   64. $37.79 decreased by 18%

R. Find the distance represented by each measurement on a map if the scale is $\frac{3}{8}$ inch = 10 miles. *(Lesson 75)*

65. 6″   66. 10 $\frac{1}{2}$″

S. If the scale of a map is $\frac{7}{8}$ inch = 8 miles, how much length on the map is needed to represent each distance? *(Lesson 75)*

67. 36 mi.   68. 100 mi.

T. Give the actual length represented by each measurement on a blueprint if the scale is $\frac{5}{8}$ inch = 1 foot. *(Lesson 76)*

69. 10 in.   70. 20 $\frac{1}{2}$ in.

U. If the scale of a blueprint is $\frac{3}{8}$ inch = 1 foot, how much length is needed to represent each distance? *(Lesson 76)*

71. 15 ft.   72. 25 ft.

V. Solve these reading problems.

73. Brother Amos's neighbor has a harvester that he uses for custom jobs. If Brother Amos hires his neighbor to make his silage at a rate of $65 per hour and the neighbor can harvest 2 acres per hour, how much will the neighbor charge to harvest 25 acres of corn?

74. Brother Amos plans to pick and shell the rest of his corn. If he gets 155 bushels per acre and pays $20 per acre to have the corn shelled, how much will it cost per bushel to shell the corn? Round your answer to the nearest tenth of a cent.

82. Semester Test

Chapter 7

More Work With Percents

Seek him that maketh
the seven stars and Orion, . . .
The Lord is his name.
(Amos 5:8)

83. Percents Over 100%; Adding and Subtracting Percents

One hundred percent (100%) means everything you are considering. If you have 100% of your math problems correct, all the problems are correct. If 100% of the students are present in class, all the students are present. If a jar contains 100% orange juice, everything in the jar is orange juice. There is nothing added to it.

Another way of understanding 100% is to consider it as being equal to the number 1. This is illustrated in Example A.

Percents over 100% can easily be changed to whole or mixed numbers by moving the decimal point two places to the left and dropping the percent sign. (See Example A.) Example B gives some commonly used percents over 100%, along with their decimal equivalents.

To multiply by a percent over 100%, use exactly the same steps as for multiplying by a percent under 100%. Move the decimal point two places to the left, drop the percent sign, and multiply. See Examples C and D.

Example A	Example B
$100\% = 1.00 = 1$ Move the decimal point two places to the left and drop the percent sign.	$125\% = 1.25 = 1\frac{1}{4}$ $150\% = 1.50 = 1\frac{1}{2}$ $175\% = 1.75 = 1\frac{3}{4}$ $200\% = 2.00 = 2$ $250\% = 2.50 = 2\frac{1}{2}$ $300\% = 3.00 = 3$ $400\% = 4.00 = 4$ $500\% = 5.00 = 5$ $1{,}000\% = 10.00 = 10$
Example C Find 125% of 80. Step 1: 125% = 1.25 Step 2: $\begin{array}{r} 1.25 \\ \times\ 80 \\ \hline 100.00 = 100 \end{array}$	**Example D** Find 275% of 88. Step 1: 275% = 2.75 Step 2: $\begin{array}{r} 2.75 \\ \times\ 88 \\ \hline 2200 \\ 2200\ \\ \hline 242.00 = 242 \end{array}$

Sometimes percents are subtracted from 100%. If you have 5% of your math problems wrong, you have 95% of them correct: 100% – 5% = 95%.

To subtract a percent from 100%, simply subtract the numbers and bring down the percent sign. See Example E.

The term **discount** is often used to refer to a decrease in price. A business may advertise its inventory at a 20% discount. This means that it is being sold at 20% off the original or first price. The discount price is 100% – 20% or 80% of the regular price (Example E).

Percents can also be added to 100%. Suppose that the price of a certain item increases by 10%. The item now costs 110% of what it had, or 110% of its original price.

To add a percent to 100%, simply add the numbers and bring down the percent sign. See Example F.

Example E	Example F
At a year-end clearance sale, all dress material was discounted by 20%. What percent was the sale price of the original price?	After a winter freeze in Florida, the selling price of oranges increased 30%. What percent was the increased price of the original price?
100% – 20% 80%	100% + 30% 130%

CLASS PRACTICE

Change these percents to whole numbers or decimals.

a. 160%   b. 350%   c. 775%   d. 650%   e. 2,000%

Find the percentages for these problems.

f. 150% of 60   g. 175% of 150   h. 225% of 110

Write a percent showing what part the new price is of the original price.

i. The Mountain View Christian Bookstore had all its stock on sale at a 15% discount.

j. The bookstore received a notice from their motto supplier which read, "Beginning January 1, all prices will be increased 8%."

k. Father said, "We will need to increase the price of our mottoes by 5% to help cover our higher costs."

l. Leonard's father bought a book at a 30% closeout discount.

WRITTEN EXERCISES

A. *Change these percents to whole numbers or decimals.*

1. 110%   2. 140%   3. 300%   4. 450%
5. 550%   6. 900%   7. 325%   8. 650%

B. Find the percentages of these numbers.

9. 150% of 40

10. 155% of 80

11. 175% of 110

12. 135% of 65

13. 165% of 80

14. 155% of 120

15. 350% of 150

16. 575% of 125

C. Mentally add these percents to 100%.

17. 7%   **18.** 6%   **19.** 38%   **20.** 59%

D. Subtract these percents from 100%

21. 7%   **22.** 6%   **23.** 38%   **24.** 59%

E. For each problem give a percent that shows what part the new price is of the original price.

25. What percent of the original price is the price after a 17% increase?

26. What percent of the original price is the price after a 14% decrease?

27. In 1979, gasoline prices increased by about 60%.

28. In 1970, gasoline prices were about 72% lower than they were in 1990. What percent of the 1990 price was the 1970 price?

29. From 1980 to 1991, prices increased in the United States by an average of 65%.

30. From 1980 to 1991, prices increased in Canada by an average of 88%.

Jesus Christ the same yesterday, and today, and forever.
Hebrews 13:8

F. Solve these reading problems.

31. In 1990, prices for new automobiles were 229% of what they had been in 1970. A certain automobile was priced $4,000 in 1970. What would a similar automobile have cost in 1990?

32. In 1990, gasoline prices were 362% of what they had been in 1970. If a certain grade of gasoline sold for $0.30 in 1970, what was the price in 1990? Give the remainder as a fraction of a cent.

33. Marlin's parents have a small clothing store. To find the selling price of each item, they add 55% to the amount they paid for it. What percent of their cost is the selling price of the clothes?

34. Because of rising costs, Marlin's parents needed to increase the price of dress material 10%. The new price was what percent of the original price?

35. During June one year, $\frac{5}{7}$ of the rain fell in the third week of the month. Write a decimal to show what part of the rain fell in the third week of June. Round your answer to the nearest hundredth.

36. In grades 7–10, six of the seventeen students are in the seventh grade. Write a decimal showing what part of the students are in seventh grade. Round your answer to the nearest thousandth.

REVIEW EXERCISES

G. Complete this chart. *(Lesson 72)*

	Fraction	Decimal	Percent
37.	$\frac{41}{50}$		
39.			60%

	Fraction	Decimal	Percent
38.	$\frac{17}{30}$		
40.		0.19	

H. Multiply these fractions mentally. *(Lesson 44)*

41. $\frac{1}{4}$ of 36   42. $\frac{1}{7}$ of 35   43. $\frac{3}{5}$ of 25   44. $\frac{5}{8}$ of 40

I. Use short division to solve these problems without copying them. Express any remainder as a whole number. *(Lesson 17)*

45. $3\overline{)7{,}512}$ 46. $6\overline{)2{,}340}$ 47. $7\overline{)4{,}321}$ 48. $9\overline{)7{,}717}$

84. Another Way to Find a Percent More or Less

Percents are often used to calculate increases or decreases in price. During times of inflation (when prices rise), a business may increase the selling prices by a fixed percent. In Example A the price is increased by 5%.

Sometimes a business puts all items on sale for a certain percent less than the regular price. This is illustrated in Example B, where the sale price is 20% off the regular price.

In Lesson 74 you learned one way to solve problems like these. You first multiplied to find the amount of increase or decrease, and then you added it to, or subtracted it from, the original amount. Another way is to add or subtract the percent before multiplying. To calculate an increase or a decrease by this method, use the following steps.

1. Find the percent by which you will multiply the original number. If the number is to be increased by a given percent, add that percent to 100%. If it is to be decreased, subtract that percent from 100%.

2. Change the new percent to a decimal by dropping the percent sign and moving the decimal point two places to the left.

3. Multiply the original number by the decimal found in Step 2.

4. If the answer is a dollar amount with three or more decimal places, round it to the nearest cent.

Example A	Example B
Find a 5% increase on an item marked $12.60.	Find the reduced price of an item on sale at a 20% discount if the regular price is $19.98.
Step 1: 100% + 5% = 105%	Step 1: 100% - 20% = 80%
Step 2: 105% = 1.05	Step 2: 80% = 0.80 = 0.8

Step 3: $12.60
         × 1.05
         $13.23
	Step 3: $19.98
	         × 0.8
	         $15.984

Step 4: No rounding is needed.	Step 4: $15.984 rounds to $15.98

CLASS PRACTICE

Find the new price after the increase or decrease. Round to the nearest cent.

a. $15.00 increased by 15%

b. $9.95 decreased by 20%

c. $18.75 increased by 35%

d. $7.95 decreased by 30%

WRITTEN EXERCISES

A. *Find the new price after each increase. Round to the nearest cent.*

1. $25.00 increased by 5%
2. $20.00 increased by 8%
3. $35.00 increased by 20%
4. $8.00 increased by 15%
5. $5.95 increased by 15%
6. $7.99 increased by 12%
7. $15.95 increased by 25%
8. $18.95 increased by 18%

B. *Find the new price after each decrease. Round to the nearest cent.*

9. $30.00 decreased by 8%
10. $15.00 decreased by 10%
11. $26.00 decreased by 14%
12. $7.50 decreased by 30%
13. $6.95 decreased by 12%
14. $8.98 decreased by 18%
15. $14.99 decreased by 25%
16. $19.95 decreased by 35%

C. *Find the new price after each increase or decrease. Round to the nearest cent.*

17. $28.00 decreased by 10%
18. $10.00 increased by 15%
19. $38.00 increased by 12%
20. $8.75 increased by 22%
21. $9.69 increased by 35%
22. $2.95 decreased by 20%
23. $15.75 decreased by 40%
24. $29.49 increased by 18%

D. *Solve these reading problems. Use proportions for numbers 29 and 30.*

25. At the Stanwick Hardware Store, all seeds were discounted 25% toward the end of the growing season. Mother purchased a one-pound pack of corn seed that normally sold for $8.75. What was the sale price of the seeds?

26. The Martins have a "Pick your own" strawberry patch. During the peak of the strawberry season, the berries sold for $1.75 per quart. Near the end of the season, when the berries were not as good, they were sold for 40% less than the regular price. What was the reduced price?

27. The Martins were thankful for the bountiful strawberry crop with which the Lord blessed them. This year they harvested 35% more berries than they had last year. If they harvested 1,800 quarts of berries last year, how many did they harvest this year?

28. Two years ago, when the weather was very dry, the Martins' berry harvest was 32% smaller than it was last year. If they harvested 1,800 quarts of strawberries last year, what was the harvest two years ago?

29. The Martins themselves pick some berries to sell. Of the 1,800 quarts they harvested last year, customers picked 3 quarts for every 2 quarts the Martins picked. How many quarts did customers pick?

30. Of the 1,800 quarts of berries, the Martins kept 1 out of every 9 quarts for their own use. How many quarts did the Martins keep?

REVIEW EXERCISES

E. Express these rates as whole numbers or decimals. *(Lesson 83)*

31. 160%   **32.** 240%   **33.** 420%   **34.** 950%

F. Find these percentages. *(Lesson 83)*

35. 150% of 78   **36.** 180% of 95

37. 214% of 63   **38.** 450% of 125

G. Find the average of each set. Express remainders as fractions. *(Lesson 19)*

39. 42, 51, 64, 38, 66   **40.** 213, 214, 200, 225, 207

85. Working With Fractions of Percents

Some percents are not whole percents. Example C illustrates a percent that is less than 1%. This percent, $\frac{1}{2}$%, is $\frac{1}{2}$ as much as 1 percent. Example D illustrates that $5\frac{1}{2}$% is halfway between 5% and 6%.

Example A — 1%

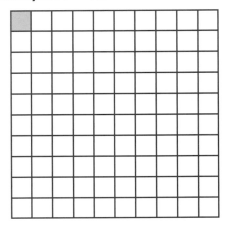

Example B — 5%

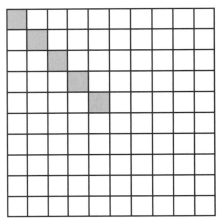

Example C
$\frac{1}{2}$% = 0.5% = 0.005

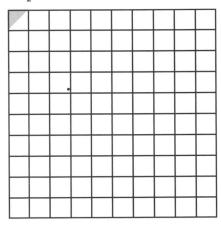

Example D
$5\frac{1}{2}$% = 5.5% = 0.055

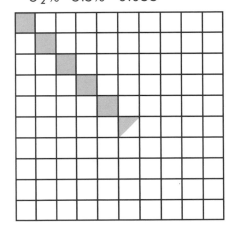

Percents that contain fractions are used in the same way as other percents. However, an extra step is required when using these percents: the fraction in the percent must be expressed as a decimal. Study the steps and examples below.

Step 1: Change the fraction in the percent to a decimal. This number is still a percent, but it is expressed as a decimal.

Step 2: Change the percent to a decimal by moving the decimal point two places to the left and dropping the percent sign.

Step 3: Solve the problem as indicated.

Example E	**Example F**
Find $\frac{1}{2}$% of 650.	Find $3\frac{3}{4}$% of 425.
Step 1: $\frac{1}{2}$% = 0.5%	Step 1: $3\frac{3}{4}$% = 3.75%
Step 2: 0.5% = 0.005	Step 2: 3.75% = 0.0375
Step 3: 650	Step 3: 425
$\times$ 0.005	$\times$ 0.0375
3.250 = 3.25	2125
	2975
	1275
	15.9375

CLASS PRACTICE

Change these fractional percents to decimals.

 a. $\frac{1}{4}$% b. $\frac{3}{5}$% c. $1\frac{3}{4}$% d. $10\frac{4}{5}$%

Find these percentages.

 e. $\frac{3}{4}$% of 180   f. $6\frac{1}{4}$% of 130   g. $125\frac{1}{2}$% of 160

WRITTEN EXERCISES

 A. *Change these percents to decimals.*

 1. $\frac{7}{10}$%   2. $\frac{2}{5}$%   3. $\frac{1}{10}$%   4. $\frac{3}{10}$%

 5. $2\frac{1}{4}$%   6. $5\frac{7}{10}$%   7. $15\frac{3}{4}$%   8. $20\frac{7}{10}$%

 B. *Find these percentages.*

 9. $\frac{1}{2}$% of 75   10. $\frac{1}{2}$% of 225

11. $\frac{1}{4}$% of 150   12. $\frac{3}{10}$% of 90

13. $\frac{3}{5}$% of 200   14. $\frac{9}{10}$% of 350

15. $1\frac{3}{4}$% of 175   16. $2\frac{1}{2}$% of 320

17. $6\frac{4}{5}$% of 130   18. $8\frac{7}{10}$% of 40

19. $75\frac{1}{2}$% of 90   20. $120\frac{1}{4}$% of 600

C. *Solve these reading problems.*

21. Brother Lewis bought a soccer ball for the school. The ball cost $15.75 plus $5\frac{1}{2}$% sales tax. How much was the sales tax?

22. Every year, Uncle Dwight pays real estate taxes equal to $1\frac{7}{10}$% of the value of his property. If his property is worth $125,000, how much are his real estate taxes every year?

23. Brother Eby pays real estate taxes equal to $\frac{3}{4}$% of the value of his farm. If his property is worth $375,000, how much are his real estate taxes?

24. When Father dried 5,000 pounds of shelled corn, it lost 9% of its weight. What did the corn weigh after it was dried?

25. Cairo, Egypt, is in a desert region that receives an average of 1.1 inches of annual precipitation. At Seattle, Washington, the annual precipitation is 2,618% of the amount at Cairo. To the nearest tenth of an inch, what is the average precipitation in Seattle?

26. Cairo is in the Nile River Valley, which can support a large population only because of the Nile River. This valley covers only about $3\frac{3}{5}$% of the area of Egypt, but almost 99% of the people live there. If the area of Egypt is 386,660 square miles, what is the area of the Nile River Valley to the nearest square mile?

REVIEW EXERCISES

D. *Find the amounts after these increases or decreases.* (Lesson 84)

27. 15% more than $50.00

28. 5% increase over 90

29. 20% less than 180

30. 12% less than $75.00

E. *Find the actual distances represented by these measurements on a map if the scale is $\frac{5}{8}$ inch = 2 miles.* (Lesson 75)

31. 4 in.

32. 11 in.

33. $6\frac{1}{2}$ in.

34. $15\frac{3}{4}$ in.

F. *Solve these division problems.* (Lesson 48)

35. $4 \div \frac{3}{8}$

36. $7 \div \frac{5}{6}$

37. $3\frac{1}{3} \div 1\frac{3}{7}$

38. $5\frac{1}{4} \div 1\frac{1}{6}$

86. Finding What Percent One Number Is of Another

Look at the two rectangles below. Do you know which one has the greater part shaded? This is difficult to tell simply by looking at them. By using percents, however, you can easily determine which rectangle has the greater part shaded.

Example A

46 of 50 blocks are dark.
____ % are shaded.

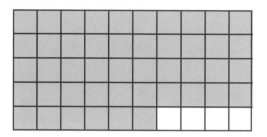

Example B

33 of 36 blocks are dark.
____ % are shaded.

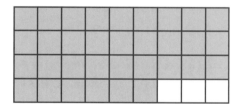

In Lesson 73, you found percentages by multiplying the base times the rate. In this lesson you will work with problems in which the percentage and the base are known, but the rate is unknown.

To find the rate when the base and the percentage are known, divide the percentage by the base. The formula is shown in the following block.

$$\text{Rate} = \frac{\text{Percentage}}{\text{Base}} \quad \text{or} \quad R = \frac{P}{B}$$

This formula is applied by using the following steps.

1. Divide the percentage by the base. Divide to the hundredths' place, and express any remainder as a fraction. **When finding a score for school work, round the answer to the nearest hundredth.**

2. Change the decimal to a percent by moving the decimal point two places to the right and adding a percent sign.

Find what percent of the squares in Example A are shaded.	Find what percent of the squares in Example B are shaded.
Step 1: $$\begin{array}{r} 0.92 \\ 50\overline{)46.00} \\ \underline{450} \\ 100 \\ \underline{100} \\ 0 \end{array}$$	Step 1: $$0.91\tfrac{24}{36} = 0.91\tfrac{2}{3}$$ $$\begin{array}{r} 36\overline{)33.00} \\ \underline{324} \\ 60 \\ \underline{36} \\ 24 \end{array}$$
Step 2: $0.92 = 92\%$	Step 2: $0.91\tfrac{2}{3} = 91\tfrac{2}{3}\%$

CLASS PRACTICE

Find these percents.

a. 12 is _____ % of 16

b. 9 is _____ % of 14

c. What was Dale's grade if he had 23 of 25 math problems correct?

d. Carlos had 28 correct out of 31 problems on a recent math test. What was his grade?

WRITTEN EXERCISES

A. *Find these percents. They are all whole-number percents.*

1. 3 is _____% of 12

2. 5 is _____% of 25

3. 8 is _____% of 25

4. 12 is _____% of 150

5. 18 is _____% of 40

6. 24 is _____% of 25

B. *Find these percents. Some of them include fractions.*

7. 13 is _____% of 15

8. 16 is _____% of 18

9. 23 is _____% of 26

10. 22 is _____% of 66

11. 35 is _____% of 42

12. 18 is _____% of 24

13. 36 is _____% of 54

14. 31 is _____% of 35

15. 1 is _____% of 14

16. 3 is _____% of 16

17. 11 is _____% of 28

18. 63 is _____% of 72

C. Solve these reading problems.

19. What was Mark's grade on a math quiz if he had 14 of 16 problems correct?

20. Michael had 31 out of 35 answers correct on his Bible doctrine test. What was his grade?

21. When Andrew Johnson was President, the Senate voted whether or not to remove him from office. The Constitution requires a $66\frac{2}{3}$ % affirmative vote to accomplish this. Of the 54 senators, 35 voted to remove President Johnson from office. To the nearest tenth, what percent is that?

22. The school board of the Ridgeview Mennonite School consists of 9 members. To hold a board meeting, a quorum of 80% of the board members is required. What percent of the board members are present if 8 of them are there?

23. The seventh grade students are making scale drawings of the tabernacle. They are drawing to a scale of $\frac{3}{4}$ inch = 2 cubits. The length of the tabernacle was 30 cubits. How long should the students' drawings of the tabernacle be?

24. On the scale drawing, the length of the holy place was $7\frac{1}{2}$ inches. What was the actual length of the holy place? (See problem 23.)

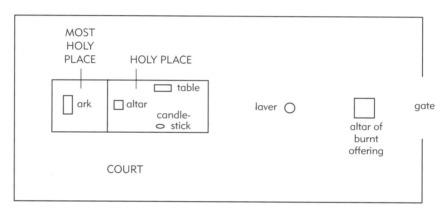

REVIEW EXERCISES

D. Find the following percentages. *(Lesson 85)*

25. $2\frac{3}{4}$ % of 205

26. $3\frac{3}{5}$ % of 75

27. $7\frac{3}{10}$ % of 670

28. $110\frac{1}{2}$ % of 250

E. Find the amounts after these increases or decreases. *(Lesson 84)*

29. 15% increase over $50

30. 75% increase over $45

31. 25% decrease from $70

32. 45% decrease from $95

F. Write a ratio to compare each of the following. *(Lesson 67)*

33. 5 inches precipitation compared to 40 inches precipitation

34. 14 acres compared to 2 acres

87. Finding a Number When a Percent of It Is Known

In some percent problems, the percentage and the rate are known but the base is unknown. Look at Example A below. The number of shaded blocks (10) is stated, and the rate (25%) is also stated. The part that is not stated is the total number of blocks (the base). This is the part that must be found.

Example A

10 shaded blocks are 25% of _____ blocks in all.

10 is 25% of _____.

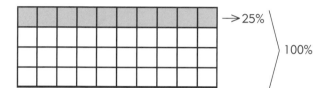

Example B

14 shaded blocks are 40% of _____ blocks in all.

14 is 40% of _____.

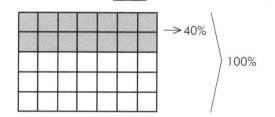

To find the base when the percentage and the rate are known, divide the percentage by the rate. (The percent is changed to a decimal for division.) The formula is shown below and is used to solve Examples A and B. You can prove that the answers are correct by counting the blocks.

$$\text{Base} = \frac{\text{Percentage}}{\text{Rate}} \quad \text{or} \quad B = \frac{P}{R}$$

Compute the total number of blocks in Example A.	Compute the total number of blocks in Example B.
$\text{Base} = \dfrac{\text{Percentage}}{\text{Rate}} = \dfrac{10}{25\%}$ $\dfrac{10}{25\%} = \dfrac{10}{0.25} = 10 \div 0.25$ $40. = 40 \text{ blocks}$ $0.25\overline{)10.00}$ $\underline{100}$ 00	$B = \dfrac{P}{R} = \dfrac{14}{40\%}$ $\dfrac{14}{40\%} = \dfrac{14}{0.40} = 14 \div 0.4$ $35. = 35 \text{ blocks}$ $0.4\overline{)14.0}$ $\underline{12}$ 20 $\underline{20}$ 0

CLASS PRACTICE

Find the base in each problem.

a. $P = 16$
    $R = 64\%$
    $B = \underline{\hphantom{xxx}}$

b. $P = 30;$
    $R = 30\%;$
    $B = \underline{\hphantom{xxx}}$

c. 12 is 15% of ____

d. 63 is 18% of ____

e. 2 is 8% of ____

f. Eugene had 3 problems wrong, or 10% of all the problems assigned. How many problems were assigned?

WRITTEN EXERCISES

A. Find the bases. They are all whole numbers.

1. $P = 20$
    $R = 50\%$
    $B = \underline{\hphantom{xxx}}$

2. $P = 15$
    $R = 50\%$
    $B = \underline{\hphantom{xxx}}$

3. $P = 12$
    $R = 25\%$
    $B = \underline{\hphantom{xxx}}$

4. $P = 18$
    $R = 25\%$
    $B = \underline{\hphantom{xxx}}$

5. $P = 25$
    $R = 20\%$
    $B = \underline{\hphantom{xxx}}$

6. $P = 45$
    $R = 10\%$
    $B = \underline{\hphantom{xxx}}$

7. $P = 14$
    $R = 35\%$
    $B = \underline{\hphantom{xxx}}$

8. $P = 11$
    $R = 55\%$
    $B = \underline{\hphantom{xxx}}$

9. $P = 18$
    $R = 75\%$
    $B = \underline{\hphantom{xxx}}$

10. $P = 24$
     $R = 80\%$
     $B = \underline{\hphantom{xxx}}$

11. 27 is 45% of ____

12. 54 is 72% of ____

13. 4 is 5% of ____

14. 6 is 8% of ____

15. 88 is 32% of ____

16. 76 is 19% of ____

B. Solve these reading problems.

17. Brother Nolt uses the dressed weights of the livestock he slaughters to estimate their live weights. He calculates that a hog's dressed weight is 67% of its live weight. What would he estimate as the live weight of a hog if its dressed weight is 134 pounds?

18. Brother Nolt estimates that the dressed weight of a steer is 60% of its live weight. What would he estimate the live weight of a steer to have been if the dressed weight is 750 pounds?

19. The Stony Ledge Hardware Store collects a 5% state sales tax on the taxable items it sells. If over $100 in sales tax is collected each year, the tax must be sent to the state every three months. What amount of taxable sales results in $100 of sales tax?

20. Brother Harold mixes a dairy feed that consists of 40% corn. How many pounds of feed can he mix if he has 800 pounds of corn?

21. For the same type of feed, Brother Harold uses 900 pounds of oats to mix a 3,000-pound batch. How much oats would he use to mix a 5,000-pound batch? (Use a proportion to solve this problem.)

22. Brother Harold includes 500 pounds of wheat in every ton of feed he mixes. How much feed can he mix if he has 1,250 pounds of wheat on hand? (Use a proportion.)

REVIEW EXERCISES

C. Find these percents. Some of them include fractions. (Lesson 86)

23. 7 is _____% of 35

24. 15 is _____% of 25

25. $P = 30$
    $B = 75$
    $R = $ _____

26. $P = 20$
    $B = 66$
    $R = $ _____

D. Find these percentages. (Lesson 85)

27. $3\frac{1}{2}$% of 45 is _____

28. $7\frac{3}{4}$% of 52 is _____

E. Find the answers to these problems. (Lesson 49)

29. 30 is $\frac{4}{5}$ of _____

30. 55 is $\frac{5}{7}$ of _____

31. 28 is $\frac{7}{9}$ of _____

32. 32 is $\frac{4}{9}$ of _____

88. Understanding the Percent Formulas

In Lessons 73, 86, and 87, you used three different formulas to find the base, the rate, and the percentage. These three formulas are different, yet they are related. All three of them use the same three terms. Each kind of percent problem is solved by using two of the parts to find the third part. Because these formulas are so closely related, they are called the **percent formulas**. They are summarized below.

Finding the Percentage (Lesson 73)

The following formula is used to find a percentage when the base and the rate are known. A percentage is a number that is a part of another number.

$$\text{Percentage } = \text{ Base } \times \text{ Rate } \quad \text{or} \quad P = BR$$

Finding the Rate (Lesson 86)

The following formula is used to find the rate when the base and the percentage are known. The rate shows what part one number (the percentage) is of another (the base). The rate is followed by the percent sign (%) or the word *percent*.

$$\text{Rate } = \frac{\text{Percentage}}{\text{Base}} \quad \text{or} \quad R = \frac{P}{B}$$

Finding the Base (Lesson 87)

The following formula is used to find the base when the percentage and the rate are known. The base is the whole number of which the other number (the percentage) is a part.

$$\text{Base } = \frac{\text{Percentage}}{\text{Rate}} \quad \text{or} \quad B = \frac{P}{R}$$

When you solve reading problems involving percents, you must determine which part you need to find—the base, the rate, or the percentage. Once that is decided, you simply apply the correct formula and perform the calculations properly.

Example A

John Mark completed 95% of his 40 math problems correctly. How many problems were correctly done?

> 95% is the rate.
> 40 math problems are all the problems, or the base.

The percentage is needed. This problem is solved by applying the formula for finding the percentage.

$$\text{Percentage } = \text{ Base } \times \text{ Rate } = 40 \times 95\% = 38 \text{ problems}$$

Example B

John Mark had 38 out of 40 math problems correct. What was his grade?

38 is the part of the 40 problems done correctly. It is the percentage.
40 math problems are all the problems, or the base.
The rate is needed. This problem is solved by applying the formula for finding the rate.

$$\text{Rate} = \frac{\text{Percentage}}{\text{Base}} = \frac{38}{40} = $$

$$\begin{array}{r} 0.95 = 95\% \\ 40\overline{)38.00} \\ \underline{360} \\ 200 \\ \underline{200} \\ 0 \end{array}$$

Example C

John Mark had 38 problems correct, or 95% of all the math problems. What was the total number of problems in the assignment?

38 is the part of the problems done correctly. It is the percentage.
95% is the rate.
The base is needed. This problem is solved by applying the formula for finding the base.

$$\text{Base} = \frac{\text{Percentage}}{\text{Rate}} = \frac{38}{95\%} = $$

$$\begin{array}{r} 40 = 40 \text{ problems} \\ 0.95\overline{)38.00} \\ \underline{380} \\ 00 \end{array}$$

CLASS PRACTICE

Find the missing parts.

a. $B = 40$
$R = 88\%$
$P = \underline{\hphantom{000}}$

b. $B = 32$
$P = 24$
$R = \underline{\hphantom{000}}$

c. $P = 54$
$R = 9\%$
$B = \underline{\hphantom{000}}$

d. 65% of 75 is _____

e. 60 is _____% of 75

f. 9 is 36% of _____

WRITTEN EXERCISES

A. Use the base and the rate to find the percentage.

1. 28% of 34 is _____

2. 45% of 62 is _____

3. 72% of 89 is _____

4. $B = 28; R = 32\%$

5. $B = 77; R = 48\%$

6. $B = 58; R = 39\%$

B. Use the base and the percentage to find the rate.

7. 26 is _____% of 50

8. 32 is _____% of 40

9. 48 is _____% of 75

10. $B = 45; P = 27$

11. $B = 40; P = 16$

12. $B = 50; P = 17$

C. Use the rate and the percentage to find the base.

13. 14 is 50% of _____

14. 18 is 25% of _____

15. 12 is 15% of _____

16. $R = 16\%; P = 24$

17. $R = 32\%; P = 8$

18. $R = 45\%; P = 54$

D. Solve for the missing part of the formula in each problem.

19. 18 is 45% of _____

20. 35% of 24 is _____

21. 16 is _____% of 40

22. $B = 54$; $R = 63\%$

23. $R = 24\%$; $P = 60$

24. $B = 28$; $P = 21$

E. To solve these reading problems, first write the base, the rate, and the percentage, using *n* for the part that is missing. Then solve the problem. Express any remainders as fractions.

25. Brother James is a merchant. He knows that the amount he pays for an item should be 70% of its selling price. If he pays $31.50 for a pair of shoes, what should he sell them for?

Base = _____   Rate = _____   Percentage = _____

26. Brother James sells a certain fabric for $3.20 per yard. What did he pay per yard if he paid 70% of his selling price?

Base = _____   Rate = _____   Percentage = _____

27. At the end of one week, Brother James had sold $400 in merchandise subject to state sales tax. He owed the state treasury $28. What was the rate of sales tax in his state?

B = _____ R = _____ P = _____

28. At noon one summer day, Father said that he and the boys had gotten in 40% of the hay they had cut that week. If they had put 5 layers of hay bales in the barn, what was the total number of layers that they could expect from that cutting?

B = _____ R = _____ P = _____

29. David unloaded 45 of the 120 hay bales on one wagon load. What percent did he unload?

B = _____ R = _____ P = _____

30. A farmer harvested 1,250 bushels of apples and sold 80% of them. How many bushels of apples did he sell?

B = _____ R = _____ P = _____

And God said, Behold, I have given you every herb bearing seed, which is upon the face of all the earth, and every tree, in the which is the fruit of a tree yielding seed; to you it shall be for meat.   Genesis 1:29

REVIEW EXERCISES

F. Find the amount after each increase or decrease. *(Lesson 84)*

31. $35.00 increased by 14%

32. $28.50 decreased by 15%

33. 65 increased by 35%

34. 88 decreased by 46%

G. Solve these division problems mentally. *(Lesson 20)*

35. $168 \div 24$

36. $242 \div 22$

37. $900 \div 50$

38. $1,300 \div 50$

39. $600 \div 25$

40. $800 \div 25$

89. Working With Commissions

One practical way in which percents are used is in the calculating of sales commissions. When something is sold on commission, the owner has another person sell his products. The seller receives a percent of his sales, or a **commission**.

Working with sales commissions is one way in which the three percent formulas are applied in everyday life. Sales commission problems involve the same three parts and the same three formulas as those discussed in the last lesson. However, the terms in the formulas are given new names that relate to commissions.

Sale—This term means the same as **base**. It is the entire amount; in this case, the entire selling price.

Rate—This is the percent, the same as the rate in other percent problems. It is also called the **rate of commission**.

Commission—This term means the same as **percentage**. It is the part of the sale that the seller receives. Commission is usually rounded to the nearest cent.

Finding the Commission (Percentage)

The same formula is used to find a sales commission as is used to find the percentage in a percent problem.

Percentage = Base × Rate   *or*   commission = sales × rate

Example A

Edward sold two rabbits at a local livestock auction for $12.00. How much commission did the auction receive if the rate of commission was 12%?

commission = sales × rate = $12.00 × 12% (0.12) = $1.44

Finding the Rate of Commission (Rate)

The same formula is used to find the rate of commission as is used to find the rate in a percentage problem.

Rate = $\dfrac{\text{Percentage}}{\text{Base}}$ *or*   rate of commission = $\dfrac{\text{commission}}{\text{sales}}$

Example B

The Millers took a sofa to a neighbor's sale, where it was sold for $50. The auctioneer deducted $6.50 as his commission. What was the rate of commission?

rate = $\dfrac{\text{commission}}{\text{sales}}$ = $\dfrac{\$6.50}{\$50}$ = 0.13 = 13%

Finding the Amount of Sales (Base)

The same formula is used to find the amount of sales as is used to find the base when the rate and the percentage are known.

$$\text{Base} = \frac{\text{Percentage}}{\text{Rate}} \quad \text{or} \quad \text{sales} = \frac{\text{commission}}{\text{rate}}$$

Example C

When Father sold a dairy cow at the Meadow Brook livestock auction, a commission of $73.50 was deducted from the check that Father received. The rate of commission was 7%. What was the selling price of the cow?

$$\text{sales} = \frac{\text{commission}}{\text{rate}} = \frac{\$73.50}{7\%} = 0.07\overline{)73.50}^{\$1050} = \$1,050$$

CLASS PRACTICE

Find the sales, the rate, or the commission.

a. $r = 5\%$
    $c = \$14$
    $s = $ _____

b. $s = \$300$
    $c = \$27$
    $r = $ _____

c. $s = \$375$
    $r = 7\%$
    $c = $ _____

d. $s = \$350$
    $r = 3\frac{1}{2}\%$
    $c = $ _____

WRITTEN EXERCISES

A. Use the sales and the rates to find the commissions. Round to the nearest cent.

1. $s = \$500$
    $r = 4\%$
    $c = $ _____

2. $s = \$750$
    $r = 3\%$
    $c = $ _____

3. $s = \$425.89$
    $r = 7\%$
    $c = $ _____

4. $s = \$288.99$
    $r = 5\%$
    $c = $ _____

5. $s = \$325$
    $r = 4\frac{1}{2}\%$
    $c = $ _____

6. $s = \$775$
    $r = 5\frac{1}{4}\%$
    $c = $ _____

B. Use the sales and the commissions to find the rates. All the rates are whole percents.

7. $s = \$500$
    $c = \$30$
    $r = $ _____

8. $s = \$800$
    $c = \$64$
    $r = $ _____

9. $s = \$250$
    $c = \$17.50$
    $r = $ _____

10. $s = \$350$
    $c = \$38.50$
    $r = $ _____

11. $s = \$775$
    $c = \$15.50$
    $r = $ _____

12. $s = \$995$
    $c = \$69.65$
    $r = $ _____

C. Use the rates and the commissions to find the sales. No rounding will be necessary.

13. $r = 8\%$
    $c = \$20$
    $s = $ _____

14. $r = 7\%$
    $c = \$35.00$
    $s = $ _____

15. $r = 11\%$
    $c = \$15.40$
    $s = $ _____

16. $r = 12\%$
$c = \$33.60$
$s =$ _____

17. $r = 7\%$
$c = \$13.37$
$s =$ _____

18. $r = 9\%$
$c = \$16.56$
$s =$ _____

D. Find the missing parts.

19. $s = \$300$
$c = \$24$
$r =$ _____

20. $s = \$700$
$c = \$91$
$r =$ _____

21. $r = 3\%$
$c = \$45$
$s =$ _____

22. $r = 6\%$
$c = \$54.30$
$s =$ _____

23. $s = \$750$
$r = 4\frac{1}{2}\%$
$c =$ _____

24. $s = \$675$
$r = 2\frac{1}{4}\%$
$c =$ _____

E. Solve these reading problems.

25. Father took a used tiller to a consignment sale. The tiller sold for $350.00, and the auctioneer charged a 6% commission. What was the commission?

26. The Sensenigs sold a dairy cow for $1,100 at a cattle sale. The sales stable took $77 off the selling price for its commission. What was the rate of commission?

27. A realtor sold a tract of land for $15,000. He charged a commission of $750. What was the rate of commission?

28. Paul took some old books to a book sale. When he received his check, a commission of $9.00 had been deducted. The rate of commission for a small lot of books was 40%. What did the books sell for?

REVIEW EXERCISES

F. Apply the correct formula to solve each of these percent problems. *(Lesson 88)*

29. $B = \$60$
$R = 9\%$
$P =$ _____

30. $R = 4\%$
$P = \$35$
$B =$ _____

31. $B = \$75$
$P = \$2.25$
$R =$ _____

32. $B = \$150$
$P = \$10.50$
$R =$ _____

G. Find these percentages. *(Lesson 85)*

33. $1\frac{1}{2}\%$ of 160

34. $3\frac{3}{4}\%$ of 190

H. Use proportions to solve these reading problems. *(Lesson 70)*

35. There are 3 sixth graders for every 2 seventh graders in Room 4 in the Lakeside Christian Day School. There are 20 students in the room. How many of them are seventh graders?

36. The Lakeside School has 1 teacher for every 18 students. When everyone is present, there are 133 people in the school, including teachers and students. How many students are there?

90. Calculating the Rate of Increase or Decrease

When there is a change in amounts, the change is often expressed as a percent of change. When the amount increases, it is stated as a percent of increase; and when it decreases, the change is stated as a percent of decrease. Both kinds of change are found by using the steps below.

Step 1: Find the amount of change by finding the difference between the two amounts.

Step 2: Find the rate of change by finding what percent the amount of change is of the original amount (the amount before the change). The rate of change is found by dividing the amount of change by the original amount. If the division problem does not come out evenly, divide to the thousandths' place and round the number to the nearest hundredth.

Step 3: Change the decimal to a percent.

Example A

One year Brother Roy harvested 45 bushels of wheat per acre. The next year he harvested 54 bushels of wheat per acre. What was the rate of increase?

Step 1: $54 - 45 = 9$ bu. per acre

Step 2: $\frac{9}{45} = 45\overline{)9.00}^{0.20} = 0.20$

Step 3: $0.20 = 20\%$ increase

Example B

One year Brother Roy harvested 54 bushels of wheat per acre. The next year he harvested 45 bushels of wheat per acre. What was the rate of decrease?

Step 1: $54 - 45 = 9$ bu. per acre

Step 2: $\frac{9}{54} = 54\overline{)9.000}^{0.166} = 0.17$ (to the nearest hundredth)

Step 3: $0.17 = 17\%$ decrease

CLASS PRACTICE

Find the rate of increase or decrease.

	Original Price	New Price		Original Price	New Price
a.	$12.00	$15.00	b.	$20.00	$18.00
c.	$35.00	$30.00	d.	$60.00	$65.00

WRITTEN EXERCISES

A. Find the rate of increase. The answers are all whole percents.

	Original Price	New Price		Original Price	New Price
1.	$40.00	$50.00	2.	$50.00	$60.00
3.	$16.00	$18.88	4.	$22.00	$25.30

B. Find the rate of decrease. The answers are all whole percents.

	Original Price	New Price		Original Price	New Price
5.	$20.00	$10.00	6.	$60.00	$45.00
7.	$18.50	$14.80	8.	$26.20	$17.03

C. Find the rate of increase or decrease. The answers are all whole percents. Label the change as *increase* or *decrease*.

	Original Price	New Price		Original Price	New Price
9.	$35.00	$42.35	10.	$61.00	$56.73
11.	$67.25	$61.87	12.	$92.50	$114.70

D. Find the rate of increase or decrease. Round your answers to the nearest whole percent. Label the change as *increase* or *decrease*.

	Original Price	New Price		Original Price	New Price
13.	$18.00	$17.00	14.	$30.00	$32.00
15.	$15.00	$17.00	16.	$27.00	$33.00

Honour the Lord with thy substance, and with the firstfruits of all thine increase.

Proverbs 3:9

E. Solve these reading problems. Round to the nearest whole percent.

17. The price of a textbook increased from $8.00 to $9.00. What was the rate of increase?

18. A rake normally priced at $15.00 is now on sale for $12.00. What is the rate of discount?

19. In the United States one year, the average price that farmers received for a hundred-weight of milk increased from $13.56 to $13.73. What was the rate of increase?

20. During the same period, the average price for a dairy cow increased from $1,030 to $1,160. What was the rate of increase?

21. Larry's father sold a car for $6,000. The man who sold the car for him received a commission of $240. What was the rate of commission?

22. A car auction charged a commission of $120.00 for selling a car. The rate of commission was 8%. What was the selling price of the car?

REVIEW EXERCISES

F. Find the missing parts in these commission problems. *(Lesson 89)*

	Sales	Rate	Commission		Sales	Rate	Commission
23.	$600.00	4%	_____	24.	$250.00	_____	$15.00
25.	$130.00	_____	$11.70	26.	_____	6%	$33.00
27.	_____	17%	$12.75	28.	$88.79	14%	_____

G. Apply the percent formulas to solve these problems. *(Lesson 88)*

	Base	Rate	Percentage		Base	Rate	Percentage
29.	_____	5%	$35.25	30.	$65.00	_____	$8.45
31.	$125.00	_____	$13.75	32.	$88.76	15%	_____
33.	78	28%	_____	34.	_____	12%	46.2

91. Multiplying Mentally by Changing Percents to Fractions

Some percent problems can be greatly simplified by changing the percent to a fraction. If the fraction is one with which it is easy to calculate, you may even be able to solve the problem mentally. For example, to find 50% of a number, find $\frac{1}{2}$ of the number.

This method can be used to solve all three kinds of percent problems.

Finding Percentages Mentally

Example A:
　Find 25% of 40.　　　　Think: $\frac{1}{4}$ of 40 = 40 ÷ 4 = 10

Example B:
　Find $66\frac{2}{3}$% of 33.　　Think: $\frac{2}{3}$ of 33 = 33 ÷ 3 × 2 = 22

Finding Rates Mentally

To find the rate mentally, divide the percentage by the base. Do this by making a fraction of the two numbers, with the percentage as the numerator and the base as the denominator. Reduce the fraction to lowest terms, and mentally change it to a percent if possible. All the fractions in this lesson have percent equivalents that you were assigned to memorize.

Example C:
　20 is ____% of 30.　　Think: $\frac{20}{30} = \frac{2}{3} = 66\frac{2}{3}$%

Example D:
　12 is ____% of 30.　　Think: $\frac{12}{30} = \frac{2}{5} = 40$%

Finding Bases Mentally

To find the base mentally, change the rate to a fraction; then divide the percentage by this fraction. For this kind of problem, all the rates in this lesson are equivalent to unit fractions. To divide a whole number by a unit fraction, multiply the number by the denominator of the fraction.

Example E:
　15 is 50% of ____　　Think: 15 is $\frac{1}{2}$ of 30 (15 × 2 = 30)

Example F:
　10 is 25% of ____　　Think: 10 is $\frac{1}{4}$ of 40 (10 × 4 = 40)

CLASS PRACTICE

Find the answers mentally.

a. 25% of 48

b. $37\frac{1}{2}$% of 32

c. 12 is 25% of _____

d. 6 is $12\frac{1}{2}$% of _____

e. 4 is _____% of 12

f. 12 is _____% of 60

WRITTEN EXERCISES

A. **Find these percentages by first changing the rates to fractions.**

1. 50% of 80

2. 25% of 20

3. $33\frac{1}{3}$% of 27

4. 20% of 55

5. $12\frac{1}{2}$% of 56

6. 10% of 70

7. 75% of 24

8. $66\frac{2}{3}$% of 21

9. 60% of 35

10. $37\frac{1}{2}$% of 48

11. $87\frac{1}{2}$% of 32

12. 80% of 55

B. **Find these bases by first changing the rates to fractions.**

13. 16 is 50% of _____

14. 12 is 25% of _____

15. 5 is $33\frac{1}{3}$% of _____

16. 5 is $12\frac{1}{2}$% of _____

17. 9 is 20% of _____

18. 65 is 10% of _____

19. 6 is 25% of _____

20. 9 is $33\frac{1}{3}$% of _____

C. **Find these rates by making fractions and mentally changing them to percents.**

21. 20 is _____% of 40

22. 10 is _____% of 30

23. 2 is _____% of 8

24. 3 is _____% of 24

25. 5 is _____% of 25

26. 18 is _____% of 30

27. 15 is _____% of 20

28. 16 is _____% of 24

D. **Solve these reading problems. You should be able to do numbers 29–32 mentally.**

29. At a year-end sale, Philip bought a $5.00 road atlas at 20% off the regular price. How much did he save?

30. Of the 72 students at Philip's school, $12\frac{1}{2}$% of them are in Grade 7. How many seventh grade students attend this school?

31. In another school, grades 1 and 2 have 11 students, or 25% of the students in school. How many students attend that school?

32. Priscilla paid $0.88 less than the regular price for the book *Dear Princess*. If the price was reduced 10%, what was the regular price?

33. One year Mother bought a pack of seeds for $6.00. The same kind and amount of seeds would have cost $5.00 one year earlier. What was the rate of increase?

34. During one year, the total number of farms in Pennsylvania dropped from 55,000 to 54,000. To the nearest whole percent, what was the rate of decrease?

While the earth remaineth, seedtime and harvest, and cold and heat,

and summer and winter, and day and night shall not cease.

Genesis 8:22

REVIEW EXERCISES

E. Find the rate of increase or decrease. Round your answers to the nearest whole percent. *(Lesson 90)*

	Original Price	New Price			Original Price	New Price
35.	$12.00	$13.00		**36.**	$26.00	$23.00
37.	$19.00	$18.00		**38.**	$44.00	$48.00

F. Find the missing parts in these commission problems. *(Lesson 89)*

	Sales	Rate	Commission			Sales	Rate	Commission
39.	$800.00	14%	____		**40.**	$375.00	____	$33.75
41.	$630.00	____	$18.90		**42.**	____	9%	$54.00

G. Complete this chart. *(Lesson 72)*

	Fraction	Decimal	Percent
43.	$\frac{17}{25}$		
45.			18%

	Fraction	Decimal	Percent
44.	$\frac{7}{20}$		
46.		0.22	

92. Reading Problems: Solving Multistep Problems

Some reading problems are simple; they can be solved by using only one step. Many others, however, require a number of steps. This means that reading problems can become quite complex, the same as problems faced in real life.

Consider the following problems. They all have the same basic facts, but each problem requires one more step than the one before it.

Example A: One-Step Reading Problem

Marlene bought a loaf of bread for $1.15 and a tablet for $1.59. What was her total bill?

Only one step is required. The total bill is found by adding the two amounts.
$1.15 + $1.59 = $2.74

Example B: Two-Step Reading Problem

Marlene bought a loaf of bread for $1.15 and a tablet for $1.59. If she paid 6% sales tax on the tablet, what was her total bill?

The sales tax should be calculated first. Then all the amounts should be added together.

Step 1: $1.59 × 0.06 = $0.10
Step 2: $1.59 + 0.10 + 1.15 = $2.84

Example C: Three-Step Reading Problem

Marlene bought a loaf of bread for $1.15 and a tablet for $1.59. The tablet was subject to 6% sales tax. If Marlene gave the cashier $5.00, how much change should she receive?

In addition to the steps in Example B, the total bill must be subtracted from $5.00 to find the amount of change.

Step 1: $1.59 × 0.06 = $0.10
Step 2: $1.59 + 0.10 + 1.15 = $2.84
Step 3: $5.00 − 2.84 = $2.16

Example D: Four-Step Reading Problem

Marlene bought a loaf of bread for $1.15 and a tablet for $1.59. The tablet was subject to 6% sales tax. Marlene gave the cashier $5.00 and asked that $1.00 worth of quarters be included in the change. How many $1 bills should Marlene receive?

In addition to the steps in Example C, $1.00 in quarters must be subtracted from the amount of change to determine the number of $1 bills Marlene should receive.

Step 1: $1.59 × 0.06 = $0.10
Step 2: $1.59 + 0.10 + 1.15 = $2.84
Step 3: $5.00 − 2.84 = $2.16
Step 4: $2.16 − 1.00 = $1.16

Marlene should receive one $1 bill.

In solving multistep reading problems, use the following steps.

Step 1: Read the problem carefully. Note the facts that are given and the question that is asked.

Step 2: Pick out the clue words that indicate whether addition, subtraction, multiplication, or division are to be used.

Step 3: Solve the problem one step at a time.

Step 4: Check your answer to make sure it is logical.

CLASS PRACTICE

a. Dale bought a calf that weighed 225 pounds. The calf gained an average of 2.8 pounds each day. What was its weight after 1 year (365 days)?

b. The calf was fed a grain diet. The cost of the feed was $0.085 per pound, and the calf ate 7.5 pounds of feed for every pound of weight it gained. By the time the calf's weight increased from 225 pounds to 600 pounds, what was the cost of the feed it had eaten?

c. A merchant sold 350 bushels of apples for a farmer at $4.25 per bushel. If the rate of commission was 5%, find the amount of commission the merchant received.

d. The next year the merchant sold 420 bushels of apples for the farmer at $4.40 per bushel. If the rate of commission was 6%, find the amount that the farmer received.

WRITTEN EXERCISES

A. Solve these multistep reading problems.

1. Water weighs 62.4 pounds per cubic foot. A water tank used by a builder weighs 175 pounds and can hold 36 cubic feet. What is the total weight of the tank when it is full of water?

2. The Martins had their fuel oil tank refilled when it still held 50 gallons. Its total capacity was 275 gallons, and the price of fuel oil was $0.799 per gallon. What did the Martins pay for the fuel?

3. How much change will Martha receive from a $5 bill if she buys 3 jars of mayonnaise for $1.49 each?

4. On a trip away from home, Brother David purchased 18 gallons of gasoline at $1.14 per gallon and paid $2.80 in highway toll. On the return trip he paid the same amount of toll and purchased 12 gallons of gasoline at $1.12 per gallon. What was the cost of his trip?

5. Brother Lester sold 125 quarts of strawberries at $1.35 per quart. He paid his helpers $0.20 per quart for picking 75 quarts of the berries. How much of the money did Brother Lester have left?

6. One winter Brother Jason bought 9 tons of coal for $109.50 per ton. He received a 2% discount because he paid when the coal was delivered. How much could Brother Jason deduct from his bill?

Study to shew thyself approved unto God, a workman that needeth not to be ashamed, rightly dividing the word of truth. 2 Timothy 2:15

7. The next winter Brother Jason bought 8 tons of coal for $113.50 per ton. Because he paid when the coal was delivered, he again received a 2% discount. How much did he pay for the coal?

8. Uncle Jonathan purchased three tracts of land measuring 46 acres, 68 acres, and 95 acres. He paid a total of $355,300 for the land. What was the average price per acre?

9. One month Brother John worked 183 hours at $8.25 per hour. His employer deducted $248.87 in taxes from his pay check. What was Brother John's take-home pay?

10. The Stauffers paid $20.00 for a coat to sell in their clothing store. They marked it with a price 40% higher than they had paid for it. A few months later they sold it at a discount of 10% off the marked price. What was the sale price?

11. Inflation is the increase of prices. The inflation rate in the United States in a recent year was about 4%. Suppose a 4-acre plot of land is worth $9,000 per acre at the beginning of the year, and its price increases by 4%. How much will the land be worth at the end of the year?

12. One year Brother Miller's harvest of corn silage was an average of 16 tons per acre. The next year, with increased rainfall, the harvest was 25% greater. If silage was worth $20 per ton in the second year, what was the value of the corn silage from one acre?

REVIEW EXERCISES

B. *Solve these percent problems mentally.* (Lesson 91)

13. 25% of 28

14. $62\frac{1}{2}$ % of 24

15. 11 is 25% of _____

16. 8 is $12\frac{1}{2}$ % of _____

17. 5 is _____% of 25

18. 9 is _____% of 72

C. *Find the rate of increase or decrease. Round your answers to the nearest whole percent.* (Lesson 90)

	Original Price	New Price		Original Price	New Price
19.	$ 7.00	$11.00	20.	$24.00	$22.00
21.	$19.00	$24.00	22.	$22.00	$17.00

D. *Find the amount after each increase or decrease.* (Lesson 84)

23. 12% more than $35.00

24. 9% increase over 85

25. 16% less than 175

26. 7% less than $66.00

E. *Change these linear measures.* (Lesson 25)

27. 19 ft. = _____ in.

28. 21 ft. = _____ yd.

29. 251 in. = _____ ft.

30. 23 ft. = _____ yd.

31. $12\frac{1}{2}$ ft. = _____ in.

32. $3\frac{1}{2}$ yd. = _____ ft.

93. Working With the Histogram

You have learned that an average is a summary of the numbers in a group. It shows what each number would be if all the numbers were the same. Consider the following example.

18, 61, 45, 92

First the numbers are added: 18 + 61 + 45 + 92 = 216
Then the sum is divided by 4: 216 ÷ 4 = 54 (average)
Adding 18 + 61 + 45 + 92 is the same as adding 54 + 54 + 54 + 54.

The average of the numbers above is 54. But 54 is not even close to some numbers in the group. In fact, it is three times as large as 18! An average is useful when one "middle" value is needed. But when a wide range of values is to be shown, it is more meaningful to use another method of summarizing the numbers. This is especially true when a large number of values are spread over a wide range.

The **histogram** is one other way to summarize numbers. This is a special kind of graph that gives a range of values (such as 1–100) and shows how the values within that range are distributed. The histogram resembles the bar graph in some ways, but its bars do not represent separate values that are being compared. Instead, the horizontal scale of a histogram represents a connected series of values (such as years), which are divided into blocks of equal size (such as ten years). The height of each bar represents the number of items in that particular part of the range.

The histogram below shows the number of states that entered the United States in each of the 20-year periods from 1790 to 1990. You could also add and divide to find that an average of almost 4 states (3.7) was added during each 20-year period. But the histogram gives a more meaningful picture.

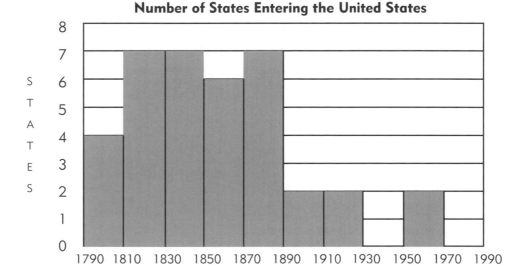

Number of States Entering the United States

Source: *World Book Encyclopedia*

Drawing a histogram requires much the same basic steps as those for drawing a bar graph.

1. Collect the facts for the various groups of numbers that you will be showing.
2. Decide what scale you will use. The largest number on the histogram must be equal to or slightly greater than the largest number in the data you are presenting. For example, if the largest number is 1,785, you would probably use a scale that counts by 200's from 0 to 1,800 or 2,000.
3. Start with zero, and mark off the scale you chose in step 2. The scale must increase at a constant rate. For example, if the scale increases by 200 for every two blocks on your graph paper, the entire scale must increase by that rate.
4. Label the vertical scale.
5. Draw each bar to the correct height, and label it. The bars should all be the same width.
6. Write a title for the histogram.
7. Write the source of the information in the lower right corner of the histogram.

CLASS PRACTICE

Refer to the following histogram to answer the questions below.

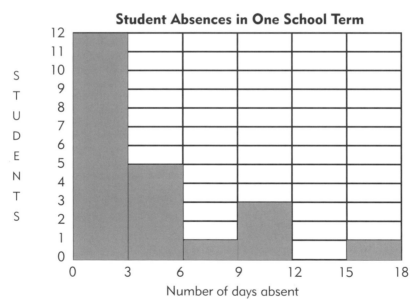

a. How many students were absent from 15 to 18 days?

b. Which range of absences includes no students?

c. Which range has the highest number of students?

d. How many students were absent more than 6 days?

e. How many students were absent 6 days or less?

f. How many students are in the class?

g. The total number of absences for the term was 99. What was the average number of days each student was absent? (Compute with your answer to f above.) Note that your answer does not give as good a picture as the histogram does.

WRITTEN EXERCISES

A. *Refer to the following histogram to answer the questions below.*

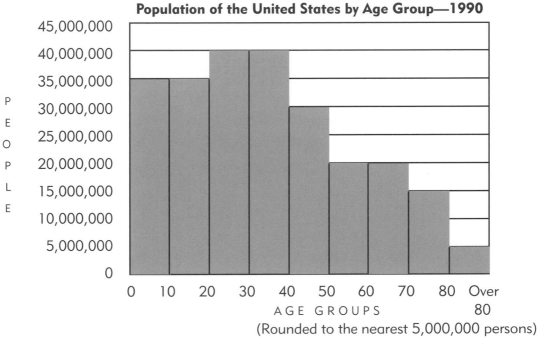

Population of the United States by Age Group—1990

AGE GROUPS
(Rounded to the nearest 5,000,000 persons)
Source: *U.S. Bureau of Census*

1. How many people in the United States were ten years old and younger?
2. How many people in the United States were over 80 years old?
3. There were 30,000,000 people in which age bracket?
4. How many people were from 11 to 20 years old?
5. How many people were 30 years old and younger?
6. How many people were over 30 years old?

B. *Prepare a histogram for each of these sets of information.*

7. The students received the following percent grades on a recent test: 60% to 69%, 1; 70% to 79%, 3; 80% to 89%, 8; 90% to 100%, 5. You do not need to give a source for this data.

8. The number of cities in the United States whose population passed 500,000 during the following periods are as follows: 1801 to 1850, 1; 1851 to 1900, 5; 1901 to 1950, 12; and 1951 to 1990, 12. The source for this information is the *1995 World Almanac*.

REVIEW EXERCISES

C. *Solve these reading problems.*

9. One year the total rainfall for a community was 14 inches. The next year the rainfall was 80 percent as much. What was the rainfall the second year?

10. If the sales tax rate is 6% and a tax of $6.42 is paid, what is the amount of the purchase?

11. A 2,000-pound batch of feed includes 1,220 pounds of ground ear corn. The ground corn is what percent of the total mix?

12. A family's monthly income is $1,250, of which 24% is used to pay rent. What is the monthly rent payment?

13. A family has an annual income of $18,000. If $9\frac{1}{2}$% of that amount is spent on real estate taxes, how much are those taxes?

14. In 1990, about $1\frac{1}{5}$% of the United States population was over age 85. If a city has 10,000 residents and $1\frac{1}{5}$% of them are over age 85, how many people is that?

D. *Solve these problems mentally by first changing the percents to fractions.* (Lesson 91)

15. 50% of 90

16. 25% of 40

17. 20% of 45

18. $66\frac{2}{3}$% of 33

19. $12\frac{1}{2}$% of 40

20. $37\frac{1}{2}$% of 48

21. 15 is _____% of 25

22. 25 is _____% of 40

23. 6 is 25% of _____

24. 9 is $33\frac{1}{3}$% of _____

E. *Solve these percentage problems.* (Lesson 85)

25. $4\frac{1}{2}$% of 28

26. $3\frac{3}{4}$% of 85

27. $4\frac{1}{8}$% of 43

28. $2\frac{5}{8}$% of 76

94. Chapter 7 Review

A. Change these percents to whole or mixed numbers. *(Lesson 83)*

1. 171%
2. 140%
3. 500%
4. 625%

B. Find the new price after each increase or decrease. Round to the nearest cent. *(Lesson 84)*

5. $15.00 decreased by 8%
6. $37.00 increased by 11%
7. $14.95 increased by 24%
8. $17.98 decreased by 19%
9. $17.47 increased by 28%
10. $63.22 decreased by 88%
11. $57.83 decreased by 30%
12. $77.82 increased by 17%

C. Change these percents to decimals. *(Lesson 85)*

13. $\frac{3}{10}$%
14. $\frac{3}{4}$ %
15. $18\frac{3}{5}$ %
16. $22\frac{3}{8}$ %

D. Solve these percent problems. *(Lessons 83–88)*

17. 175% of 40
18. 130% of 80
19. 210% of 110
20. 462% of 65
21. $\frac{1}{2}$ % of 87
22. $\frac{4}{5}$ % of 430
23. $\frac{3}{4}$ % of 180
24. $\frac{9}{10}$% of 95
25. $2\frac{3}{4}$ % of 215
26. $3\frac{1}{2}$ % of 450
27. $7\frac{3}{5}$ % of 320
28. $6\frac{7}{10}$% of 75
29. $75\frac{1}{2}$ % of 90
30. 5 is ____ % of 25
31. 9 is ____% of 75
32. 18 is ____% of 40

33. $P = 32$
$R = 40\%$
$B = $ ____

34. $P = 24$
$R = 30\%$
$B = $ ____

35. $P = 36$
$R = 48\%$
$B = $ ____

36. $P = 39$
$R = 75\%$
$B = $ ____

37. $R = 24\%$
$P = 18$
$B = $ ____

38. $R = 55\%$
$P = 88$
$B = $ ____

39. 27 is 45% of _____

40. 16 is _____% of 125

41. $B = 42$
$R = 28\%$
$P =$ _____

42. $B = 75$
$P = 33$
$R =$ _____

E. Find the missing parts in these commission problems. *(Lesson 89)*

43. $s = \$650$
$r = 6\%$
$c =$ _____

44. $s = \$775$
$r = 7\%$
$c =$ _____

45. $s = \$543.99$
$r = 9\%$
$c =$ _____

46. $s = \$275$
$c = \$19.25$
$r =$ _____

47. $s = \$650$
$c = \$78$
$r =$ _____

48. $s = \$375$
$c = \$30$
$r =$ _____

49. $r = 8\%$
$c = \$30$
$s =$ _____

50. $r = 12\%$
$c = \$15.36$
$s =$ _____

51. $r = 9\%$
$c = \$33.75$
$s =$ _____

52. $s = \$670$
$r = 4\frac{1}{2}\%$
$c =$ _____

F. Find the rate of increase or decrease. Round your answers to the nearest whole percent. *(Lesson 90)*

	Original Price	New Price		Original Price	New Price
53.	$15.00	$18.00	**54.**	$46.00	$49.68
55.	$22.00	$17.00	**56.**	$36.00	$33.00

G. Solve these problems mentally by first changing the rates to fractions. *(Lesson 91)*

57. 50% of 50

58. $33\frac{1}{3}\%$ of 39

59. $62\frac{1}{2}\%$ of 64

60. 60% of 45

61. 19 is 50% of _____

62. 9 is 25% of _____

63. 7 is $33\frac{1}{3}\%$ of _____

64. 11 is $12\frac{1}{2}\%$ of _____

65. 12 is _____% of 48

66. 10 is _____% of 80

67. 6 is _____% of 9

68. 5 is _____% of 20

H. Refer to this histogram to answer the following questions. *(Lesson 93)*

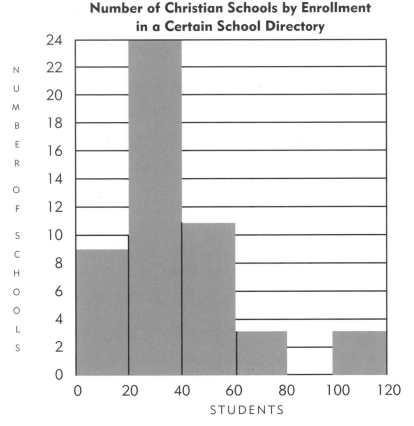

Number of Christian Schools by Enrollment in a Certain School Directory

69. Which size school occurs most frequently in this school directory?

70. How many schools have 20 students or less?

71. How many schools have 60 students or less?

72. How many schools have more than 60 students?

I. Prepare a histogram for each set of facts. *(Lesson 93)*

73. The students received the following percent grades on a recent homework assignment: 61% to 70%, 1; 71% to 80%, 3; 81% to 90%, 9; 91% to 100%, 7. You do not need to give a source for this data.

74. The areas of the provinces of Canada are listed below.

Square Miles	Number of Provinces
1 to 100,000	3
100,001 to 200,000	1
200,001 to 300,000	3
300,001 to 400,000	1
400,001 to 500,000	1
500,001 to 600,000	1

Source: *World Book Encyclopedia*

J. Solve these reading problems.

75. There were 125 seeds in a small packet. If 95% of them germinate, how many is that? Round your answer to the next lower whole number.

76. One day 114 students were present at school. This was 95% of all the students. How many students attend the school?

77. On the Stoltzfus farm, the average yield of corn was 140 bushels per acre one year and 160 bushels per acre the next year. What was the rate of increase? Round your answer to the nearest whole percent.

78. One year Mother froze 125 quarts of sweet corn. The following year she froze 115 quarts. To the nearest whole percent, what was the rate of decrease?

79. One year the average corn yield on the Landis farm was 155 bushels per acre. The selling price was $2.50 per bushel. The shelling cost was $20 per acre, and other costs were $225 per acre. What was the profit per acre?

80. Father bought 10 acres of standing corn from a neighbor and made silage out of it. The corn yielded 18 tons of silage per acre, for which Father paid $18.00 per ton. The cost of harvesting was $60.00 per hour, and the harvester cut 2 acres of corn per hour. What was the total cost of the silage?

95. Chapter 7 Test

Chapter 8

Money and Banking

Wherefore, brethren, look ye out among you seven men of honest report, full of the Holy Ghost and wisdom, whom we may appoint over this business.

(Acts 6:3)

96. Calculating Profit and Loss

God has commanded that everyone should work. Fathers work both to provide for their families and to share with others. The money earned from operating a business or a farm is called **profit**.

For a business or farm to operate, it needs to receive money for the work it does or the product it sells. This money is called **income**. Businesses such as repair shops earn most of their income through the services they perform. Those such as grocery stores and lumber companies earn their income by buying and selling products.

Not all the money that a business or farm receives is profit. Usually some money must be spent in order to generate that profit. The funds that are spent in operating a business are called **expenses**.

Profit is what a business has remaining after its expenses are paid. Thus profit equals the income of a business minus its expenses.

$$profit \ = \ income \ - \ expenses$$

When a business spends more money than it receives, it is said to have a **loss**. Stated another way, a business loses money when its expenses exceed its income. To determine the amount of the loss, subtract the income from the expenses.

$$loss \ = \ expenses \ - \ income$$

Example A

One week, the Brubaker Tire Shop had $1,200 income and $750 in expenses. What was the profit or loss? Because income was greater than expenses, the business earned a profit.

$$profit = income - expenses$$
$$profit = \$1,200 - 750$$
$$profit = \$450$$

Example B

Another week, the Brubaker Tire Shop had $900 income and $1,300 in expenses. What was the profit or loss? Because expenses were greater than income, the business had a loss.

$$loss = expenses - income$$
$$loss = \$1,300 - 900$$
$$loss = \$400$$

Income, expenses, and profit are directly related to each other. Expenses are equal to income minus profit (Example C). Income is equal to expenses plus profit (Example D).

Example C

If the Brubaker Tire Shop had $1,100 income one week and a profit of $425, what were the expenses?

expenses = income − profit
expenses = $1,100 − 425
expenses = $675

Example D

If the Brubaker Tire Shop had $400 profit one week and total expenses of $815, what was the income?

income = expenses + profit
income = $815 + 400
income = $1,215

CLASS PRACTICE

Find the missing amounts.

	Income	*Expense*	*Profit*		*Income*	*Expense*	*Profit*
a.	$800	$300	____	b.	$775	$445	____
c.	$765	$215	____	d.	$395	$263	____

	Income	*Expense*	*Loss*		*Income*	*Expense*	*Loss*
e.	$560	$640	____	f.	$775	$960	____

WRITTEN EXERCISES

A. *Find the profit.*

	Income	*Expense*	*Profit*		*Income*	*Expense*	*Profit*
1.	$150	$45	____	2.	$300	$145	____
3.	$650	$275	____	4.	$745	$730	____
5.	$3,150	$2,678	____	6.	$4,087	$2,996	____

B. *Find the loss.*

	Income	*Expense*	*Loss*		*Income*	*Expense*	*Loss*
7.	$125	$175	____	8.	$695	$730	____
9.	$725	$815	____	10.	$785	$960	____
11.	$995	$1,315	____	12.	$1,875	$2,695	____

C. *Find the profit or loss. Write* profit *or* loss *after each answer.*

	Income	Expense	Profit or Loss		Income	Expense	Profit or Loss
13.	$475	$385	____	14.	$785	$935	____
15.	$750	$860	____	16.	$935	$775	____
17.	$2,450	$3,160	____	18.	$7,325	$6,675	____

D. *Find the missing parts.*

	Income	Expense	Profit		Income	Expense	Profit
19.	$455	$375	____	20.	$785	____	$250
21.	____	$395	$225	22.	$975	$689	____
23.	$7,475	____	$338	24.	____	$2,565	$988

E. *Solve these reading problems.*

25. Jeffrey's father paid $125 for a calf. During the next six months, the calf ate $280 worth of feed. Once when the calf was sick, Jeffrey's father paid $35 to the veterinarian for medication and services. The calf was sold for $470. What was the profit?

26. Jeffrey helped his father build bluebird houses during the winter. To make 15 birdhouses, Father paid $25.00 for lumber, $1.75 for hardware, and $3.25 for stain. The birdhouses sold for $6.50 each. What was the profit?

27. During the summer months, the Bylers sell baked goods at the end of their lane. One summer their sales totaled $127.25. Father calculated that their profit was $35.75. What were their expenses?

28. The following summer, the Bylers had a profit of $42.15 and expenses of $115.62. What were their total sales that summer?

29. A local hardware dealer earns 8% profit on his sales. If he earns $4.80 on a wheelbarrow, what is the selling price of the wheelbarrow?

30. The Oak Dale Grocery Store earns 3% profit on the items sold. If the profit on a gallon of milk is $0.072, what is the selling price?

REVIEW EXERCISES

F. Solve these percent problems mentally. *(Lesson 91)*

31. 25% of 32

32. $87\frac{1}{2}$ % of 16

33. 10 is ____% of 30

34. 20 is ____% of 32

35. 15 is $33\frac{1}{3}$ % of ____

36. 12 is 20% of ____

G. Find the base in each problem. *(Lesson 87)*

37. $R = 12\%$
$P = 15$
$B =$ ____

38. $R = 40\%$
$P = 38$
$B =$ ____

39. $R = 8\%$
$P = 10$
$B =$ ____

40. $R = 5\%$
$P = 16$
$B =$ ____

H. Express these fractions as decimals. Calculate until you can identify the repeating digits, and draw a bar over those digits. *(Lesson 57)*

41. $\frac{7}{12}$

42. $\frac{9}{11}$

I. Change these English measures. *(Lesson 28)*

43. 15 sq. yd. = ____ sq. ft.

44. 15 sq. mi. = ____ a.

97. Profit and Loss as a Percent of Sales

Businesses often express their profit as a percent of the selling price. Knowing this rate helps a businessman compare the efficiency of his business with its efficiency in other years. For example, if the profit of a business was 8% of sales last year but only 3% of sales this year, the businessman needs to be concerned. His sales may actually have increased this year over last year, but his percent of profit has decreased. This businessman will likely examine his expenses to see which ones can be cut.

Knowing the percent that profit is of sales also helps in comparing the profitability of a business with that of other businesses of the same type. Books are published that give these rates for many kinds of businesses. As a businessman compares his rate of profit with that of comparable businesses, he may find ways to improve his profitability.

Finding the percent of profit means finding what percent one number is of another, as you learned in Lesson 86. In this lesson, you will round the rate to the nearest whole percent. The steps are shown below.

Step 1: Calculate the profit or loss.

Step 2: Divide the profit or loss by the total sales. If the division does not come out evenly, divide to the thousandths' place and round the answer to the nearest hundredth.

Step 3: Change the answer to a percent by moving the decimal point two places to the right and adding a percent sign.

Example A	Example B
Uncle Daniel calculates that he earns $8.50 profit when he installs a pickup truck tire for $75.00. What percent is his profit of the sale?	Uncle Daniel sold a tire that was faulty. He replaced the tire free of charge. He had expenses of $95.00 on a sale of $65.00. What percent was the loss of this sale?

Example A

Step 1: profit = $8.50

Step 2:
$$\begin{array}{r} 0.113 \\ \$75\overline{)\$8.500} \\ \underline{75} \\ 100 \\ \underline{75} \\ 250 \\ \underline{225} \\ 25 \end{array}$$
= 0.11 to nearest hundredth

Step 3: 0.11 = 11% profit

Example B

Step 1: loss = $95.00 – $65.00
loss = $30.00

Step 2:
$$\begin{array}{r} 0.461 \\ \$65\overline{)\$30.000} \\ \underline{260} \\ 400 \\ \underline{390} \\ 100 \\ \underline{65} \\ 35 \end{array}$$
= 0.46 to nearest hundredth

Step 3: 0.46 = 46% loss

CLASS PRACTICE

Find the percent of profit or loss on these sales.

	Sales	Profit or Loss	Percent of Sales		Sales	Profit or Loss	Percent of Sales
a.	$450	$63	____	b.	$150	$12	____
c.	$325	$27	____	d.	$260	$28	____

WRITTEN EXERCISES

A. Find the percent of profit or loss on these sales. All the answers are whole percents.

	Sales	Profit or Loss	Percent of Sales		Sales	Profit or Loss	Percent of Sales
1.	$750	$75	____	2.	$500	$40	____
3.	$425	$34	____	4.	$700	$42	____
5.	$675	$81	____	6.	$150	$3	____
7.	$900	$72	____	8.	$450	$63	____

B. Find the percent of profit or loss on these sales. Round the answers to the nearest whole percent.

	Sales	Profit or Loss	Percent of Sales		Sales	Profit or Loss	Percent of Sales
9.	$750	$47	____	10.	$325	$68	____
11.	$275	$30	____	12.	$650	$35	____
13.	$950	$85	____	14.	$675	$85	____
15.	$550	$65	____	16.	$325	$22	____

C. Find the profit or loss in each case. Then find what percent the profit or loss is of the selling price (income). Round your answers to the nearest whole percent and include the label *profit* or *loss*.

	Income	Expenses		Income	Expenses
17.	$450	$525	18.	$700	$550
19.	$850	$690	20.	$450	$595

D. Solve these reading problems.

21. The Birch Valley Stove Company makes a profit of $63 on each wood stove sold for $525. What is the rate of profit from the sale of one such wood stove?

22. Uncle Willis calculated that he earned a profit of $8.00 per hog on one group he raised. The hogs sold for $118 each. What was the rate of profit?

23. On another group of hogs that Uncle Willis raised, he calculated that he had invested $104.00 in each hog. The hogs sold for an average of $99.00 each. What was his rate of loss?

24. Father bought a damaged car for $2,000 and repaired it during the winter months. He spent $850 for repairs and sold the car for $3,200. What was his rate of profit?

25. The Bowmans raise produce to sell at a roadside stand. One week they sold 60% of their watermelons for $3.50 each and the rest for $2.50 each. If they sold 70 watermelons in all, what were the total receipts?

REVIEW EXERCISES

E. Find the missing parts of these percent problems. *(Lesson 88)*

26. $B = 80$
    $R = 6\%$
    $P = $ _____

27. $R = 8\%$
    $P = \$36$
    $B = $ _____

28. $B = \$400$
    $P = \$356$
    $R = $ _____

29. $B = 87.6$
    $R = 4\frac{1}{2}\%$
    $P = $ _____

F. Solve these addition problems. *(Lesson 58)*

30. $4.3 + 6 + 0.05609 + 3.771$

31. $5 + 163 + 0.06084 + 4.00039$

G. Change these measures. *(Lesson 29)*

32. $15\frac{1}{2}$ min. = _____ sec.

33. 17 decades = _____ yr.

34. 27 wk. = _____ days

35. 4,400 yr. = _____ millennia

Whatsoever thy hand findeth to do,
do it with thy might.
Ecclesiastes 9:10

98. Calculating Sales Tax

Governments receive most of their operating funds by taxation. There are many kinds of taxes. Some are based on income, some on the value of real estate, and some on the amount of sales.

In the United States, many state governments and some local governments charge a tax on sales at a given rate of the sale. Usually this sales tax is charged on all sales except those items that are specifically exempt, such as food or clothing.

Finding the amount of sales tax on a specific sale means finding a percentage of a number (Lesson 73). The steps are shown below. Note that Step 3 is needed only when finding the total amount of the sale, including sales tax.

1. Express the rate as a decimal.
2. Multiply the sale by the rate, and round the answer to the nearest cent.
3. Add the sales tax to the amount of the sale.

Example A	**Example B**
Philip bought a notebook for $7.95. The notebook was subject to a $5\frac{1}{2}\%$ sales tax. What was the sales tax on the notebook?	Father bought an atlas for $5.95. If the atlas was a taxable item and the tax rate was 6%, how much did Father pay in all?
Step 1: $5\frac{1}{2}\% = 0.055$	Step 1: $6\% = 0.06$

Step 2: $7.95
  $\times 0.055$
  $0.43725 = 0.44 to the
  nearest cent
	Step 2: $5.95
	  $\times 0.06$
	  $0.357 = 0.36 to the
	  nearest cent

Step 3: (Not needed)	Step 3: $5.95
	  $+ 0.36$
	  $6.31

CLASS PRACTICE

Find the sales tax and the total cost of each sale.

	Amount of Sale	Tax Rate		Amount of Sale	Tax Rate
a.	$4.65	5%	b.	$15.75	7%
c.	$12.95	4%	d.	$18.95	$5\frac{1}{2}\%$

WRITTEN EXERCISES

A. *Find the sales tax on each sale.*

Amount of Sale	Tax Rate		Amount of Sale	Tax Rate
1. $2.75	6%	2.	$13.75	7%
3. $14.25	4%	4.	$29.95	3%
5. $179.89	7%	6.	$225.69	4%
7. $5,500.00	6%	8.	$8,995.00	7%
9. $455.00	$8\frac{1}{4}$%	10.	$650.00	$5\frac{1}{2}$%

B. *Find the total amount of each sale, including sales tax.*

Amount of Sale	Tax Rate		Amount of Sale	Tax Rate
11. $25.50	6%	12.	$75.25	3%
13. $35.00	2%	14.	$85.50	4%
15. $550.00	6%	16.	$950.00	7%
17. $6,200.00	5%	18.	$7,800.00	4%
19. $750.00	$6\frac{1}{4}$%	20.	$850.00	$7\frac{1}{4}$%

C. *Solve these reading problems.*

21. Martha bought a pack of pencils for $0.84 and a tablet for $1.19. Find the sales tax if both items are taxable at the rate of 4%.

22. Mildred purchased a Bible for $15.95 and a motto for $5.95. The sales tax rate in her state is 6%. How much sales tax must she pay if the Bible is exempt from sales tax?

23. Sandra bought dress material for $12.60 and quilting material for $25.00. The sales tax rate is $5\frac{1}{2}$%. What was Sandra's total bill if only the quilting material was taxable?

24. The Martins bought a new garden tiller for $850 and an attachment for $75. The sales tax rate in their state was $6\frac{1}{4}$%. What was the total cost of the tiller and the attachment including sales tax?

25. The cost and other expenses of the tiller came to a total of $770. If the selling price was $850, what was the rate of profit?

26. A seed corn salesman earned $25.00 on a sale. This was 5% of the selling price. What was the amount of the sale?

REVIEW EXERCISES

D. Find the profit or loss on these sales. Write profit **or** loss **after each answer.** *(Lesson 96)*

	Income	Expense		Income	Expense
27.	$85.50	$97.95	**28.**	$65.50	$43.95
29.	$125.50	$85.60	**30.**	$99.75	$135.99

E. Find the rate of profit or loss on these sales. *(Lesson 97)*

31.	sale: $60	profit: $9	**32.**	sale: $85	loss: $12
33.	sale: $135	loss: $15	**34.**	sale: $215	profit: $26

F. Find the missing parts of these commission problems. *(Lesson 89)*

	Sale	Rate	Comission		Sale	Rate	Comission
35.	$750	6%	____	**36.**	$80	____	$12

G. Solve each problem mentally by moving the decimal point. *(Lesson 59)*

37. $4.215 \div 100$ **38.** $47.56 \times 1,000$

H. Find the time in the following time zones if it is 12:00 noon in the Central Time Zone. *(Lesson 30)*

39. Hawaii–Aleutian Time Zone   **40.** Newfoundland Time Zone

And Jesus answering said unto them, "Render to Caesar the things that are Caesar's, and to God the things that are God's."

Mark 12:17

99. Calculating Interest

When a family borrows a house to live in, they pay rent to the owner of the house. When a farmer borrows land to farm, he pays rent to the owner of the land. When a person borrows money, he usually pays the lender for the use of the money. The money he pays is called interest.

Finding the Amount of Interest

To calculate interest, the following three factors must be known.

Principal—The amount of money borrowed.

Rate—The percent used to compute interest, with the principal as the base.

Time—The length of time for which the money is borrowed, usually expressed in years. These three factors are multiplied to find the amount of interest.

> To find the amount of interest, multiply the principal, the rate, and the time. The formula is as follows:
>
> interest = principal × rate × time, or $i = prt$

Example A

Father borrowed $6,000 at 5% interest. He paid interest one year later. How much was the interest?

interest = principal × rate × time
interest = $6,000 × 0.05 × 1

$$\begin{array}{ll} \$6,000 & \text{principal} \\ \underline{\hspace{0.3em}0.05} & \text{rate} \\ \$300.00 & \\ \underline{\times\ 1} & \text{time} \\ \$300.00 & \end{array}$$

(The last multiplication is not needed when the time is 1 year.)

Example B

Uncle David borrowed $8,000 for 3 years. He paid 6% interest at the end of each year. How much interest did Uncle David pay in three years?

$i = prt$
$i = \$8,000 × 0.06 × 3$

$$\begin{array}{ll} \$8,000 & \text{principal} \\ \underline{\hspace{0.3em}0.06} & \text{rate} \\ \$480.00 & \\ \underline{\times\ 3} & \text{time} \\ \$1,440.00 & \end{array}$$

Finding the Rate of Interest

To find the rate of interest when the principal and the annual interest are known, divide the annual interest by the principal.

Example C   Brother Ernest paid Brother David $400 interest per year on a business loan of $8,000. What was the rate of interest?

$$\text{rate} = \frac{\text{interest}}{\text{principal}} \quad \text{or} \quad r = \frac{i}{p} \qquad \frac{400}{8,000} = 0.05 = 5\%$$

Finding the principal

To find the principal when the annual interest and the rate are known, divide the annual interest by the rate.

Example D   Brother Leonard paid Brother Mark $200 interest for one year at a rate of 4%. What was the principal?

$$\text{principal} = \frac{\text{interest}}{\text{rate}} \quad \text{or} \quad p = \frac{i}{r} \quad \frac{200}{0.04} = \$5,000$$

CLASS PRACTICE

Find the interest.

	p	r	t
a.	$5,000	5%	1 year
c.	$8,000	$5\frac{1}{2}$%	5 years

	p	r	t
b.	$3,500	6%	2 years
d.	$6,000	$5\frac{1}{4}$%	3 years

Find the rate or the principal.

e. annual interest = $500
   principal = $12,500
   rate = _____

f. annual interest = $600
   rate = 8%
   principal = _____

WRITTEN EXERCISES

A. Find the interest.

	p	r	t
1.	$3,000	7%	1 year
3.	$5,000	5%	2 years
5.	$7,500	3%	3 years
7.	$3,800	6%	5 years
9.	$6,000	$5\frac{1}{2}$%	3 years

	p	r	t
2.	$3,500	6%	1 year
4.	$4,500	4%	2 years
6.	$9,250	4%	4 years
8.	$10,500	5%	7 years
10.	$8,000	$5\frac{1}{4}$%	4 years

B. Use the annual interest and the principal to find the rate.

	i	p
11.	$300	$6,000
13.	$700	$17,500
15.	$200	$2,500

	i	p
12.	$800	$20,000
14.	$600	$7,500
16.	$300	$5,000

C. Use the annual interest and the rate to find the principal.

	i	r
17.	$500	8%
19.	$1,200	6%
21.	$450	5%

	i	r
18.	$200	4%
20.	$720	9%
22.	$900	8%

D. Solve these reading problems.

23. Father borrowed $8,000 from Grandfather to buy a used tractor. He paid 3% interest on the loan. How much was the interest for one year?

24. When Brother Sanford's barn burned down, Father lent him $15,000 without charging him interest. How much interest could the $15,000 have earned in one year at $3\frac{1}{2}$%?

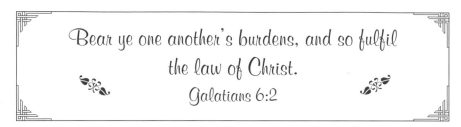

Bear ye one another's burdens, and so fulfil
the law of Christ.
Galatians 6:2

25. How much money must be invested to earn $50.00 interest per year if the interest rate is 4%?

26. Father paid $125 as one year's interest on a loan of $2,500. What was the rate of interest?

27. Father lent $500 to Brother David at the beginning of the year. After one year, the interest and the principal together totaled $520. What was the rate of interest?

28. Father went to Philadelphia and bought a backhoe for $6,500. The rate of sales tax there was 7%. Later he bought a trailer for the backhoe and paid $5,000 plus 6% Pennsylvania sales tax. What was the total sales tax that Father paid?

REVIEW EXERCISES

E. Find the sales tax on these sales. (Lesson 98)

29. sale: $25.50
rate: $5\frac{1}{2}$%

30. sale: $225.00
rate: $8\frac{1}{4}$%

F. Express the profit or loss as a percent of the sales. Round the answer to the nearest whole percent. (Lesson 97)

	Sale	Profit or Loss		Sale	Profit or Loss
31.	$750	$50	**32.**	$450	$80
33.	$800	$65	**34.**	$750	$90

G. Find the percent of increase or decrease. Label your answers increase or decrease. (Lesson 90)

	Original Price	New Price		Original Price	New Price
35.	$30	$34	**36.**	$45	$40

H. Find the missing parts. (Lesson 32)

	Time	Rate	Distance		Time	Rate	Distance
37.	3 hr.	49 m.p.h.	_____	**38.**	5 hr.	_____	320 mi.

100. Finding Interest for Part of a Year

An interest rate like 8% means 8% is paid on a principal that is borrowed for a whole year. But since money is often borrowed for periods other than exact years, it is necessary to calculate interest for part years. This lesson shows two ways of doing this.

By the Month

When the time for a loan is given in months, the following steps are used to calculate the interest. Examples A and B illustrate these steps.

1. Write a fraction to express the time as part of a year. Use the number of months as the numerator and 12 as the denominator.

2. Reduce the fraction if it is not in lowest terms. But if it is an improper fraction, do not change it to a mixed number.

3. Multiply the principal by the rate. This answer is the interest for a whole year.

4. Multiply the answer found in step 3 by the fraction from steps 1 and 2. Round the answer to the nearest cent.

Example A	Example B
Find the interest on $600 for 5 months at a rate of 7%.	Find the interest on $500 for 18 months at a rate of 6%.
1. 5 months = $\frac{5}{12}$ year	1. 18 months = $\frac{18}{12}$
2. $\frac{5}{12}$ is in lowest terms.	2. $\frac{18}{12} = \frac{3}{2}$
3. $600 \times 0.07 = $42	3. $500 \times 0.06 = $30
4. $\frac{\overset{7}{\cancel{42}}}{1} \times \frac{5}{\underset{2}{\cancel{12}}} = \frac{35}{2} = 17.50	4. $\frac{\overset{15}{\cancel{30}}}{1} \times \frac{3}{\underset{1}{\cancel{2}}} = 45

By the Day

The time of a loan may be given in days rather than months. As with months, the days need to be expressed as part of a year.

In calculating interest, businessmen often consider a year as being equal to 360 days rather than 365 or 366 days. This simplifies calculations because 360 is a multiple of ten and it can be divided by many factors. A year of 360 days is called a business year.

The number 360 becomes the denominator of the fraction showing part of a year. This fraction can often be reduced. The following steps and examples show how to find interest for a given number of days, based on a 360-day business year.

1. Write a fraction to express the time as part of a year. Use the number of days as the numerator and 360 as the denominator.

2. Reduce the fraction if it is not in lowest terms. (In this lesson, all the fractions can be reduced.)

3. Multiply the principal by the rate. This answer is the interest for a whole year.
4. Multiply the answer found in step 3 by the fraction from steps 1 and 2. Round the answer to the nearest cent.

Example C	**Example D**
Find the interest on $800 for 60 days at 6%.	Find the interest on $900 for 150 days at 5%.
1. 60 days = $\frac{60}{360}$ year	1. 150 days = $\frac{150}{360}$
2. $\frac{60}{360} = \frac{1}{6}$	2. $\frac{150}{360} = \frac{5}{12}$
3. $800 × 0.06 = $48	3. $900 × 0.05 = $45
4. $\frac{\overset{8}{\cancel{48}}}{1} × \frac{1}{\underset{1}{\cancel{6}}} = \frac{8}{1} = \$8.00$	4. $\frac{\overset{15}{45}}{1} × \frac{5}{\underset{4}{\cancel{12}}} = \frac{75}{4} = \$18.75$

CLASS PRACTICE

Find the interest.

	p	r	t		p	r	t
a.	$800	7%	11 months	b.	$900	5%	9 months
c.	$750	6%	120 days	d.	$1,000	9%	200 days

WRITTEN EXERCISES

A. *Find the interest.*

	p	r	t		p	r	t
1.	$300	7%	1 year	2.	$500	6%	3 years
3.	$900	9%	4 years	4.	$900	7%	6 years
5.	$800	$4\frac{3}{4}$%	6 years	6.	$500	$5\frac{1}{4}$%	7 years
7.	$2,000	7%	4 years	8.	$4,500	9%	5 years
9.	$100	4%	3 months	10.	$300	6%	1 month
11.	$500	5%	10 months	12.	$700	9%	4 months
13.	$800	$5\frac{1}{2}$%	6 months	14.	$575	$5\frac{1}{4}$%	8 months
15.	$1,200	3%	30 months	16.	$3,000	12%	20 months

B. *Express the time as part of a year to solve these problems. Remember to use a 360-day year.*

	p	r	t		p	r	t
17.	$500	6%	60 days	18.	$600	8%	180 days
19.	$600	4%	300 days	20.	$350	5%	10 days
21.	$450	6%	45 days	22.	$700	9%	90 days
23.	$3,000	11%	75 days	24.	$4,500	12%	120 days

C. Solve these reading problems.

25. Uncle David borrowed $2,000 for $\frac{1}{2}$ year at 5% interest. What was the interest on that amount?

26. Father borrowed $25,000 when he built an addition to the chicken house. He pays interest every three months at a rate of 8%. How much interest does he pay in three months?

27. Brother Ronald has a business of selling and repairing lawn mowers. He can order a shipment of mowers without paying for them immediately, but there is a charge of 9% interest for this service. How much interest does he pay on $8,000 for 75 days?

28. The Masts are selling their house to move to a new area of church outreach. They purchased another house before their first one was sold. The bank lent them $110,000 for 45 days until they received the money for their first house. At a rate of 9%, how much interest did they need to pay?

29. The Masts bought their house five years ago for $95,000. They sold it for 15% more than they paid for it. What was the selling price?

30. The price for a gallon of milk increased by 8% over an earlier price of $2.15. What was the new price?

REVIEW EXERCISES

D. Find the amount of sales tax. *(Lesson 98)*

31. sale: $655
rate: 6%

32. sale $722.91
rate: 5%

E. Find the profit or loss. Write *profit* or *loss* **after each answer.** *(Lesson 96)*

33. income: $375

expenses: $452

34. income: $715

expenses: $321

F. Solve these problems mentally by changing the percents or decimals to fractions. *(Lessons 61, 91)*

35. 0.75 of 48

36. 0.9 of 50

37. 25% of 36

38. 80% of 45

39. 15 is 25% of _____

40. 30 is $12\frac{1}{2}$% of _____

G. Find the new price after each increase or decrease. *(Lesson 84)*

Original Price	Rate of Change		Original Price	Rate of Change
41. $35.00	12% increase		**42.** $45.00	16% decrease

101. Working With Compound Interest

In the last two lessons you worked with **simple interest**, which is paid to the lender as soon as it is due. Simple interest is not added to the principal, so the principal remains the same.

When money is kept in a savings account, the bank usually does not pay interest directly to the account holder each time it is due. Instead, the interest is added to the balance in the account. The interest becomes part of the principal; and the next time interest is paid, it is calculated on the new principal. Interest paid on the original principal plus interest that was added previously is called **compound interest**.

Compound interest accumulates more rapidly than simple interest paid at the same rate. In Example A, the first column shows what happens when simple interest is paid. The person would receive $50 each **interest period**, which is one year in this case. In five years, the total interest would be $250.00. The second column shows compound interest, with the interest for each period being added to the account. Then the person would receive a total of $276.28 interest in five years.

Example A		
	$1,000 at 5% Simple Interest	$1,000 at 5% interest Compounded Annually
January 1, Year 1 deposit	$1,000.00	$1,000.00
December 31, Year 1	$1,050.00	$1,050.00
December 31, Year 2	$1,100.00	$1,102.50
December 31, Year 3	$1,150.00	$1,157.63
December 31, Year 4	$1,200.00	$1,215.51
December 31, Year 5	$1,250.00	$1,276.28

Calculations for compound interest are more complex than for simple interest. Because the interest is added to the account, a separate calculation is required for each interest period.

Steps for Finding Interest Compounded Annually

1. Change the interest rate to a decimal, and add it to 1. This decimal is the multiplier that will be used for each year.

2. Multiply the principal by the decimal found in step 1, and round the product to the nearest cent. This answer is the principal and interest after one year (the new balance in the account).

3. Repeat step 2 for each year that interest is being compounded. Always multiply the new balance from the previous year by the multiplier from step 1.

Example B

Suppose $700 is deposited in a savings account that pays 4% interest compounded annually. How much will be in the account after 3 years?

Step 1: 4% = 0.04 1 + 0.04 = 1.04	Step 2: $700 × 1.04 2800 700 $728.00 (new balance after 1 year)
Step 3: $728 × 1.04 2912 728 $757.12 (new balance after 2 years)	Step 3: $757.12 (repeated) × 1.04 302848 75712 $787.4048 = $787.40 (to nearest cent) after 3 years

To find the total compound interest, subtract the beginning principal from the final balance.

Example C

Find the total interest earned in Example B. $787.40
    – 700.00
    $87.40

CLASS PRACTICE

Calculate the final balance in each savings account if interest is compounded annually. Then find the total interest paid.

	p	r	t		p	r	t
a.	$100	5%	2 years	b.	$500	6%	3 years
c.	$400	4%	3 years	d.	$700	8%	4 years

WRITTEN EXERCISES

A. *Calculate the final balance in each savings account if interest is compounded annually.*

	p	r	t		p	r	t
1.	$100	6%	2 years	2.	$100	7%	2 years
3.	$200	6%	2 years	4.	$300	4%	2 years
5.	$400	8%	3 years	6.	$500	9%	3 years
7.	$200	4%	3 years	8.	$300	5%	3 years

B. The following examples show the beginning and ending amounts in various savings accounts. Find the total interest paid.

Beginning Principal	Final Balance		Beginning Principal	Final Balance
9. $500.00	$638.14	10.	$600.00	$802.94
11. $750.00	$1,063.89	12.	$775.00	$1,416.73
13. $2,550.00	$4,617.22	14.	$3,750.00	$4,224.34

C. Calculate the final balance in each savings account if the interest is compounded annually. Then find the total interest paid.

	p	r	t		p	r	t
15.	$100	4%	2 years	16.	$200	7%	2 years
17.	$500	5%	3 years	18.	$400	6%	3 years

D. Solve these reading problems.

19. Father had $800 in a savings account at 4% interest compounded annually. What was the balance at the end of 2 years?

20. Uncle Marvin opened a savings account with $1,500. The savings account bears 5% interest compounded each year. If he leaves both the principal and the interest in the account, what will be the balance at the end of three years?

21. Brother David has a savings account of $2,500 at 5% interest compounded annually. How much interest will he earn if he leaves all the interest and the principal in the account for two years?

22. When a person puts money in the bank for an extended period of time, he can place the money on a certificate of deposit. Such an account yields interest at a higher rate than for regular savings accounts. How much interest would be paid on a 3-year certificate of deposit if the principal is $4,000 and the interest rate is 6% compounded annually?

23. A certain business reported a profit of $25,000 on $600,000 of sales. What percent was the profit of the sales? Round your answer to the nearest whole percent.

24. The following year, the profit of the same business was 4% of sales. The sales for that year amounted to $590,000. What was the profit?

REVIEW EXERCISES

E. Express each profit or loss as a percent of the sales. Round to the nearest whole percent. *(Lesson 97)*

25. sales: $275　　profit: $18　　　26. sales: $425　　loss: $41

F. Solve these percent problems. *(Lesson 85)*

27. $3\frac{3}{4}\%$ of 775　　　　　　28. $27\frac{7}{10}\%$ of 475

G. Solve these division problems. *(Lessons 63)*

29. $0.6\overline{)4.215}$　　　　　　30. $0.45\overline{)1.125}$

102. Calculating Unit Prices

When we go shopping, it is not always easy to tell which product is the better buy because of differences in quantity. For example, is it cheaper to buy 14 ounces of cereal for $2.25 or 16 ounces for $2.50? The best way to compare prices like these is to calculate the **unit price** (price for one unit) of each item. A unit may be one separate piece (such as one pencil out of a dozen) or one unit of measure (such as one ounce or one yard).

In Example A below, the unit price is the price per tablet. In Example B, the unit price is the price per copy.

To find a unit price, use the following steps.

1. Divide the price of the item by the number of units in that item. If necessary, divide to the ten-thousandths' place.

2. Round the answer to the nearest tenth of a cent (thousandth of a dollar).

Example A	**Example B**
36 tablets for $11.31	50 copies of the tract *The Bible and Dress* for $2.40
Step 1: $0.3141 36)$11.3100 108 51 36 150 144 60 36 24	Step 1: $0.048 50)$2.400 200 400 400 0
Step 2: $0.3141 to the nearest tenth of a cent (thousandth of a dollar) is $0.314, or 31.4¢.	Step 2: The answer does not need to be rounded. It is exactly $0.048, or 4.8¢.

When the unit prices of two items are found, you can compare them and see which one is the better buy.

In the store, it is often not convenient to use pencil and paper to calculate unit prices. Therefore, you will find it useful to know how to calculate unit prices mentally, such as dividing by 10 or 100.

CLASS PRACTICE

Find these unit prices to the nearest tenth of a cent.

   a. 72 pens for $5.34

   b. 36 markers for $13.32

Find these unit prices mentally.

   c. 10 boxes of paper clips for $1.40

   d. 12 pencils for $1.08

WRITTEN EXERCISES

   A. *Find these unit prices mentally. Do not round the answers.*

   1. 10 pads of graph paper for $16.90

   2. 10 boxes of staples for $9.95

   3. 100 trash bags for $3.59

   4. 10 pounds of cheese for $14.90

   B. *Find the unit price for each item, to the nearest tenth of a cent.*

   5. 12 highlighters for $4.24

   6. 120 paper clamps for $7.70

   7. 36 binder clips for $1.59

   8. 36 erasers for $14.97

   9. 250 file folders for $69.80

   10. 36 tablets for $19.41

   11. 72 rolls of masking tape for $23.52

   12. 20 reams of copier paper for $65.60

   13. 12 pads of self-stick notes for $2.29

   14. 1,000 shipping envelopes for $51.49

   15. 3 lb. of onions for $0.89

   16. 12 rolls for $0.99

   17. 15 oz. of cereal for $1.99

   18. 9 oranges for $1.00

   19. 64 oz. of orange juice for $0.99

   20. 6 rolls for $0.99

   C. *Solve these reading problems.*

   21. Father paid $23.30 for the 9 books in the "God Is Good" set. What was the price per book?

   22. The Spring Mountain congregation ordered 75 subscriptions of the periodical *The Light of Life* to mail to individuals in their community. The total cost of the subscriptions was $63.75. What was the cost per subscription?

   23. The school treasurer ordered 72 dozen pencils for $78.48. What was the cost per pencil? (First express the dozens of pencils as the number of individual pencils.)

   24. The treasurer also ordered 3 cases of paper towels for $74.97. Three cases was a total of 12,000 towels. What was the cost per towel?

   25. What is the interest on $4,000 for 3 years at a rate of 4% compounded annually?

   26. Sarah Ann bought a copy of *Zion's Praises* for $10.00 plus $5\frac{1}{2}$% sales tax. What was her total bill?

REVIEW EXERCISES

D. Calculate the total amount of interest paid if it is compounded annually.
(Lesson 101)

	p	*r*	*t*			*p*	*r*	*t*
27.	$400	5%	2 years		**28.**	$500	6%	3 years

E. Calculate the simple interest on these amounts. *(Lesson 99)*

	p	*r*	*t*			*p*	*r*	*t*
29.	$1,275	7%	4 years		**30.**	$2,650	6%	5 years

F. Calculate the sales tax on these sales. *(Lesson 98)*

31. sale: $25.79
rate: 3%

32. sale: $49.75
rate: 6%

G. Solve these percent problems. *(Lesson 86)*

33. 33 is _____ % of 110

34. 48 is _____ % of 75

103. Keeping a Multicolumn Expense Record

Farmers and other businessmen need to keep records of their income and expenses for several reasons. The records enable the businessman to determine whether he is making a profit. Another reason is that both Canada and the United States, as well as many individual states and provinces, levy income taxes. Businessmen are required to keep accurate records of their income and expenses so that their income taxes can be filed properly.

One convenient way to keep records is to enter the amounts received in a cash-receipts journal and to enter the checks written in a cash-disbursements journal. This lesson deals with the cash-disbursements journal. The cash-receipts journal is a similar journal used to record income.

To understand how a cash-disbursements journal is maintained, study the example below and read the comments after the journal.

Example A

The Rustville Lawn Supply Company wrote the following checks during one week. Notice how they were entered in the cash-disbursements journal.

On February 3, check #935 for $95.75 to Rustville Supply for parts for used mowers.

On February 5, check #936 for $650.00 to Marvin Smith for rent for the building used in the business.

On February 6, check #937 for $175.68 to the North Power Company for electricity for the month of January.

On February 6, check #938 for $879.94 to Monroe Equipment for lawn mowers.

On February 7, check #939 for $125.66 to Rustville Supply for spark plugs and other mower parts.

On February 8, check #940 for $55.72 to Lewis Engines for mower engines.

RUSTVILLE LAWN SUPPLY COMPANY
Cash-Disbursements Journal for 1997

#	Date	Description	Amount	EXPENSES		
				Mowers And Parts	*Rent & Rentals*	*Electric & Phone*
935	2-3	Rustville Supply	$95.75	$95.75		
936	2-5	Marvin Smith	650.00		$650.00	
937	2-6	North Power Co.	175.68			$175.68
938	2-6	Monroe Equipment	879.94	879.94		
939	2-7	Rustville Supply	125.66	125.66		
940	2-8	Lewis Engines	55.72	55.72		
TOTALS			$1,982.75	$1,157.07	$650.00	$175.68

CHECK

Total Mowers and Parts Expenses $1,157.07
Total Rent Expense 650.00
Total Electric and Phone Expense . . . . <u>175.68</u>
Grand Total $1,982.75
(must agree with total in "Amount" column)

Notice that each time a check was written, the amount was entered in the "Amount" column. It was also entered in the correct column for that kind of expense. A dollar sign was used at the top of each column and in the "Totals" row.

At the end of the week, all the columns were totaled. Because all the check amounts are entered twice—once in the first column and once in one of the expense columns—the total of the three expense columns must equal the total in the "Amount" column. This is a way of checking the accuracy of the addition in the journal.

CLASS PRACTICE

Complete the following cash-disbursements journal, using a copy of the form below.

During the first full week of March, the following checks were written.

On March 3, check #972 for $119.71 to North Power Company for electricity.

On March 4, check #973 for $48.86 to Eastern Telephone Company for the February telephone bill.

On March 4, check #974 for $650.00 to Marvin Smith for building rent.

On March 6, check #975 for $1,978.38 to Monroe Equipment for lawn equipment.

On March 6, check #976 for $71.46 to A & K Rentals for equipment rental.

On March 7, check #977 for $89.96 to Lewis Engines for mower engine parts.

RUSTVILLE LAWN SUPPLY COMPANY
Cash-Disbursements Journal for 1997

		#	Date	Description	Amount	EXPENSES		
						Mowers and Parts	Rent & Rentals	Electric & Phone
a.								
b.								
c.								
d.								
e.								
f.								
		TOTALS			g.	h.	i.	j.

WRITTEN EXERCISES

A. *On a copy of the form below, prepare a cash disbursements journal, using the information given for the first full week in April.*

On April 7, check #991 for $650.00 to Marvin Smith for building rent.

On April 7, check #992 for $95.61 to Edison Electric.

On April 8, check #993 for $945.32 to Monroe Equipment for lawn mowers.

On April 9, check #994 for $2,864.23 to Monroe Equipment for lawn equipment.

On April 11, check #995 for $128.87 to Lewis Engines for mower engines.

On April 11, check #996 for $843.29 to Valley Mowers for mowers.

RUSTVILLE LAWN SUPPLY COMPANY
Cash-Disbursements Journal for 20—

	#	Date	Description	Amount	EXPENSES Mowers and Parts	EXPENSES Rent & Rentals	EXPENSES Electric & Phone
1.							
2.							
3.							
4.							
5.							
6.							
		TOTALS		7.	8.	9.	10.

B. *Solve these reading problems.*

11. A business office ordered 500 shipping envelopes for $18.96. What was the price per envelope to the nearest tenth of a cent?

12. The business also ordered 500 heavy-duty filing folders for $43.30. What was the unit price to the nearest tenth of a cent?

13. The Gospel of Luke and the Acts of the Apostles are both considered as having been written by Luke. These two books contain 52 of the 260 chapters in the New Testament. What percent of the chapters in the New Testament are found in these two books?

14. The Gospel of Luke and the Acts of the Apostles contain 2,158 verses. The entire New Testament contains 7,957 verses. To the nearest whole number, what percent of the verses of the New Testament are found in these two books?

15. Father borrowed $4,000 from Grandfather for two years at 3% simple interest. What is the total amount of interest and principal that Father will pay back?

16. Brother Samuel lent $15,000 to the mission board without charging interest. How much interest could the money have earned in two years at a rate of 5% compounded annually?

REVIEW EXERCISES

C. *Find the unit price for each item to the nearest tenth of a cent.* *(Lesson 102)*

17. 6 dry cell batteries for $5.25

18. 6 cassette tapes for $4.89

19. 5 macaroni dinners for $1.00

20. 3 cans of soup for $2.00

D. *Find the interest on these accounts if it is compounded annually.* *(Lesson 101)*

	p	r	t		p	r	t
21.	$500	4%	3 years	22.	$400	6%	2 years

E. *Calculate the simple interest on these amounts.* *(Lesson 99)*

	p	r	t		p	r	t
23.	$875.00	7%	6 years	24.	$985.00	9%	3 years

F. *Find the base in each problem.* *(Lesson 87)*

25. 18 is 72% of _____

26. 20 is 80% of _____

27. 27 is 45% of _____

28. 36 is 90% of _____

104. Reading Problems: More Multistep Problems

Lesson 92 dealt specifically with reading problems that require more than one step. This lesson provides more practice in working with problems of this kind.

When solving a reading problem, remember to use the following steps. There is no substitute for thoroughly reading and understanding the problem.

Step 1: Read the problem carefully. Note the facts that are given and the question that is asked.

Step 2: Look for clue words that indicate whether addition, subtraction, multiplication, or division are to be used.

Step 3: Solve the problem one step at a time.

Step 4: Check your answer to make sure it is logical.

CLASS PRACTICE

Solve these reading problems.

a. One year Brother John's fields produced at the following average rates: wheat—54 bushels per acre from 7.5 acres; barley—84 bushels per acre from 9.25 acres; and oats—95 bushels per acre from 10.6 acres. How much grain did he harvest from the three fields together?

b. From a 10.5-acre corn field, Brother Nelson harvested an average of 110 bushels of shelled corn per acre. He sold 40% of the corn at $2.25 per bushel. He later sold the remainder at $2.45 per bushel. What were his total receipts for the corn from this field?

c. Brother Dwight operates a sawmill. One year he had $175,600 in income. He had expenses totaling $148,700. What percent of the sales was his profit?

d. A customer at the Willow Dell Clothing Store purchased shoes for $29.95 and an iron for $25.75. The iron was subject to 6% sales tax, but the shoes were tax exempt. How much change should the customer receive from $60.00?

e. How much more interest does $500 earn in 3 years at 6% compounded annually than at 6% simple interest?

WRITTEN EXERCISES

A. Solve these reading problems.

1. One year the Landis family had an income of $95,650 from their dairy farm. Expenses were $18,525 for feed, $8,532 for repairs, $3,250 for fertilizer, $16,750 for depreciation, and $29,450 for other expenses. What was their profit that year?

2. Brother Jones, a carpenter, had an income of $75,529 one year. His expenses were $15,421 for lumber, $2,410 for small equipment, $18,734 for labor, and $13,785 for other expenses. What was Brother Jones's profit that year?

3. Brother John had a 19-acre alfalfa field that produced an average of 1.3 tons per acre in one cutting. The total market value of this hay was $2,925. What was the value per ton?

4. Brother John also had two fields of clover and timothy. The yield was 1.4 tons per acre from the 13-acre field and 2.1 tons per acre from the 9-acre field. The hay from these fields had a market value of $83.20 per ton. What was the total value of the clover and timothy?

5. One year Uncle Thomas sold fattened cattle worth $262,800. He had paid $162,000 for them, and his other expenses were $75,500. What percent of the total sales was his profit? Round your answer to the nearest whole percent.

6. A customer at the Willow Dell Clothing Store purchased dress fabric for $17.49 and pillows for $18.75. The pillows were subject to 6% sales tax, but the fabric was tax exempt. What was the total amount that the customer paid?

7. How much more interest does $900 earn in 3 years at 5% compounded annually than at 5% simple interest?

8. Father borrowed $6,000 one spring to buy a tractor. He repaid the loan with 6% interest 120 days later. How much interest did he pay?

9. One evening Brother Glenn made a 9-minute, long-distance telephone call that cost $1.26. The next day he made a 7-minute call to the same number during business hours, but this time the cost was $1.61. How much higher was the charge per minute for the second call?

10. The charge for international calls can be considerably higher than for calls within the same country. One month Brother Glenn was billed $12.60 for a 20-minute call from his home in Pennsylvania to Manitoba, but the charge for a call to California was $0.50 for 2 minutes. How much higher was the charge per minute for the international call than for the one to California?

11. The Sermon on the Mount is recorded in Matthew 5, 6, and 7. There are 48 verses in chapter 5, 34 verses in chapter 6, and 29 verses in chapter 7. The entire book of Matthew contains 1,071 verses. To the nearest whole number, what percent of the verses in Matthew are in chapters 5, 6, and 7?

12. There are 1,071 verses in the Gospel of Matthew, 678 verses in the Gospel of Mark, 1,151 verses in the Gospel of Luke, and 879 verses in the Gospel of John. The New Testament has a total of 7,957 verses. To the nearest whole number, what percent of the verses in the New Testament are in the four Gospels?

REVIEW EXERCISES

B. Write the amounts that belong in the spaces numbered 13–17 in a copy of the following cash-disbursements journal, using the information given for the first week in March. Then calculate the amounts that belong in the spaces numbered 18–21. (Lesson 103)

Check #201 on March 3 for $75.62 to Black Creek Fabrics for fabric.

Check #202 on March 4 for $489.93 to Central Warehouse for fabric.

Check #203 on March 4 for $79.95 to Sauder Sewing Machine Shop for sewing machine repairs.

Check #204 on March 5 for $79.97 to Union Telephone for telephone expense.

Check #205 on March 8 for $275.65 to East Branch Power & Light for electricity.

BOWMANS' GARMENTS
Cash-Disbursements Journal

	#	Date	Description	Amount	Material	Repairs	Electric & Phone
						EXPENSES	
13.							
14.							
15.							
16.							
17.							
	TOTALS			18.	19.	20.	21.

C. Find the unit price for each item, to the nearest tenth of a cent. (Lesson 102)

22. 6 spools of thread for $10.00

23. 3 zippers for $1.70

24. 3 yards of elastic for $2.95

25. 6 spools of thread for $7.00

D. Find the simple interest. (Lesson 100)

	p	r	t		p	r	t
26.	$200	6%	30 days	**27.**	$400	5%	90 days

E. Solve these percent problems. (Lesson 88)

28. 15% of 70

29. 25% of 40

30. 15 is 30% of ____

31. 32 is 40% of ____

32. 12 is ____% of 48

33. 16 is ____% of 48

---

105. Chapter 8 Review

A. Find the profit or loss. Write *profit* **or** *loss* **after each answer.** *(Lesson 96)*

1. income: $525
   expense: $460

2. income: $683
   expense: $776

3. income: $359
   expense: $426

4. income: $734
   expense: $453

B. Find the missing parts. *(Lesson 96)*

	Income	Expense	Profit
5.	$765	$432	____
7.	____	$277	$261

	Income	Expense	Profit
6.	$840	____	$327
8.	$634	$543	____

C. Find the rate of each profit or loss, based on the sale. Round the answers to the nearest whole percent. *(Lesson 97)*

	Sales	Profit or Loss	Rate
9.	$820	$82	____
11.	$414	$38	____
13.	$475	$78	____

	Sales	Profit or Loss	Rate
10.	$640	$32	____
12.	$525	$98	____
14.	$750	$61	____

D. Find the sales tax on each sale. *(Lesson 98)*

15. sale: $3.54
    tax rate: 4%

16. sale: $35.75
    tax rate: 6%

17. sale: $89.94
    tax rate: 5%

18. sale: $62.89
    tax rate: 7%

E. Find the total amount of each sale, including sales tax. *(Lesson 98)*

19. sale: $15.90
    tax rate: 3%

20. sale: $27.90
    tax rate: 2%

21. sale: $49.95
    tax rate: 8%

22. sale: $78.49
    tax rate: 7%

F. Find the simple interest on these amounts. *(Lessons 99, 100)*

	p	r	t			p	r	t
23.	$2,000	6%	1 year		24.	$4,800	5%	1 year
25.	$900	7%	8 months		26.	$800	8%	5 months
27.	$1,500	9%	75 days		28.	$3,200	5%	150 days

G. Use the annual interest and the principal to find the rate. *(Lesson 99)*

	i	p			i	p
29.	$200	$4,000		30.	$500	$6,250
31.	$400	$5,000		32.	$252	$4,200

H. Use the annual interest and the rate to find the principal. *(Lesson 99)*

	i	r			i	r
33.	$600	8%		34.	$1,500	6%
35.	$639	9%		36.	$776	8%

I. Calculate the total amount in each savings account if the interest is compounded annually. *(Lesson 101)*

	p	r	t			p	r	t
37.	$100	8%	2 years		38.	$100	9%	2 years
39.	$200	7%	3 years		40.	$400	6%	3 years

J. Find the compound interest for each of these accounts. *(Lesson 101)*

	p	r	t			p	r	t
41.	$100	5%	2 years		42.	$300	7%	2 years
43.	$500	6%	3 years		44.	$600	8%	3 years

K. Find these unit prices mentally. *(Lesson 102)*

45. 10 reams of copy paper for $32.95   46. 10 yards of elastic for $2.80

L. Find the unit price for each item, to the nearest tenth of a cent. *(Lesson 102)*

47. 12 doilies for $15.50   48. 3 zippers for $1.45

49. 4 curved needles for $2.65   50. 12 barrettes for $2.75

M. Write the amounts that belong in the spaces numbered 51–54 in a copy of the following cash-disbursements journal, using the information given for checks written on March 12. Then calculate the amounts that belong in the spaces numbered 55–58. *(Lesson 103)*

Check #641 for $325.66 to Monroe's Fuel for gasoline.

Check #642 for $127.95 to Jones's Lawn Equipment for snow blower repairs.

Check #643 for $27.52 to Dale's Service Station for gasoline.

Check #644 for $89.95 to East Pennbrooke Telephone for the February telephone bill (miscellaneous expense).

MONROEVILLE LAWN SERVICE
Cash-Disbursements Journal for 20—

	#	*Date*	*Description*	*Amount*	*Fuel*	*Repairs*	*Misc.*
						EXPENSES	
51.							
52.							
53.							
54.							
	TOTALS			55.	56.	57.	58.

N. Solve these reading problems.

59. Anthony helped his father build calf hutches. The cost of each one was $15.25 for materials and $3.75 for other expenses. The hutches sold for $65.00 apiece. What was the profit?

60. Anthony and his father also built swing sets. The expenses for each one were $45.00, and the selling price was $115.00. To the nearest whole percent, what was the rate of profit?

61. Anthony's father needed to charge $5\frac{1}{2}\%$ sales tax on the swing sets. What was the sales tax on a swing set that sold for $115.00?

62. Father paid $22.98 for 20 gallons of gasoline. To the nearest tenth of a cent, what was the cost per gallon?

63. Edwin's father borrowed $30,000 at 6% interest to buy a batch of steers. He repaid the loan after 10 months. What was the interest?

64. What is the interest on $5,000 for 3 years at 4% compounded annually?

106. Chapter 8 Test

Chapter 9

Geometry:
Working With Lines and Planes

And the Lord said unto Joshua, See, I have given into thine hand Jericho, . . .
And seven priests shall bear before the ark seven trumpets of rams' horns:
and the seventh day ye shall compass the city seven times . . .

By faith the walls of Jericho fell down, after they were compassed about seven days.
(Joshua 6:2–4, Hebrews 11:30)

107. Introduction to Geometric Terms

Geometry is a branch of mathematics that deals with lines, angles, planes, and solids. The word *geometry* comes from two Greek words that mean "earth or land" and "to measure"; so the literal meaning of *geometry* is "to measure land."

Many of the geometric terms used in this chapter are listed below. Following each term is a brief definition of that term. Be sure to memorize the terms and their meanings; they are used frequently in the next two chapters.

Point—A location represented by a dot. A point has no length or width; it is simply a location. The symbol for a point is a dot, often labeled with a capital letter. The point at the right is called "point A."

A
•

Line—A straight line that extends without end in two directions. A line is labeled by using two capital letters at two points on the line. Arrows at the ends show that the line continues without end. The symbol at the right is read "line BC."

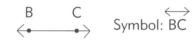

Symbol: $\overleftrightarrow{BC}$

Line Segment—A part of a line with two endpoints. A line segment is named by a capital letter at each endpoint. The symbol at the right is read "line segment DE."

Symbol: $\overline{DE}$

Ray—A line with only one endpoint. An arrow shows that the ray extends without end in one direction. A ray is named by two capital letters, one at the endpoint and one at a point on the ray, with the letter of the endpoint first. The symbol at the right is read "ray FG."

Symbol: $\overrightarrow{FG}$

Angle—A figure formed by two rays with the same endpoint, or two line segments that meet at a point. The rays or line segments are the **sides** of the angle, and the meeting point is the **vertex**. Angles are named by using three letters. (The letter for the vertex is always in the middle.) The symbol for *angle* is ∠. The angle at the right may be called "angle HIJ" or "angle JIH." It may also be named ∠I, read "angle I," because the vertex is point I.

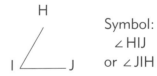

Symbol: ∠HIJ or ∠JIH

Right Angle—An angle that is formed by perpendicular lines (like the lines at the corner of a square). The symbol ⌐ inside an angle shows that it is a right angle. The figure at the right is called "right angle KLM."

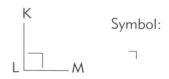

Symbol: ⌐

Perpendicular Lines—Lines that are at right angles to each other. The expression at the right is read "line NO is perpendicular to line PQ."

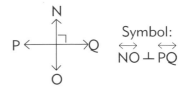

Symbol:

$\overleftrightarrow{NO} \perp \overleftrightarrow{PQ}$

Parallel Lines—Two lines that are always the same distance apart, no matter how far they extend in either direction. The expression at the right is read "line RS is parallel to line TU."

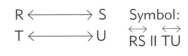

Symbol:

$\overleftrightarrow{RS} \parallel \overleftrightarrow{TU}$

Intersecting Lines—Two lines that intersect or cross at a point. In the figure at the right, intersecting lines WX and YZ cross at point V. This figure is called "intersecting lines WX and YZ."

Plane—A flat surface that extends in all directions but has no thickness. The top surface of a desk or table is an example of part of a plane.

Plane Geometry—Geometry that deals with planes. This chapter is a study of plane geometry. In Chapter 10 you will study solid geometry, which deals with figures having three dimensions.

Circle—A closed curve on which all the points are the same distance from the center.

Polygon—Any closed figure that can be drawn with line segments, that is, with straight sides. Following are the names of various polygons, based on the number of sides they have.

Triangle—Any three-sided polygon.

Quadrilateral—Any four-sided polygon.

Pentagon—Any five-sided polygon.

Hexagon—Any six-sided polygon.

Heptagon—Any seven-sided polygon.

Octagon—Any eight-sided polygon.

The quadrilateral is probably the most common kind of polygon. Therefore, quadrilaterals have various specific names as shown below.

Parallelogram—Any four-sided polygon whose opposite sides are parallel. (The corners are usually not right angles.)

Rectangle—A four-sided polygon whose corners are right angles.

Square—A rectangle whose sides are of equal length.

CLASS PRACTICE

Write the symbols for these expressions.

a. angle CDE

b. point X

c. Line AB is perpendicular to line CD.

Draw each of these figures.

d. triangle

e. quadrilateral

f. heptagon

WRITTEN EXERCISES

A. *Write the symbols for these expressions.*

1. angle OPQ

2. line segment YZ

3. line RS

4. ray TU

5. Line JK is parallel to line LM.

6. Line AB is perpendicular to line CD.

B. *Draw each of these figures.*

7. hexagon

8. parallelogram

9. octagon

10. square

11. rectangle

12. parallel lines

13. pentagon

14. circle

C. *Write the symbols for these figures.*

15.

G ─────────── H →

16.

J ←──────────→ K

L ←──────────→ M

17.

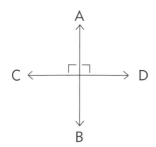

18.

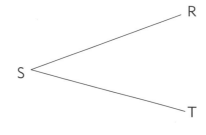

REVIEW EXERCISES

D. *Solve these reading problems.*

19. Father borrowed $8,000 for 45 days at 8% interest. How much interest did he owe?

20. Uncle Samuel borrowed $10,000 for 60 days at 9% interest. What was the total amount (interest and principal) that he needed to pay?

21. Father bought a Bible that had increased in price from $27.95 to $29.95. What was the rate of increase to the nearest whole percent?

Yea, if thou criest after knowledge, and liftest up thy voice for understanding; . . . then shalt thou understand the fear of the Lord, and find the knowledge of God.
Proverbs 2:3, 5

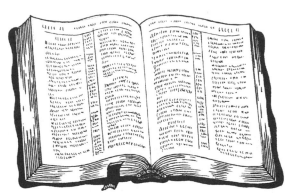

22. Paint that regularly sells for $27.00 is on sale for $20.00. What is the rate of decrease to the nearest whole percent?

23. There are 3 boys for every 4 girls at school. What is the ratio of girls to students in the school?

24. A batch of hogs ate 100 pounds of feed for every 30 pounds of weight they gained. What was the ratio of feed eaten to weight gained?

E. *Find the simple interest.* (Lessons 99, 100)

25. $p = \$5,000$	26. $p = \$6,500$	27. $p = \$2,500$	28. $p = \$3,000$
$r = 7\%$	$r = 8\%$	$r = 5\%$	$r = 7\%$
$t = 4$ yr.	$t = 6$ yr.	$t = 90$ days	$t = 7$ mo.

F. *Find the percent of increase or decrease. Label your answers.* (Lesson 90)

	Original Price	New Price		Original Price	New Price
29.	$15.00	$17.25	30.	$18.00	$14.76
31.	$25.00	$25.50	32.	$30.00	$33.60

G. *Write ratios for these facts.* (Lesson 67)

33. Write a ratio comparing 45 ears of sweet corn to 28 stalks.

34. Write a ratio comparing 500 bushels of shelled corn to 3 acres.

H. *Find the greatest common factors.* (Lesson 38)

35. 12, 16	36. 18, 30	37. 40, 60	38. 45, 75

108. Working With Angles

An angle is formed by two rays with the same endpoint, or two line segments that meet at a point. The meeting point of the angle is the **vertex**. The rays or line segments are the **sides** of the angle.

Angles are measured in degrees, which are based on the circle. A full circle has 360°, a half circle has 180°, and a quarter circle has 90°. The size of an angle depends on the number of degrees between its two sides.

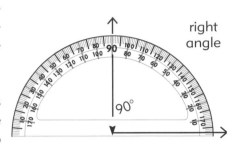

right angle

Angles are classified according to the sharpness of the vertexes. A **right angle** is formed by two perpendicular lines. This makes a 90° angle. On a clock, the hands form a right angle at three o'clock and nine o'clock.

An **acute angle** is sharper than a right angle; it has less than 90 degrees. An example of an acute angle is the hands of a clock at one o'clock.

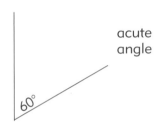

acute angle

An **obtuse angle** is more blunt than a right angle. (The word *obtuse* means "blunt.") It has more than 90 degrees but less than 180 degrees. The hands of a clock form obtuse angles at times such as five o'clock and eight o'clock.

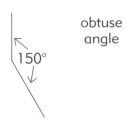

obtuse angle

A **straight angle** has 180°—as many degrees as there are in a semicircle. The hands of a clock form a straight angle at six o'clock.

The sizes of angles are measured by using an instrument called a **protractor** (prō·trăk´tər). Most protractors are semicircular with an arrow or line indicating the center of the straight edge. One scale begins with 0° on the left side of the protractor and increases to 180° on the right side. The other scale begins with 0° on the right side and increases to 180° on the left side.

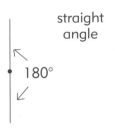

straight angle

To measure an angle, use the following steps. Notice how the angles are measured in the examples.

1. If necessary, extend the sides of the angle with a pencil mark until they are long enough to measure.
2. Lay the protractor on the angle so that the center mark is at the vertex and the straight edge is exactly on one side.
3. Read the number of degrees on the correct scale of the protractor. Be sure it is the scale that begins with 0° on the side toward which the angle opens.
4. Check to make sure your answer is logical. An acute angle has less than 90°, and an obtuse angle has more than 90°.

To draw an angle with a given number of degrees, use the following steps.

1. Draw one side of the angle with a straightedge, and mark one end as the vertex.
2. Place the straight edge of the protractor on the line segment you drew, with the center mark at the vertex.
3. Find the desired number of degrees on the correct scale of the protractor, and put a dot on the paper at that point. Be sure it is the scale that begins with 0° on the side toward which the angle opens.
4. Using a straightedge, draw a line from the vertex through the dot you made in step 3.

Bisecting an angle means dividing it into two equal angles. To bisect an angle, use the following steps.

1. Carefully measure the angle with a protractor.
2. Divide the number of degrees in the angle by 2.
3. With the protractor in the same position, find the number of degrees on the correct scale of the protractor. Put a dot on the paper at that point.
4. Using a straightedge, draw a line from the vertex through the dot you made in step 3.

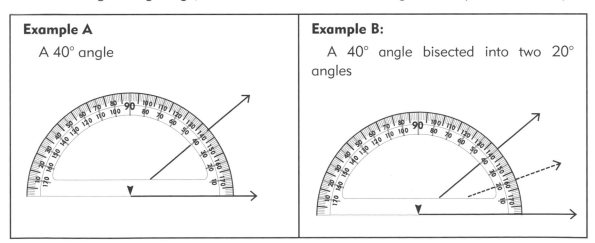

| **Example A** | **Example B:** |
| A 40° angle | A 40° angle bisected into two 20° angles |

CLASS PRACTICE

Identify each figure as a *right angle,* **an** *acute angle,* **an** *obtuse angle,* **or a** *straight angle.* ***Then use a protractor to measure the degrees.***

a.
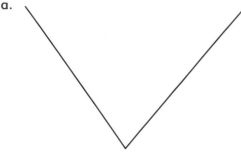

b.

Draw angles having these degrees. Then bisect each angle.

c. 50°   d. 80°   e. 140°

WRITTEN EXERCISES

A. *Identify each angle as* *acute, obtuse, right,* **or** *straight.*

1.
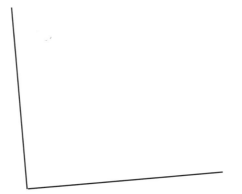

2.
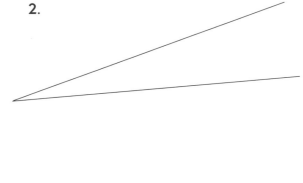

3.

4.

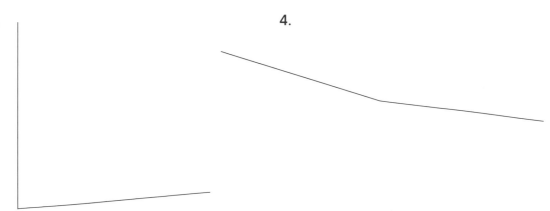

5.

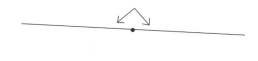

6.

7.

8.

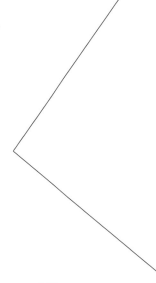

B. Measure the angles in exercises 1–8 above. All answers are multiples of 5 degrees.

9. Angle 1 = _____ degrees.

10. Angle 2 = _____ degrees.

11. Angle 3 = _____ degrees.

12. Angle 4 = _____ degrees.

13. Angle 5 = _____ degrees.

14. Angle 6 = _____ degrees.

15. Angle 7 = _____ degrees.

16. Angle 8 = _____ degrees.

C. Identify angles with the following degrees as *acute, obtuse, right,* **or** *straight.*

17. 173 degrees

18. 180 degrees

19. 90 degrees

20. 93 degrees

21. 80 degrees

22. 45 degrees

D. *Do the following exercises.*

23. Draw a 173-degree angle.

24. Draw a 180-degree angle.

25. Draw a 90-degree angle.

26. Draw a 93-degree angle.

27. Bisect an 80-degree angle.

28. Bisect a 140-degree angle.

E. *Solve these reading problems. Use proportions for numbers 31–34.*

29. The Masts' lane has the shape of a 115-degree angle. What type of angle is that?

30. Near a mission church in Guatemala is a sharp switchback curve in the shape of a 45-degree angle. What type of angle is formed by this curve?

31. Sylvia helped her mother make aprons for a sewing-circle project. She sewed 2 aprons for every 3 aprons her mother sewed. If her mother sewed 12 aprons, how many did Sylvia do?

32. The Moyers canned 2 quarts of peaches for every 3 quarts of pears. They canned 140 quarts of peaches. How many quarts of pears did they can?

33. The ratio of Randall's age to his father's age is 3 to 7. If Randall's father is 42 years old, how old is Randall?

34. One week Darvin did 19 out of every 20 math problems correctly. If he did 171 problems correctly, how many problems did he do in all?

REVIEW EXERCISES

F. *Draw geometric figures as indicated below. (Lesson 107)*

35. parallel lines MN and OP

36. a quadrilateral

37. a pentagon

38. perpendicular lines QR and ST

G. *Solve these problems mentally. (Lesson 91)*

39. 25% of 40 is _____

40. 80% of 30 is _____

41. 11 is $12\frac{1}{2}$% of _____

42. 6 is $33\frac{1}{3}$ % of _____

43. 7 is _____% of 28

44. 8 is _____% of 40

H. *Find the lowest common multiple of each pair. (Lesson 39)*

45. 15, 20

46. 14, 16

109. Working With Triangles

Any polygon with three sides and three angles is a triangle. Triangles are commonly classified in two ways: according to the types of their angles and according the lengths of their sides.

The following names and descriptions define triangles according to the types of their angles. An **acute triangle** has three acute angles. A **right triangle** has one right angle and two acute angles. An **obtuse triangle** has one obtuse angle and two acute angles. An **equiangular triangle** is a special type of acute triangle. All three of its angles are equal, containing 60°.

Example A:
  Acute Triangle

Example B:
  Right Triangle

Example C:
  Obtuse Triangle

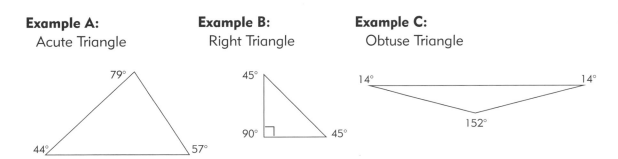

Triangles classified by comparing the lengths of their sides have the following names and descriptions. An **equilateral triangle** has three sides of equal length. Since it also has three equal angles, it is equiangular as well. An **isosceles triangle** (ī·sŏs′ə·lēz) has two sides of equal length. A **scalene triangle** (skā′lĕn) has no sides of equal length.

Example D:
  Equiangular and
  Equilateral Triangle

Example E:
  Isosceles Triangle

Example F:
  Scalene Triangle

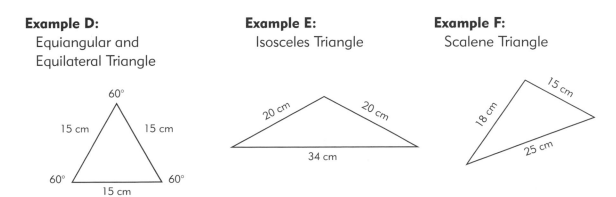

Every triangle can be classified both according to its angles and according to its sides. The acute triangle in Example A is also a scalene triangle. The right triangle in Example B and the obtuse triangle in Example C are both isosceles triangles.

All triangles are alike in that the sum of the degrees in their angles is always 180°. An equiangular triangle has three 60° angles, equaling 180 degrees. If a right triangle has a 90° angle and a 50° angle, the third angle will be a 40° angle, bringing the total number of degrees to 180°.

Triangles with the same shape are related in one of two ways. If the two triangles have the same shape but not the same size, they are **similar triangles**. If the two triangles are the same shape and size, they are exactly the same. These triangles are **congruent triangles**.

Example G:
Similar Triangles

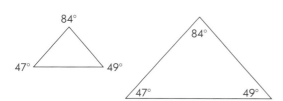

Example H:
Congruent Triangles

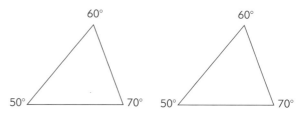

If the degrees of two angles in a triangle are known, the degrees of the third one can be found by adding the degrees in the two known angles and subtracting the sum from 180 degrees.

Example I	Step 1	Step 2
If two angles in an acute triangle have 70 degrees and 75 degrees, how many degrees are in the third angle?	70° + 75° ——— 145°	180° − 145° ——— 35°

CLASS PRACTICE

Each pair of numbers gives the degrees in two angles of a triangle. Find the degrees in the third angle. Then classify each triangle according to its angles.

a. 90°, 38°   b. 52°, 26°   c. 120°, 20°   d. 57°, 89°

Classify each triangle according to the lengths of its sides.

e. 3", 5", 5"   f. 7', 6', 5'   g. 11", 12", 11"   h. 60°, 60°, 60°

WRITTEN EXERCISES

A. *Each pair of numbers gives the degrees in two angles of a triangle. Find the degrees in the third angle.*

1. 50°, 70°   2. 30°, 60°   3. 105°, 30°   4. 60°, 60°

5. 38°, 52°   6. 47°, 61°   7. 99°, 77°   8. 45°, 98°

B. Classify these triangles according to their angles.

9.

10.

11.

12. 40°, 25°, 115°

13. 38°, 71°, 71°

14. 60°, 60°, 60°

C. Classify these triangles according to the lengths of their sides.

15.

16.

17.

18. 1", 2", 2"

19. 3', 4', 5'

20. 7', 7', 7'

D. Identify these sets of triangles as congruent or similar.

21.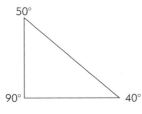

22.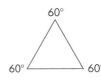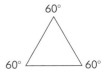

23.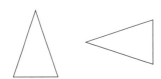

24.

E. Use a protractor to find the degrees in the angles of these triangles. All answers are multiples of five degrees.

25. Angle A = _____°
    Angle B = _____°
    Angle C = _____°

26. Angle D = _____°
    Angle E = _____°
    Angle F = _____°

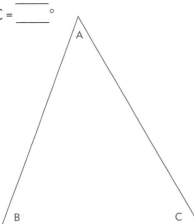

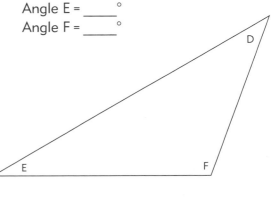

F. *Solve these reading problems.*

27. The Nolts' property is triangular. One of the angles of the boundary measures 80° and another angle measures 74°. What is the size of the third angle of the boundary?

28. The gable end of the Nolts' house forms a triangle. The two angles at the eaves are 34 degrees each. How many degrees are in the angle at the peak of the roof?

29. Classify the triangle described in problem 27 according to its angles.

30. Classify the triangle described in problem 28 according to its angles.

REVIEW EXERCISES

G. *Write the symbols for these geometric figures.* (Lesson 107)

31.

$$\overline{}$$
A   B

32.

A ⟷ B

C ⟷ D

33.

34.

H. *Find the simple interest.* (Lessons 99, 100)

35. p = $2,500
r = 5%
t = 3 yr.

36. p = $3,200
r = 6%
t = 6 yr.

37. p = $3,000
r = 4%
t = 11 mo.

38. p = $4,000
r = 7%
t = 75 days

I. *Use proportions to solve these reading problems.* (Lesson 69)

39. Glenn was mixing feed in which 4 pounds of salt was to be added for every 1,000 pounds of the finished batch. If he added 30 pounds of salt, how much feed was he making?

40. A business office has a row of filing cabinets in which 12 cabinets take up 17 feet of wall space. At that rate, how much wall space would a row of 8 filing cabinets take?

41. Dale helped to plant sweet corn one day after school. He dropped 12 corn seeds every 5 feet. At that rate, how many corn seeds would he drop in 600 feet?

42. The Zimmermans have a chicken house in which there are 3 cages for every 8 feet. How many cages are in a 304-foot row?

110. Using a Compass to Make Geometric Designs

A compass is an instrument used to draw circles. It looks somewhat like a pair of scissors with a pencil where the one point should be. Isaiah 44:13 mentions a carpenter's compass. Although that compass was not exactly like the ones we use, it was also used to make circles.

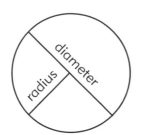

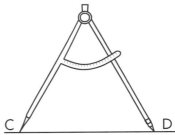

To draw a circle having a specified size, follow the steps below.

1. Find the radius of the circle. If you know the diameter of the circle, divide the diameter in half.

2. Using a ruler, set the distance between the pivot point and the pencil point of the compass. This will be the same as the radius of the circle.

3. Place the pivot point on the point chosen for the center of the circle. Be sure the circle will not extend off your paper in any direction; then carefully draw a circle around the center point. Do not place too much pressure on the compass, or the compass setting will change and the circle will not be closed.

Example A	**Example B**
Draw a circle with a radius of $1\frac{1}{4}$ inches.	Draw a circle with a diameter of 2 inches.
Step 1: The radius is $1\frac{1}{4}$ ".	Step 1: Because the diameter is 2", the radius is 1".
Step 2: Use a ruler to set the pivot point and the pencil point $1\frac{1}{4}$ " apart.	Step 2: Use a ruler to set the pivot point and the pencil point 1" apart.
Step 3: Place the compass and draw the circle.	Step 3: Place the compass and draw the circle.

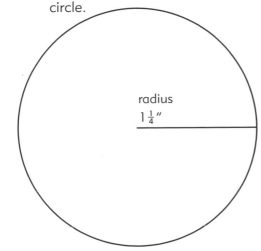

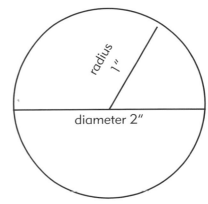

A compass can be used along with a straightedge to make various geometric designs. Following are the steps for drawing a regular hexagon. A regular hexagon has six sides of equal length.

1. Use the compass to draw a circle about the size of the regular hexagon you wish to make.
2. Mark an X anywhere on the circle.
3. Keep the points of the compass the same distance apart as they were to draw the circle. Place the pivot point of the compass on the X. Draw a small **arc** (curved line that is part of a circle) on the circle. Be careful not to use too much pressure.
4. Place the pivot point on the point where the arc and the circle intersect. Now draw another arc further around on the circle.
5. Repeat step 4 until the sixth arc is drawn. If you drew your arcs carefully, the sixth arc should be on the X where you started.
6. Use a straightedge to draw lines between the points where the arcs intersect the circle.
7. Erase the circle. You should now have a regular hexagon.

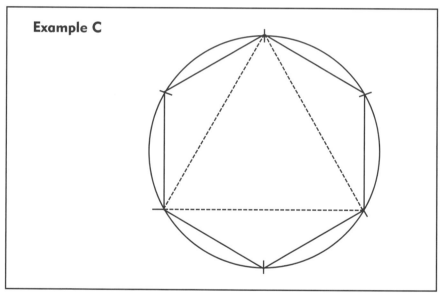

Example C

The same method can be used to draw an equilateral triangle. This is done by drawing lines between every other arc on the circle, as shown by the dashed lines on the diagram.

CLASS PRACTICE

Draw these circles as indicated.

a. radius: 2 inches   b. radius: 3 inches   c. diameter: 5 inches

Draw these polygons as indicated.

d. Use the circle you drew for *b* above to draw a regular hexagon.
e. Use the circle you drew for *c* above to draw an equilateral triangle.

WRITTEN EXERCISES

A. *Draw circles having these radii.*

1. $1\frac{1}{2}$ inches
2. 2 inches
3. $2\frac{1}{2}$ inches
4. 3 inches

B. *Draw circles having these diameters. Use the same center point for all the circles.*

5. 5 inches
6. 4 inches
7. 3 inches
8. 2 inches

C. *Use a compass and a ruler to draw these polygons.*

9. Draw a regular hexagon in a circle with a 2-inch diameter.
10. Draw a regular hexagon in a circle with a 3-inch diameter.
11. Draw an equilateral triangle in a circle with a 2-inch diameter.
12. Draw an equilateral triangle in a circle with a $2\frac{1}{2}$-inch diameter.

D. *Use the principles taught in the lesson to make one of these figures.*

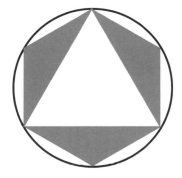 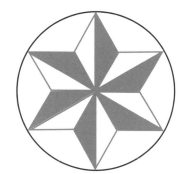 

REVIEW EXERCISES

E. *Solve these reading problems.* (Lesson 109)

13. The sides of a triangle measure 5 inches, 6 inches, and 7 inches. Classify this triangle according to its sides.
14. Two sides of a triangle are 9 inches long. The third side is 12 inches long. Classify this triangle according to its sides.
15. Two angles in a triangle each have 65 degrees. How many degrees are in the third angle?
16. An obtuse triangle has a 98-degree obtuse angle and a 48-degree acute angle. How many degrees are in the other acute angle?

17. If a right triangle is also an isosceles triangle, we know the degrees in each of the three angles. The one is a right angle and the other two are equal angles. What are the degrees in each of the three angles?

18. If a right triangle has one 60-degree angle, what is the size of the third angle?

F. Find the compound interest for each account. *(Lesson 101)*

19. $p = \$100$	20. $p = \$200$	21. $p = \$500$	22. $p = \$600$
$r = 5\%$	$r = 7\%$	$r = 6\%$	$r = 5\%$
$t = 2$ yr.	$t = 2$ yr.	$t = 3$ yr.	$t = 3$ yr.

G. Identify the type of angle shown in each problem. *(Lesson 108)*

23. $27°$ 24. $89°$ 25. $97°$ 26. $90°$

H. Reduce these fractions to lowest terms. Label the parts of the first two fractions. *(Lessons 40, 41)*

27. $\frac{15}{27}$ 28. $\frac{35}{49}$ 29. $\frac{39}{65}$ 30. $\frac{34}{85}$

111. Finding Perimeters

A **perimeter** is a closed boundary line that marks off part of a plane. It can also mean the total length of such a boundary line.

To find the perimeter of any polygon, add the lengths of all the sides. Label the answer with the same unit that is used to measure the sides. (See Example A.)

> **To find the perimeter of any polygon, add the lengths of all the sides.**

Example A

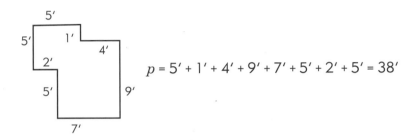

$$p = 5' + 1' + 4' + 9' + 7' + 5' + 2' + 5' = 38'$$

Because a square has four equal sides, a special formula is used to find its perimeter. The formula in the box is used in Example B below.

> To find the perimeter (p) of a square, multiply 4 times the length of one side (s).
>
> **Memorize this formula for the perimeter of a square.**
>
> perimeter = 4 × side, or $p = 4s$

Example B

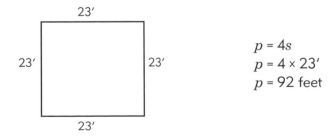

$$p = 4s$$
$$p = 4 \times 23'$$
$$p = 92 \text{ feet}$$

A special formula is also used to find the perimeter of a rectangle. The formula in this box is used in Example C below.

> To find the perimeter (p) of a rectangle, find the sum of the length (l) and the width (w). Multiply this sum by 2.
>
> **Memorize this formula for the perimeter of a rectangle.**
>
> perimeter = 2 × (length + width), or $p = 2(l + w)$

Example C

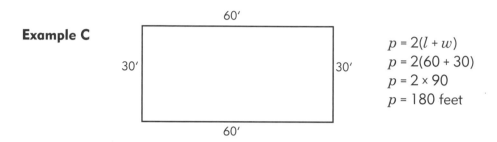

$p = 2(l + w)$
$p = 2(60 + 30)$
$p = 2 \times 90$
$p = 180$ feet

The perimeter of a parallelogram is found in the same way as the perimeter of a rectangle. But instead of using the true length and width of the parallelogram, the actual lengths of its sides are added and multiplied. (See Example D.)

Example D

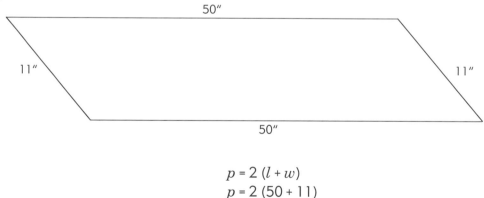

$p = 2 (l + w)$
$p = 2 (50 + 11)$
$p = 2 \times 61$
$p = 122$ inches

CLASS PRACTICE

Find the perimeters of polygons with these dimensions.

a. hexagon: 5′ by 4′ by 7′ by 4′ by 3′ by 9′   b. triangle: 7″ by 4″ by 9″

c. square: $s = 4″$ d. rectangle: l = 5′, w = 4′

WRITTEN EXERCISES

A. *Find the perimeters of these polygons.*

1. pentagon: 7″ by 8″ by 3″ by 9″ by 10″

2. quadrilateral: 7″ by 5″ by 12″ by 9″

3. triangle: 15′ by 17′ by 21′

4. heptagon: 3″ by 4″ by 4″ by 5″ by 6″ by 6″ by 7″

B. *Find the perimeters of these squares.*

5. $s = 7'$ 6. $s = 19'$ 7. $s = 30'$ 8. $s = 35'$

9. $s = 9.5''$ 10. $s = 17.7'$ 11. $s = 12\frac{1}{2}'$ 12. $s = 15\frac{1}{4}''$

C. *Find the perimeters of these rectangles. Try to do numbers 13–16 mentally.*

13. $l = 8'$
    $w = 7'$

14. $l = 11''$
    $w = 9''$

15. $l = 15''$
    $w = 10''$

16. $l = 18'$
    $w = 12'$

17. $l = 72'$
    $w = 45'$

18. $l = 145'$
    $w = 107'$

19. $l = 24.7'$
    $w = 14.9'$

20. $l = 19.95$ mi.
    $w = 12.47$ mi.

D. *Find the perimeters of these parallelograms.*

21. $l = 18'$
    $w = 16'$

22. $l = 28'$
    $w = 23'$

23. $l = 13\frac{3}{4}''$
    $w = 11\frac{1}{2}''$

24. $l = 15\frac{3}{16}''$
    $w = 7\frac{3}{4}''$

E. *Solve these reading problems.*

25. Brother Eugene is making a square Gospel sign. Each side is 14 inches long. When he is finished painting it, he will cover the edge with a protective strip. How long a strip will he need?

26. Another sign Brother Eugene is making is rectangular. Its length is 20 inches and its width is 16 inches. How long a protective border will he need for the edges of this sign?

27. Brother Gerald is using a piece of carpet 12 feet long and 4 feet wide to make a runner at school. He plans to use carpet tubing to bind the raw edges of the carpet. How much tubing will he need?

> Him
> that cometh
> to me
> I will in no wise
> cast out.
> John 6:37

28. The Wadel's house measures 44 feet by 32 feet. What is the perimeter of the house?

29. The cost of a one-year subscription (52 issues) of *The Christian Pathway* is $7.15. What is the cost per issue to the nearest tenth of a cent?

30. The cost for a one-year subscription (12 issues) to *The Christian School Builder* is $9.35. To the nearest tenth of a cent, what is the cost per issue?

REVIEW EXERCISES

F. *Measure the degrees in the angles of these triangles. All the angles are multiples of 5 degrees.* *(Lesson 109)*

31.

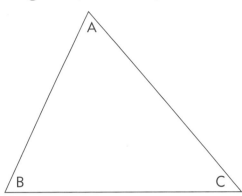

32.

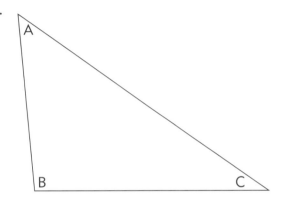

G. *Write the symbols for these geometric figures.* *(Lesson 107)*

33.

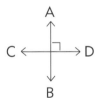

34.   A $\longleftrightarrow$ B
          C $\longleftrightarrow$ D

H. *Find the unit price of each item to the nearest tenth of a cent.* *(Lesson 102)*

35. 3 loaves of bread for $2.00   **36.** 12 flower bulbs for $2.25

I. *Solve these addition problems.* *(Lesson 42)*

37. $3\frac{2}{5}$
         $+2\frac{2}{3}$

38. $5\frac{5}{6}$
         $+2\frac{3}{4}$

112. Radius, Diameter, and Circumference of a Circle

A circle is different from a polygon in that it does not have straight edges. It is also different in that every point on the edge of a circle is the same distance from the center.

Any straight line drawn from the center of a circle to its edge is a **radius**. The plural of radius is **radii** (rā´dē·ī). Because every point on the edge of a circle is an equal distance from the center, all the radii are the same length. A circle has an unlimited number of radii.

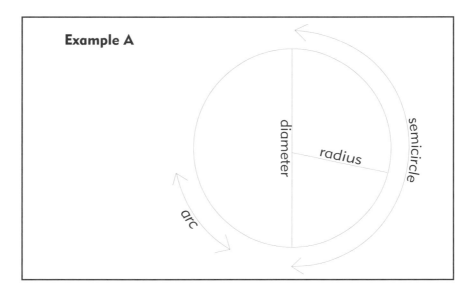

Example A

Any straight line drawn from one edge of the circle through its center to the opposite edge is a **diameter**. All the diameters in a circle are the same length. A circle also has an unlimited number of diameters.

An **arc** is any part of the curve of a circle. A **semicircle** is an arc that makes half a circle.

The perimeter or distance around a circle has a special name, **circumference**. Because a circle is round, the circumference cannot be found by adding the lengths of its sides. Also, it is difficult to measure a curved line with a ruler. However, the ratio of the circumference to the diameter of every circle is the same. This ratio is called **pi** (pronounced like "pie"). The symbol for *pi* is π, the Greek letter *p*.

It was known in Bible times that the ratio of the circumference of a circle to its diameter is about 3 to 1. This relationship can be seen in 2 Chronicles 4:2, where the compass (circumference) of the molten sea is given as 30 cubits, and the distance from brim to brim (its diameter) is given as 10 cubits—a ratio of 3 to 1.

The ratio 3 to 1 does work well for mental calculation. However, more exact values for pi are used for most purposes. The values used in this course are 3.14 or $\frac{22}{7}$ ($3\frac{1}{7}$); these are accurate enough for most practical purposes. For very exact measurements, a value like 3.14159 is used. But all these values of pi are only approximate. The exact value of pi is a nonterminating, nonrepeating decimal.

The formula for finding the circumference of a circle is given in the box below. If the radius of a circle is given, double the radius to find the diameter. **The decimal form of pi is generally used in working with whole numbers and decimals, and the fractional form in working with fractions and mixed numbers and numbers that are multiples of 7.**

> To find the circumference (c) of a circle, multiply π times the diameter (d). The value of π is 3.14 or $\frac{22}{7}$.
>
> **Memorize this formula for the circumference of a circle.**
>
> circumference = π × diameter, or $c = \pi d$

Example B	**Example C**
Find the diameter of a circle with a radius of 4 inches. 2 × 4 inches = 8 inches	Find the circumference of a circle with a 5-inch diameter. $c = \pi d$ $c = 3.14 \times 5$ inches $c = 15.7$ inches
Example D	**Example E**
Find the circumference of a circle with a diameter of 7 inches. Use $\frac{22}{7}$ for π. $c = \pi d$ $c = \frac{22}{7} \times 7$ $c = 22$ inches	Find the circumference of a circle with a 5-inch radius. diameter = 2 × 5 = 10 $c = \pi d$ $c = 3.14 \times 10$ inches $c = 31.4$ inches

CLASS PRACTICE

Find the diameters of circles with these radii.

a. $r = 9''$ b. $r = 14''$

c. $r = 3.95$ cm   d. $r = 7\frac{7}{16}''$

Find the circumferences of circles with these diameters and radii. Use $\frac{22}{7}$ for π in solving g and h.

e. $d = 6''$ f. $r = 2.25''$

g. $d = 21''$ h. $r = 28'$

WRITTEN EXERCISES

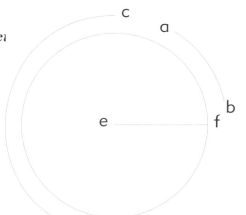

A. *Use the circle at the right to do these exerci*

1. Line segment _____ is a radius.

2. Arc _____ is a semicircle.

3. Arc _____ is an arc but not a semicircle.

4. The length of the diameter is _____.

5. The length of the radius is _____.

6. The length of the circumference is _____.

B. *Find the circumferences, using 3.14 for pi.*
Remember: d means "diameter" and r means "radius."

7. $d = 4''$	8. $d = 3''$	9. $d = 32'$	10. $d = 60'$
11. $r = 3''$	12. $r = 5.5''$	13. $r = 7.75'$	14. $r = 8.25'$

C. *Find the circumferences, using $\frac{22}{7}$ for pi.*

15. $d = 14''$	16. $d = 35''$	17. $d = 10\frac{1}{2}'$	18. $d = 56'$
19. $r = 14''$	20. $r = 21''$	21. $r = 6''$	22. $r = 8''$

D. *Solve these reading problems.*

23. Tunnels allow traffic to travel under the Hudson River between New York City and New Jersey. Each tunnel is a circular tube with an outside diameter of 29.5 feet. What is the circumference of each tube?

24. The largest circular tube tunnel is the River Mersey Tunnel between Liverpool and Birkenhead, England. These tubes have an outside diameter of 46.25 feet. What is the circumference of each tube?

25. The longest vehicular tunnel in the world is the Saint Gotthard tunnel in the Swiss Alps. It is $10\frac{1}{5}$ miles long. The second longest vehicular tunnel is the Mont Blanc tunnel in the Alps. This $7\frac{1}{2}$-mile-long tunnel carries traffic between France and Italy. How much longer is the Saint Gotthard tunnel than the Mont Blanc tunnel?

26. The longest tunnel in the world, the main tunnel of the Delaware Aqueduct, carries water underground for 85 miles from the Rondout Reservoir in the Catskill Mountains to the Hillview Reservoir near New York City. The longest railroad tunnel is the $33\frac{1}{2}$-mile-long Seikan Tunnel in Japan. How much longer is the Delaware Aqueduct than the Seikan Tunnel?

27. The diameter of the main tunnel of the Delaware Aqueduct is 19.5 feet at its largest point. What is the circumference of the tunnel at that point?

28. The New Castle Arc, one of the few political boundaries of that shape, was established between Delaware and Pennsylvania in 1681. Delaware was given all the territory within 12 miles of "ye end of ye horse dyke" in New Castle. Thus, the New Castle Arc is part of a circle with a 12-mile radius. What is the circumference of the full circle?

REVIEW EXERCISES

E. *Find the perimeters.* (Lesson 111)

29. rectangle
  l = 15.5'
  w = 12.25'

30. rectangle
  l = 17.75"
  w = 14.125"

31. square
  s = 7.875"

32. square
  s = 4.125"

F. *Identify the type of angle.* (Lesson 108)

33. 180°   **34.** 91°   **35.** 177°   **36.** 88°

G. *Measure these angles. All answers will be multiples of 5 degrees.* (Lesson 108)

37. 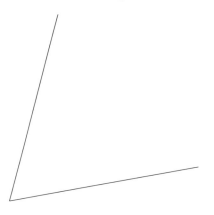   **38.**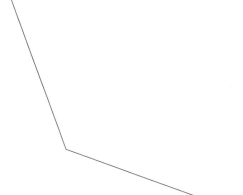

39. 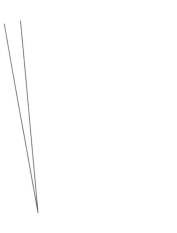   **40.**

H. *Complete this chart.* (Lesson 72)

41.

Fraction	Decimal	Percent
$\frac{27}{50}$		

42.

Fraction	Decimal	Percent
		14%

I. *Solve these subtraction problems.* (Lesson 43)

43. $4\frac{1}{4}$
        $-\ 1\frac{4}{5}$

44. $7\frac{1}{3}$
        $-\ 3\frac{1}{2}$

113. Introduction to Area

The study of area in mathematics is the study of surface. The area of your desk top, for example, is the amount of surface on the desk top. In this chapter, you will be finding the areas of some common plane figures.

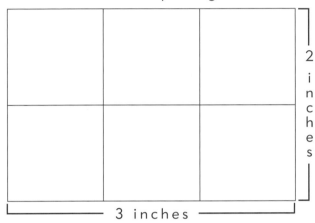

2 inches

3 inches

The area of the rectangle to the left is the amount of surface area it covers. Each block in the rectangle is 1 inch long and 1 inch wide. This makes each block 1 square inch. The whole rectangle divided into blocks shows that it has an area of 6 square inches. The area of this rectangle can also be found by multiplying the length by the width: 3 inches x 2 inches = 6 square inches.

To find the area (a) of a rectangle, multiply the length (l) times the width (w).

Memorize this formula for the area of a rectangle.

area = length × width, or $a = lw$

Because area includes both length and width, the term **square** is used in naming units that measure area. The acre and the hectare are exceptions because they themselves are units of square measure. Following are some common English and metric units of area. Notice the differences in the English abbreviations and the metric abbreviations.

Common English Units of Area		**Common Metric Units of Area**	
square inch	(sq. in.)	square millimeter	(mm^2)
square foot	(sq. ft.)	square centimeter	(cm^2)
square yard	(sq. yd.)	square meter	(m^2)
acre	(a.)	hectare	(ha)
square mile	(sq. mi.)	square kilometer	(km^2)

Example A	**Example B**
Find the area of a rectangle with these dimensions.	Find the area of a rectangle with these dimensions.
$l = 35'$; $w = 29'$	$l = 24.6$ m; $w = 13.5$ m
$a = lw$	$a = lw$
$a = 35' \times 29'$	$a = 24.6$ m $\times$ 13.5 m
$a = 1,015$ sq. ft.	$a = 332.1$ m^2

CLASS PRACTICE

Find the areas of rectangles with these dimensions.

a. $l = 17''$
$w = 14''$

b. $l = 48.5$ yd.
$w = 32.3$ yd.

c. $l = 15.3$ m
$w = 14.7$ m

d. $l = 7.9$ m
$w = 4.6$ m

WRITTEN EXERCISES

A. *Find the areas of rectangles with these dimensions. Be careful to use the correct labels.*

1. $l = 12''$
$w = 9''$

2. $l = 16''$
$w = 12''$

3. $l = 36'$
$w = 24'$

4. $l = 89'$
$w = 74'$

5. $l = 495'$
$w = 132'$

6. $l = 787'$
$w = 643'$

7. $l = 72$ yd.
$w = 46$ yd.

8. $l = 19.5$ yd.
$w = 7.7$ yd.

9. $l = 15\frac{1}{2}''$
$w = 6\frac{1}{2}''$

10. $l = 9\frac{3}{4}''$
$w = 4\frac{1}{4}''$

11. $l = 45$ mm
$w = 36$ mm

12. $l = 78$ mm
$w = 67$ mm

13. $l = 89$ cm
$w = 67$ cm

14. $l = 98$ cm
$w = 67$ cm

15. $l = 145$ m
$w = 98$ m

16. $l = 336$ m
$w = 325$ m

17. $l = 16.5$ km
$w = 14.9$ km

18. $l = 22.7$ km
$w = 13.9$ km

19. $l = 1.78$ m
$w = 0.29$ m

20. $l = 1.91$ m
$w = 0.15$ m

B. *Solve these reading problems.*

21. A rectangular warehouse measures 325 feet by 275 feet. What is the floor space in the warehouse?

22. The church sign at the Fieldville Mennonite Church measures 48 inches by 42 inches. What is the area of the sign?

23. A business paid $0.17 per square inch for a sign measuring 24 inches by 20 inches. What was the cost of the sign?

24. A rectangular field measures 700 feet by 600 feet. Is the field larger or smaller than 10 acres? (You will need to know the number of square feet in an acre.)

25. Barbara is baking cookies on a cookie sheet that measures 16 by 20 inches. Each cookie on the sheet requires a space of 16 square inches. How many cookies can she bake on a sheet?

26. Each finished cookie has a diameter of 3 inches. What is the circumference of each cookie?

REVIEW EXERCISES

C. Find the circumferences of circles having these sizes. *(Lesson 112)*

27. $d = 5$ ft. 28. $d = 17$ in. 29. $r = 11$ in. 30. $r = 13$ in.

D. Find the perimeters of polygons having these dimensions. *(Lesson 111)*

31. *rectangle*
$l = 17.5''$
$w = 14.5''$

32. *square*
$s = 16.5''$

E. Classify these triangles according to their angles. *(Lesson 109)*

33.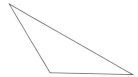

34.

F. Find the profit or loss, and label each answer *profit* **or** *loss.* *(Lesson 96)*

35. income: $78; expenses: $43

36. income: $89; expenses: $105

G. Find these percentages. *(Lesson 73)*

37. 38% of 29

38. 91% of 67

H. Write the reciprocals of these numbers. *(Lesson 47)*

39. $4\frac{1}{2}$

40. 10

I. Solve these multiplication problems. *(Lessons, 45)*

41. $1\frac{3}{4} \times 1\frac{1}{2}$

42. $5\frac{2}{3} \times 4\frac{3}{8}$

114. Area of a Square and a Parallelogram

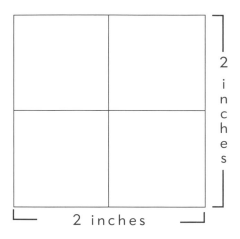

2 inches

2 inches

In Lesson 113, you reviewed the formula for finding the area of a rectangle. Because a square is a special type of rectangle, the formula $a = lw$ can be used to find the area of a square, but there is also a special formula for squares.

Because all sides of a square are of equal length, multiplying the length of one side by that of another side is the same as multiplying the length by itself. To find the area of a square, multiply the length of one side by itself.

A small raised 2 placed after a number means that the number is to be multiplied by itself. That is, the number is to be used as a factor two times. Thus, 5^2 means that 5 should be multiplied by itself: $5^2 = 5 \times 5 = 25$. The small raised 2 is called an **exponent** (ĭk·spō´nənt).

To read the expression 5^2, say "five to the second power" or "five squared." The formula for finding the area of a square includes the exponent 2.

> To find the area (a) of a square, multiply the length of one side (s) by itself.
> **Memorize this formula for the area of a square.**
> area = side × side, or $a = s^2$

> **Example A**
>
> Find the area of a square with sides 9 inches long.
> $a = s^2$ means $a = s \times s$
> $a = 9$ inches $\times$ 9 inches $= 81$ square inches

A parallelogram is like a rectangle in that it has two sets of parallel sides. But a parallelogram is not a rectangle because its corners are usually not right angles.

The area of a parallelogram is found by multiplying the length of the **base** times the **height**. The base is the lower or upper side of the parallelogram. The height is the perpendicular distance between the two bases, shown by a dotted line on the diagram. The height is *not* found by measuring the length of the slanted sides.

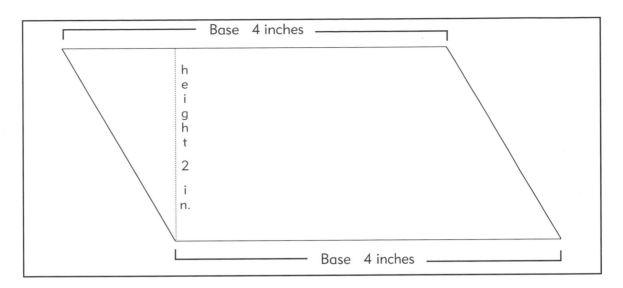

To find the area (a) of a parallelogram, multiply the length of the base (b) times the height (h).

Memorize this formula for the area of a parallelogram.

area = base × height, or $a = bh$

Example B

Find the area of a parallelogram having a base of 4 inches and height of 2 inches.

$a = bh$

$a = 4$ in. × 2 in.

$a = 8$ sq. in.

CLASS PRACTICE

Find the areas of squares having these sizes.

a. $s = 14''$	**b.** $s = 27''$	**c.** $s = 21$ cm	**d.** $s = 17.5$ cm

Find the areas of parallelograms with these dimensions.

e. $b = 9''$	**f.** $b = 23''$	**g.** $b = 14$ cm	**h.** $b = 3.68$ m
$h = 8''$	$h = 16''$	$h = 12$ cm	$h = 1.19$ m

WRITTEN EXERCISES

A. *Find the area of squares having these sizes.*

1. $s = 12''$	**2.** $s = 16''$	**3.** $s = 17$ cm	**4.** $s = 23$ cm
5. $s = 4.5$ yd.	**6.** $s = 3.75$ yd.	**7.** $s = 2.7$ km	**8.** $s = 3.5$ km
9. $s = 6\frac{1}{2}$ feet	**10.** $s = 13\frac{2}{3}$ yd.		

B. Find the areas of parallelograms with these dimensions.

11. $b = 17''$
    $h = 15''$

12. $b = 27''$
    $h = 17''$

13. $b = 48'$
    $h = 32'$

14. $b = 145'$
    $h = 113'$

15. $b = 13.5$ mi.
    $h = 11.7$ mi.

16. $b = 19.8$ mi.
    $h = 15.9$ mi.

17. $b = 23.7$ km
    $h = 19.3$ km

18. $b = 78.9$ km
    $h = 47.6$ km

19. $b = 9\frac{1}{2}$ ft.
    $h = 7\frac{3}{4}$ ft.

20. $b = 15\frac{2}{3}$ yd.
    $h = 7\frac{1}{3}$ yd.

C. Solve these reading problems

21. A certain city block is a 660-foot square. What is its area?

22. How far would you need to walk to go around the block described in problem 21?

23. The Shale Ridge Christian School is built on a square lot with 325-foot sides. What is the area of the lot?

24. A certain field in the shape of a parallelogram has a base of 425 feet and a height of 840 feet. What is its area?

25. Charles spaded a circular area in the front yard for Mother's flower bed. When he was finished, he put a border of bricks around the bed. If the diameter of the flower bed was 12 feet, what was the length of the border?

26. One traffic circle has a radius of 275 feet. What is the distance around the circle?

REVIEW EXERCISES

D. Find the areas of these rectangles. *(Lesson 113)*

27. $l = 45$ ft.
    $w = 39$ ft.

28. $l = 41.9$ m
    $w = 31.7$ m

E. Find the circumferences of circles having these sizes, using $\frac{22}{7}$ for pi. *(Lesson 112)*

29. $d = 14''$

30. $d = 21'$

F. Express the profit as a percent of sales, to the nearest whole number. *(Lesson 97)*

31. sales: $150   profit: $25

32. sales: $95   profit: $16

G. Find the amount of increase or decrease and the new price. *(Lesson 74)*

	Original Price	Percent of Increase		Original Price	Percent of Decrease
33.	$17.40	15%	34.	$21.50	16%

H. Find the actual distance if the scale of miles is $\frac{3}{4}$ inch = 2 miles. *(Lesson 75)*

35. $2\frac{1}{2}$ inches

36. $3\frac{3}{4}$ inches

115. Area of a Triangle

Finding the area of a rectangle or parallelogram is fairly simple because their opposite sides are parallel. Triangles do not have parallel sides, so an extra step is required. In the diagram below, notice that two congruent triangles are placed together to form a parallelogram. This can be done with any triangle; if a congruent triangle is placed beside it, the result is a parallelogram.

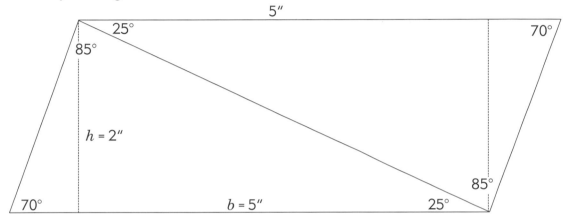

The diagram above shows that the area of a triangle is half that of a parallelogram having the same base and height. This points to the formula for the area of a triangle, which is given in the box.

To find the area (a) of a triangle, multiply $\frac{1}{2}$ times the length of the base (b) times the height (h).

Memorize this formula for the area of a triangle.

area = $\frac{1}{2}$ × base × height, or $a = \frac{1}{2}bh$

Example A	**Example B**
Find the area of one triangle shown above.	Find the area of a triangle having a base of 7 inches and a height of 6 inches.
$a = \frac{1}{2}bh$	$a = \frac{1}{2}bh$
$a = \frac{1}{2} \times 5 \times 2$	$a = \frac{1}{2} \times 7 \times 6$
$a = \frac{1}{2} \times 10$	$a = \frac{1}{2} \times 42$
$a = 5$ square inches	$a = 21$ square inches

CLASS PRACTICE

Find the areas of triangles having these dimensions.

a. $b = 5$ in.
    $h = 3$ in.

b. $b = 12$ in.
    $h = 9$ in.

c. $b = 17$ cm
    $h = 13$ cm

d. $b = 12.5$ cm
    $h = 11$ cm

WRITTEN EXERCISES

A. *Find the areas of triangles having these dimensions.*

1. $b = 8$ in.
    $h = 4$ in.

2. $b = 9$ in.
    $h = 8$ in.

3. $b = 12$ in.
    $h = 12$ in.

4. $b = 15$ in.
    $h = 14$ in.

5. $b = 20$ in.
    $h = 14$ in.

6. $b = 25$ in.
    $h = 16$ in.

7. $b = 18$ in.
    $h = 16$ in.

8. $b = 45$ in.
    $h = 28$ in.

9. $b = 25$ mm
    $h = 19$ mm

10. $b = 34$ mm
     $h = 22$ mm

11. $b = 45$ cm
     $h = 37$ cm

12. $b = 72$ cm
     $h = 49$ cm

13. $b = 19.2$ m
     $h = 16.8$ m

14. $b = 25.9$ m
     $h = 18.7$ m

15. $b = 32.6$ m
     $h = 27.8$ m

16. $b = 61.6$ m
     $h = 48.6$ m

B. *Measure these triangles. Find their areas in square inches.*

17.

18.

C. *Solve these reading problems.*

19. Father is cutting triangular shelves to place in a corner. The front (base) of each shelf is 24 inches and the depth (height) is 12 inches. What is the surface area of each shelf?

20. The gable end of a house has a 34-foot base. The height of the gable end is 13 feet. What is its area?

21. The Risser's house is located on a triangular lot with 250 feet of road frontage and a depth of 700 feet. What is the area of the property?

22. A triangular plate of steel has a base of 28 inches and a height of 20 inches. If both sides are painted, what is the total area covered?

23. Sharon bought a Bible storybook that cost $15.95 plus 7% sales tax. How much did she pay in all?

24. The Martins are replacing the roof shingles on their house. Each side of the roof measures 44 feet by 21 feet. What is the total area of the roof?

REVIEW EXERCISES

D. Find the areas of polygons with these dimensions. *(Lessons 113, 114)*

25. *square*
$s = 14.9$ cm

26. *square*
$s = 9.7$ m

27. *rectangle*
$l = 14$ ft.
$w = 11.5$ ft.

28. *parallelogram*
$b = 28''$
$h = 21''$

E. Find the perimeters of these polygons. *(Lesson 111)*

29. the square in problem 25

30. the rectangle in problem 27

F. Write the symbols for these geometric figures. *(Lesson 107)*

31.

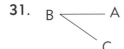

32.

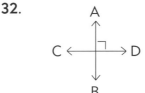

G. Find the sales tax. *(Lesson 98)*

33. sale, $28.95; rate, 6%

34. sale, $89.95; rate, $5\frac{1}{2}$%

H. Multiply these fractions mentally. *(Lesson 46)*

35. $\frac{3}{4}$ of 16 = _____

36. $\frac{5}{8}$ of 40 = _____

116. Area of a Trapezoid

Example A: Trapezoid

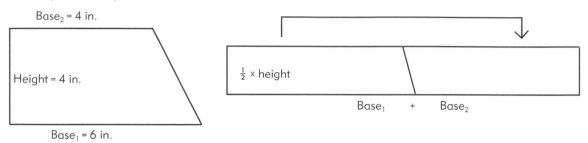

Base$_2$ = 4 in.

Height = 4 in.

Base$_1$ = 6 in.

$\frac{1}{2}$ × height

Base$_1$ + Base$_2$

A trapezoid (trăp′ ĭ·zoid) is a quadrilateral that has one set of parallel sides and one set that is not parallel. How can you find the area of such an odd-shaped figure? First think of the trapezoid as being cut horizontally in two pieces. Then think of the top half as being flipped over and set beside the bottom half, as shown in the diagram above. The result is a parallelogram with the same area as the original trapezoid, but with only half its height.

The area of a parallelogram is found by using the formula $a = bh$. To find the area of a trapezoid, you must find half its height and multiply that times the total length of the bases (found by adding the lengths of base$_1$ and base$_2$). For the trapezoid above, this works as shown below.

$$\text{area} = \tfrac{1}{2} \times 4 \times (4 + 6)$$
$$= 2 \times 10$$
$$= 20 \text{ square inches}$$

To find the area (a) of a trapezoid, multiply $\frac{1}{2}$ times the height (h) times the sum of the two bases (b).
Memorize this formula for the area of a trapezoid.
area = $\frac{1}{2}$ × height × (base$_1$ + base$_2$), or $a = \frac{1}{2} h(b_1 + b_2)$

Example B

$h = 4''$
$b_1 = 9''$
$b_2 = 5''$

9"

4"

5"

$a = \frac{1}{2} h\,(b_1 + b_2)$
$a = \frac{1}{2} \times 4 \times (9 + 5)$
$a = 2 \times 14$
$a = 28$ sq. in.

Example C

$h = 14$ cm
$b_1 = 15$ cm
$b_2 = 19$ cm

15 cm

14 cm

19 cm

$a = \frac{1}{2} h\,(b_1 + b_2)$
$a = \frac{1}{2} \times 14 \times (15 + 19)$
$a = 7 \times 34$
$a = 238$ cm^2

CLASS PRACTICE

Find the areas of trapezoids with these dimensions.

a. $h = 4''$
$b_1 = 5''$
$b_2 = 3''$

b. $h = 12''$
$b_1 = 6''$
$b_2 = 10''$

c. $h = 18''$
$b_1 = 15''$
$b_2 = 27''$

d. $h = 300'$
$b_1 = 125'$
$b_2 = 155'$

WRITTEN EXERCISES

A. *Find the areas of trapezoids with these dimensions.*

1. $h = 2''$
$b_1 = 6''$
$b_2 = 4''$

2. $h = 5''$
$b_1 = 7''$
$b_2 = 5''$

3. $h = 8''$
$b_1 = 9''$
$b_2 = 7''$

4. $h = 7'$
$b_1 = 8'$
$b_2 = 6'$

5. $h = 9''$
$b_1 = 12''$
$b_2 = 10''$

6. $h = 7''$
$b_1 = 11''$
$b_2 = 21''$

7. $h = 12''$
$b_1 = 15''$
$b_2 = 25''$

8. $h = 15'$
$b_1 = 18'$
$b_2 = 14'$

9. $h = 32$ cm
$b_1 = 21$ cm
$b_2 = 27$ cm

10. $h = 45$ cm
$b_1 = 18$ cm
$b_2 = 22$ cm

11. $h = 69$ cm
$b_1 = 78$ cm
$b_2 = 98$ cm

12. $h = 55$ cm
$b_1 = 91$ cm
$b_2 = 77$ cm

13. $h = 92$ m
$b_1 = 115$ m
$b_2 = 131$ m

14. $h = 120$ m
$b_1 = 148$ m
$b_2 = 196$ m

15. $h = 200$ ft.
$b_1 = 350$ ft.
$b_2 = 270$ ft.

16. $h = 350$ ft.
$b_1 = 425$ ft.
$b_2 = 375$ ft.

B. *Solve these reading problems.*

17. A certain city block is in the shape of a trapezoid. The lengths of the parallel streets (the bases) are 660 feet and 450 feet. The distance between the parallel streets (the height) is 650 feet. What is the area of this block?

18. Another city block is triangular. If the length of one side is 650 feet and the height is 325 feet, what is its area?

19. The floor of a rectangular cistern measures 7 feet by 8 feet. If the water pressure on the cistern floor is 220 pounds for every square foot, what is the total water pressure on the floor of the cistern?

20. A clock has a second hand that is 3 inches long. How far does the outer tip move in 1 minute?

21. The Millers have a rectangular garden that measures 110 feet by 95 feet. They are planning to put a low fence all the way around the garden to keep out rabbits. How long a fence will they need?

22. James lives near a small lake and enjoys riding his bicycle on the circular path around it, which has a diameter of $\frac{1}{2}$ mile. To the nearest tenth of a mile, how far does James ride on one trip around the lake?

REVIEW EXERCISES

C. Find the areas of polygons with these dimensions. *(Lessons 113, 114)*

23. rectangle
$l = 15$ cm
$w = 13$ cm

24. square
$s = 17$ in.

25. square
$s = 16.5$ m

26. parallelogram
$b = 15.1$ cm
$h = 11.9$ cm

D. Find the circumferences of circles having these sizes. Use $\frac{22}{7}$ for pi in Exercises 29 and 30. *(Lesson 112)*

27. $d = 12''$

28. $d = 15''$

29. $r = 7$ cm

30. $r = 84$ cm

E. Find the simple interest. *(Lesson 100)*

31. $p = \$1,700$
$r = 6\%$
$t = 210$ days

32. $p = \$2,200$
$r = 7\%$
$t = 240$ days

F. Find these percentages. *(Lesson 83)*

33. 115% of 60

34. 145% of 75

35. 215% of 120

36. 350% of 140

G. Solve these division problems. *(Lessons 47, 48)*

37. $3\frac{3}{4} \div \frac{3}{8}$

38. $2\frac{3}{5} \div \frac{1}{2}$

39. $3\frac{1}{2} \div 1\frac{1}{4}$

40. $4\frac{2}{3} \div 1\frac{1}{6}$

117. Area of a Circle

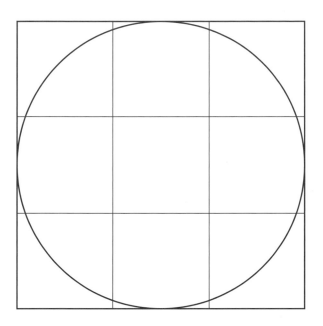

The circle at the left has a radius of $1\frac{1}{2}$ inches and a diameter of 3 inches. Each square on the block is 1 square inch. By counting carefully, you can see that the circle covers about 7 square inches.

But this method gives only a rough estimate of the area of a circle. A better and more accurate way is to calculate the area by using the value of π in a formula.

To find the area of a circle, first find the square of the radius (multiply the radius by itself). Then multiply the result times π. Use 3.14 for π unless you are instructed otherwise. If the diameter is given instead of the radius, first divide it by 2 to find the radius; then find the area.

To find the area (a) of a circle, multiply π × (radius x radius).
Memorize this formula for the area of a circle.
area = π × (radius x radius), or $a = \pi r^2$

Example A

Find the area of a circle with a radius of 5 inches.

$a = \pi \times r \times r$
$a = 3.14 \times 5 \times 5$
$a = 78.5$ sq. in.

Example B

Find the area of a circle with a diameter of 8.6 meters.

$d = 8.6$ m; $r = 8.6 \div 2 = 4.3$ m
$a = \pi \times r \times r$
$a = 3.14 \times 4.3 \times 4.3$
$a = 58.0586$ m²

CLASS PRACTICE

Find the area of each circle. Use $\frac{22}{7}$ for pi in problem d.

a. $r = 2''$ b. $r = 8$ cm   c. $d = 12$ cm   d. $r = 420$ m

WRITTEN EXERCISES

A. Find the areas of circles having these sizes. Remember: *d* means "diameter" and *r* means "radius."

1. *r* = 3 in.
2. *r* = 4 in.
3. *r* = 9 cm
4. *r* = 7 cm

5. *r* = 11 ft.
6. *r* = 13 ft.
7. *r* = 5.2 m
8. *r* = 2.7 m

9. *d* = 9 in.
10. *d* = 26 ft.
11. *d* = 47 mm
12. *d* = 16.9 cm

B. Find the areas of circles having these sizes. Use $\frac{22}{7}$ for pi.

13. *r* = 7″
14. *r* = 14″
15. *r* = 35″
16. *r* = 42″

C. Solve these reading problems. Use 3.14 for pi.

17. The largest masonry dome in existence is on the Pantheon in Rome, Italy. The Pantheon was used by the Romans for idol worship in Jesus' day. The diameter of the dome is 142 feet. What is its circumference?

18. A stainless steel dome on a public building in Pittsburgh, Pennsylvania, is one of the largest domes in the world. The diameter of this dome is 415 feet. What is the distance around its edge?

19. The diameter of the dome on the Pantheon is 142 feet. How much area does it cover? (Remember to find the radius first.)

20. What is the area covered by the dome described in problem 18?

21. An automobile tire 25 inches in diameter is driven across a spot of wet paint on the road. Every time the tire goes around, it makes another paint spot. How far apart are the spots on the road?

22. Uncle Mervin wants to build a fence around a rectangular field that is 550 feet long and 480 feet wide. He plans to use 4 strands of barbed wire. How many feet of barbed wire will he need?

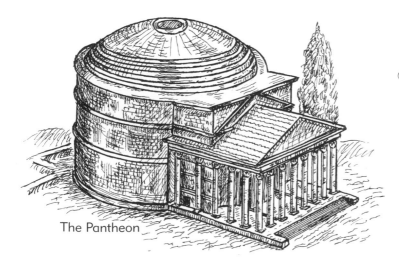

The Pantheon

Thou shalt worship the Lord thy God, and him only shalt thou serve.
Luke 4:8

REVIEW EXERCISES

D. *Find the areas of polygons with these dimensions.* (Lessons 114-116)

23. *rectangle*
l = 4.5 cm
w = 3.7 cm

24. *parallelogram*
b = 14 in.
h = 13 in.

25. *square*
s = 15.5 cm

26. *trapezoid*
h = 15 in.
b_1 = 32 in.
b_2 = 26 in.

E. *Identify the types of angles shown below.* (Lesson 108)

27.

28.

29.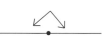

30.

F. *Find these percentages.* (Lesson 85)

31. $\frac{3}{4}$% of 70

32. $\frac{1}{2}$% of 90

33. $1\frac{1}{2}$% of 75

34. $3\frac{3}{4}$% of 78

G. *Find the new price after each increase or decrease. Round the answer to the nearest cent.* (Lesson 84)

Original Price	Percent of Increase or Decrease
35. $15.00	29% decrease
36. $16.75	20% increase

118. Working With Graphs: The Circle Graph

Bar graphs and picture graphs show how amounts compare with each other. Line graphs show how values change over a period of time. But a **circle graph** shows how a whole amount is divided into different parts.

The circle graph below shows what part of the students in the Sharon Mennonite School are in each room. You can see at a glance that no room has $\frac{1}{4}$ of all the students, but several of the rooms have about $\frac{1}{5}$ of all the students.

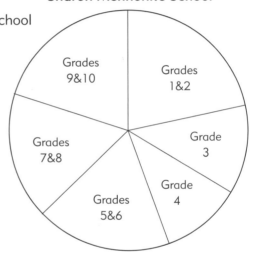

Students in Each Classroom at Sharon Mennonite School

Students in Each Classroom at Sharon Mennonite School

	No. of Students	Part of School	No. of Degrees
Grades 1, 2	24	0.218	78°
Grade 3	13	0.118	42°
Grade 4	12	0.109	39°
Grades 5, 6	20	0.182	66°
Grades 7, 8	19	0.173	62°
Grades 9, 10	22	0.200	72°
Totals	110	1.000	359°

Calculating the Sectors in a Circle Graph

In the graph above, each **sector** (part between two radii) takes up the same fractional part of the circle as that classroom is of the entire number of students. Use the following steps to calculate the number of degrees in each sector of a circle graph.

1. Write a fraction showing what part of the entire circle each sector will be. The numerator should be the number of items in that sector, and the denominator should be the total number of items that the graph represents.

2. Change each fraction you found in step 1 to a decimal rounded to the nearest thousandth. This shows what decimal part of the entire circle each sector will be.

3. A circle has 360 degrees. To find the number of degrees for each sector, multiply 360 by the decimal for that sector.

4. Check your answers to make sure they are logical. The sum of all the decimals should equal 1.000, and the sum of all the degrees should equal 360°. Because of rounding, however, there may be a difference of 1 or 2 from the sum of the decimals or the degrees.

CLASS PRACTICE

Complete the following table.

Number of Students by Classroom

	Classrooms	Students	Fraction	Decimal	Degrees
a.	Grade 1	16	___	___	___
b.	Grades 2, 3	22	___	___	___
c.	Grades 4, 5	18	___	___	___
d.	Grade 6	14	___	___	___
e.	Grades 7, 8	23	___	___	___
f.	Grades 9, 10	19	___	___	___
g.	*Totals*	112	___	___	___

WRITTEN EXERCISES

A. Study the following circle graph, and do the exercises.

1. Which region contains approximately one-fifth of the area of the United States?

2. Alaska, Hawaii and the Pacific Coast States contain about ($\frac{1}{2}, \frac{1}{3}, \frac{1}{4}, \frac{1}{5}$) of the total land area.

3. The Southwestern States and the Rocky Mountain States together contain about ($\frac{1}{4}, \frac{1}{3}, \frac{1}{2}, \frac{3}{5}$) of the total land area.

4. The information in Part B of your assignment shows that the New England States and the Middle Atlantic States contain about $\frac{1}{4}$ of the population of the United States. These regions contain about ($\frac{1}{15}, \frac{1}{5}, \frac{1}{4}$) of the total land area.

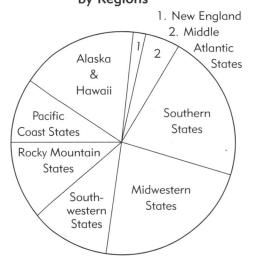

Area of the United States by Regions

1. New England
2. Middle Atlantic States

B. The following table has information for a circle graph on population distribution in the United States. Find the numbers of degrees for each sector of the graph.

Region	Population	Decimal Part	Degrees
New England States	13,050,045	0.051	5. ___
Middle Atlantic States	52,100,527	0.203	6. ___
Southern States	71,025,117	0.276	7. ___
Midwestern States	64,859,318	0.252	8. ___
Southwestern States	8,801,117	0.034	9. ___
Rocky Mountain States	5,884,719	0.023	10. ___
Pacific Coastal States	39,747,893	0.155	11. ___
Alaska and Hawaii	1,730,743	0.007	12. ___
Totals	257,199,479	1.000	13. ___

C. *Complete this chart.*

Number of States by Regions				
Region	*States*	*Fraction*	*Decimal*	*Degrees*
New England	6	14.		
Middle Atlantic	7	15.		
Southern	11	16.		
Midwestern	13	17.		
Southwestern	4	18.		
Rocky Mountain	4	19.		
Pacific Coast	3	20.		
Alaska, Hawaii	2	21.		
Totals	50	22.		

D. *Solve these reading problems.*

23. Of the 25 students in grades six and seven, 7 are eleven years old, 13 are twelve, and 5 are thirteen. How many degrees should each age group have on a circle graph?

24. Of the 100 acres on the Zooks' farm, 72 are farmland, 15 are meadow, and 13 are woodland. Find the degrees that each part of the farm should have on a circle graph.

25. Oak trees are one of the larger kinds of trees. One very large oak in Gloucestershire, England, has a trunk that is 15 feet in diameter. To the nearest foot, what is the circumference of the oak?

26. The trunk of the North American white oak grows up to 8 feet in diameter. How many square feet are covered by the trunk of such an oak?

27. Grant Township requires building lots to be one acre or larger. Is a rectangular lot 250 feet by 150 feet large enough for a building lot? If you do not remember the size of an acre, see Lesson 28.

28. In a trapezoid-shaped lot, one parallel side is 180 feet long and the other is 250 feet long. The depth (height) of the lot is 220 feet. Is this lot at least the required one acre?

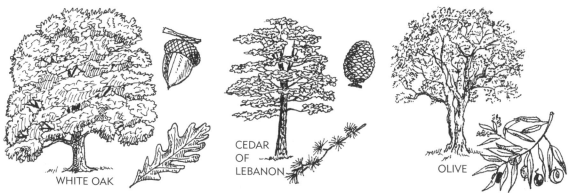

WHITE OAK

CEDAR OF LEBANON

OLIVE

Praise the Lord from the earth, ye . . . fruitful trees, and all cedars.   *Psalm 148:7, 9*

REVIEW EXERCISES

E. Find the areas of these polygons and circles. *(Lessons 114–117)*

29. *rectangle*
$l = 27'$
$w = 19'$

30. *parallelogram*
$b = 34$ cm
$h = 15$ cm

31. *square*
$s = 41$ cm

32. *trapezoid*
$h = 4.8$ m
$b_1 = 8.5$ m
$b_2 = 7.1$ m

33. *circle*
$r = 2.5$ cm

34. *circle*
$r = 13$ in.

F. Classify these triangles according to their angles. *(Lesson 109)*

35.

36.

37.

38.

G. Measure the degrees in these angles. *(Lesson 109)*

39. **40**.

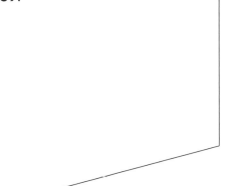 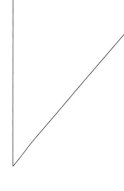

41. **42**.

 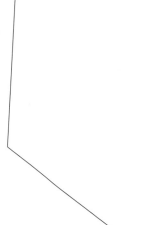

H. Find the percents. *(Lesson 86)*

43. 21 is ____% of 60

44. 36 is ____% of 80

I. Find the unknown numbers. *(Lesson 49)*

45. 16 is $\frac{4}{5}$ of ____

46. 18 is $\frac{2}{3}$ of ____

119. Reading Problems: Using a Parallel Problem

When there are fractions, decimals, or large numbers in a reading problem, it is sometimes hard to decide what steps are needed to find the answer. Often such a problem can be understood more easily if the difficult numbers are replaced by small whole numbers. The problem with small whole numbers is **parallel** to the more difficult one. When you solve this simpler parallel problem, you can understand the more difficult one and solve it by the same method.

Example

More difficult problem:

A supersonic jet traveled 525 miles in $\frac{5}{12}$ hour. What was its rate of speed?

Less difficult parallel problem:

A plane traveled 800 miles in 2 hours. What was its rate of speed?

In the parallel reading problem, the fraction is replaced by a small whole number and the other number is replaced by a round number. The second problem clearly shows that division is needed to find the answer. To solve the more difficult problem, therefore, 525 miles must be divided by $\frac{5}{12}$ hour.

Solution

Less difficult problem:

$800 \div 2 = 400$ m.p.h.

More difficult problem:

$$525 \div \frac{5}{12} = \frac{\overset{105}{\cancel{525}}}{1} \times \frac{12}{\underset{1}{\cancel{5}}} = \frac{1,260}{1} = 1,260 \text{ miles per hour}$$

To write a parallel problem that is easier to understand, replace any difficult numbers with simple whole numbers. Solve the simple problem, and then use the same method to solve the more difficult problem.

CLASS PRACTICE

Work with these problems in pairs. Use the solution to problem *b* ***as a help in solving*** *a,* ***and the solution to*** *d* ***as a help in solving*** *c.*

a. Jason worked $5\frac{1}{2}$ hours and was paid $26.40. How much would he be paid for working 8 hours?

b. Jason worked 3 hours and was paid $15. How much would he be paid for working 8 hours?

c. Marcus walked $2\frac{1}{2}$ miles in $\frac{5}{6}$ hour. What was his average rate of speed?

d. Marcus walked 5 miles in 2 hours. What was his average rate of speed?

WRITTEN EXERCISES

A. ***Work with these problems in pairs. Use the solution to number 2 as a help in solving number 1, and so forth.***

1. The Millerstown Mennonite Church paid $147.00 for 735 subscriptions to the *Star of Hope.* What was the cost per subscription?

2. The Millerstown Church paid $300 for 100 copies of the New Testament. What was the cost per copy?

3. Brother Carl traveled 412.5 miles in 7.5 hours to preach in a distant congregation. At that rate, how far did he travel in 3 hours?

4. Brother Carl traveled 400 miles in 8 hours to preach in a distant congregation. At that rate, how far did he travel in 3 hours?

And they went forth, and preached everywhere.
Mark 16:20

5. Uncle David sold 105 pounds of ground beef for $149.10. At that price, how much would he receive for 280 pounds?

6. Uncle David sold 100 pounds of ground beef for $150.00. At that price, how much would he receive for 300 pounds?

7. On a trip, Brother Martin averaged 52 miles per hour for the first $2\frac{1}{2}$ hours and 45 miles per hour for the last $1\frac{2}{3}$ hours. How many miles did he travel in all?

8. On a trip, Brother Martin averaged 50 miles per hour for the first 2 hours and 45 miles per hour for the last 2 hours. How many miles did he travel in all?

9. Father received $87.50 when he sold apples last week for $3.50 per basket. How much would he have received if he had sold the apples for $3.75 per basket?

10. Father received $90.00 when he sold apples last year for $3.00 per basket. How much would he have received if he had sold the apples for $4.00 per basket?

11. The price for one kind of feed increased 7%. It had been $175.80 per ton. What was the new price?

12. The price for one kind of feed increased 10%. It had been $150.00 per ton. What was the new price?

REVIEW EXERCISES

B. Find the missing numbers on this table for making a circle graph. *(Lesson 118)*

Number of States by Population				
Population Range	*No. of States*	*Fraction*	*Decimal*	*Degrees*
Under 1,000,000	7	**13.**		
1,000,000–2,999,999	15	**14.**		
3,000,000–4,999,999	13	**15.**		
5,000,000–9,999,999	8	**16.**		
10,000,000 and above	7	**17.**		
Totals	50	**18.**		

C. Find the areas of polygons and circles with these dimensions. *(Lessons 114–117)*

19. *rectangle*
    $l = 275'$
    $w = 145'$

20. *parallelogram*
    $b = 475'$
    $w = 325'$

21. *trapezoid*
    $h = 18$ m
    $b_1 = 19$ m
    $b_2 = 23$ m

22. *square*
    $s = 1.82$ m

23. *circle*
    $r = 10'$

24. *circle*
    $r = 1.5$ m

D. Find the unit price to the nearest tenth of a cent. *(Lesson 102)*

25. 130 gal. heating oil for $103.87

26. 250 gal. gasoline for $292.25

E. Solve these percent problems. *(Lesson 87)*

27. 12 is 30% of _____

28. 16 is 40% of _____

120. Chapter 9 Review

A. Match the following items. You will not use all the letters.

1. Any six-sided polygon
2. Any four-sided polygon
3. 3.14 or $\frac{22}{7}$
4. Formula for area of a circle
5. Formula for perimeter of a rectangle
6. Distance from the center of a circle to the edge
7. Quadrilateral with only one set of parallel sides
8. Any part of the edge of a circle
9. Distance from one edge of a circle through the center to the other edge
10. Any five-sided polygon
11. Formula for circumference of a circle
12. Formula for area of a square
13. Formula for area of a parallelogram
14. Formula for area of a trapezoid

a. $a = s^2$
b. π (pi)
c. hexagon
d. octagon
e. $p = 2(l + w)$
f. $a = bh$
g. quadrilateral
h. radius
i. $a = \frac{1}{2}bh$
j. arc
k. $a = \frac{1}{2}h(b_1 + b_2)$
l. trapezoid
m. $a = \pi r^2$
n. diameter
o. pentagon
p. $c = \pi d$

B. Write the symbols for these geometric expressions. *(Lesson 107)*

15. angle JKL
16. Line RS is parallel to line TU.
17. line OP
18. line segment YZ

C. Write the symbols for these geometric figures. *(Lesson 107)*

19. A —— B
20.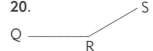
21.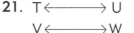
22.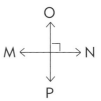

D. Identify the types of angles and triangles. *(Lessons 108, 109)*

23.
24.

25.    **26.**   **27.** 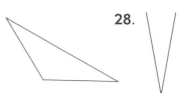   **28.**

E. Measure the angles indicated. All answers are multiples of 5 degrees.
(Lesson 108)

29. The angle in problem 23 = _____ degrees.

30. The angle in problem 24 = _____ degrees.

F. Draw the following angles. *(Lesson 108)*

31. a 145-degree angle   **32.** a 35-degree angle

G. Each pair of numbers gives the degrees in two angles of a triangle. Find the degrees in the third angle. *(Lesson 109)*

33. 42°, 61°   **34.** 75°, 35°   **35.** 105°, 68°   **36.** 32°, 32°

H. Classify these triangles according to the lengths of their sides. *(Lesson 109)*

37. 7", 9", 8"   **38.** 5', 2', 5'   **39.** 9', 9', 9'

I. Classify these triangles according to their angles. *(Lesson 109)*

40. 45°, 90°, 45°   **41.** 51°, 67°, 62°   **42.** 55°, 20°, 105°

J. Identify these sets of triangles as *congruent* **or** *similar.* *(Lesson 109)*

43. 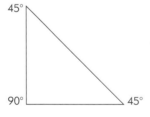   **44.**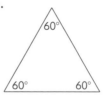

K. Find the perimeters of the figures described. *(Lessons 111, 112)*

45. *square*
   s = 14′

46. *square*
   s = 22 cm

47. *rectangle*
   l = 23″
   w = 17″

48. *rectangle*
   l = 10.5 m
   w = 7.9 m

49. *circle*
   d = 6′

50. *circle*
   d = 15″

51. *circle*
   r = 16 cm

52. *circle*
   r = 25 cm

L. Find the areas of the figures described. *(Lessons 113–117)*

53. *rectangle*
$l = 45''$
$w = 16''$

54. *rectangle*
$l = 24''$
$w = 21''$

55. *square*
$s = 14''$

56. *square*
$s = 25$ cm

57. *parallelogram*
$b = 45$ in.
$h = 36$ in.

58. *parallelogram*
$b = 5.7$ cm
$h = 4.8$ cm

59. *triangle*
$b = 12$ in.
$h = 8$ in.

60. *triangle*
$b = 25$ cm
$h = 18$ cm

61. *trapezoid*
$h = 7''$
$b_1 = 9''$
$b_2 = 7''$

62. *trapezoid*
$h = 35$ cm
$b_1 = 45$ cm
$b_2 = 37$ cm

63. *circle*
$r = 4$ in.

64. *circle*
$r = 9$ in.

65. *circle*
$d = 10$ cm

66. *circle*
$d = 15$ cm

M. Find the missing numbers on this table for making a circle graph. *(Lesson 118)*

Major Divisions of the Old Testament				
Section	*No. of Books*	*Fraction*	*Decimal*	*Degrees*
Law	5	**67.**		
History	12	**68.**		
Poetry	5	**69.**		
Major Prophets	5	**70.**		
Minor Prophets	12	**71.**		
Totals	39	**72.**		

N. Solve these problems. Numbers 73–76 are parallel sets. *(Lesson 119)*

73. One road in a new development is a cul-de-sac with a circular turnaround at the end. If the radius of the turnaround is $20\frac{1}{2}$ feet and paving costs $2.75 per square foot, what is the cost of the paving?

74. One road in a new development is a dead end with a circular turnaround at the end. If the radius of the turnaround is 20 feet and paving costs $3.00 per square foot, what is the cost of the paving?

352 Chapter 9 Geometry: Working With Lines and Planes

75. A rectangular garden 93 feet long has an area of 11,904 square feet. What is the perimeter of the garden?

76. A rectangular garden 10 feet long has an area of 90 square feet. What is the perimeter of the garden?

77. The Landis family lives on a triangular property that is 175 feet long (the base). The depth (height) of the lot is 495 feet. What is its area?

78. A school is located on a plot of land that narrows toward the back, giving it the shape of a trapezoid. It has 450 feet of road frontage and a back boundary of 300 feet. The depth of the property is 400 feet. What is its area?

121. Chapter 9 Test

Chapter 10

Geometry: Working With Solid Figures

All this came upon the king Nebuchadnezzar . . . .
The king spake, and said, "Is not this great Babylon, that I have built . . .
by the might of my power, and for the honour of my majesty?" . . .
there fell a voice from heaven, . . . "The kingdom is departed from thee . . .
and seven times shall pass over thee, until thou know that the most High
ruleth in the kingdom of men, and giveth it to whomsoever he will."
(Daniel 4:28–32)

122. Introduction to Solid Geometry

In Chapter 9 you studied lines and planes. Lines have only one dimension: length. Planes have two dimensions: length and width.

In Chapter 10 you will be working with figures that have three dimensions: length, width, and height. These figures are known as **geometric solids** because they have three dimensions. Any object with length, width, and height is a geometric solid. This is true whether the geometric solid contains mostly air, as your classroom does, or whether it is a block of solid steel. Geometric solids all have **volume**, or the ability to contain matter. Your classroom contains air, desks, and so forth. A block of steel contains steel.

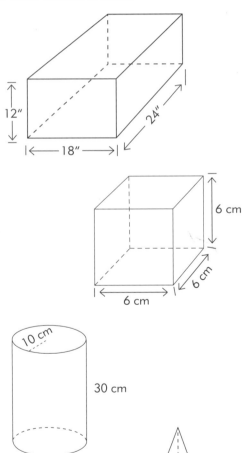

One common geometric solid is the **rectangular solid.** A rectangular solid has six rectangular or square sides. A cardboard box is an example of a rectangular solid. The six sides of a rectangular solid make three pairs of congruent rectangles.

The **cube** is a special type of rectangular solid; all six sides are congruent squares. The length, width, and height of a cube are equal.

The **cylinder** has two flat, circular bases that are parallel to each other. The **lateral surface** (side) of a cylinder forms a rectangle if it is rolled out flat. A tin can is an example of a cylinder.

The **cone** has one circular base and a lateral surface that comes to a point. Some ice cream cones are conical (cone-shaped).

CLASS PRACTICE

Identify these geometric solids.

a.

b.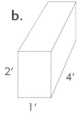

c.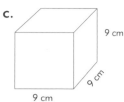

d.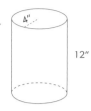

Give the correct vocabulary word for each definition.

e. Any figure that has length, width, and height.

f. A figure with three pairs of congruent rectangles.

g. A figure with two congruent circular bases.

h. A figure with six congruent squares.

i. A figure with one circular base and a lateral surface that narrows to a point.

WRITTEN EXERCISES

A. *For each blank, write the name of the correct plane figure.*

1. The base of a cylinder forms a _____.

2. If rolled out flat, the side of a cylinder would form a _____.

3. The base of a cube is a _____.

4. The base of a rectangular solid is either a rectangle or a _____.

5. The base of a cone is a _____.

B. *Find the answers.*

6. Find the area of the base of a cone if the radius is 4 inches.

7. Find the area of one side of a cube if one edge measures 9 centimeters.

8. Find the area of one base of a rectangular solid if the length is 41 millimeters and the width is 27 millimeters.

9. Find the circumference of the base of a cone having a diameter of 7 inches.

10. Find the area of one base of a rectangular solid if the length is $7\frac{1}{2}$ inches and the width is 6 inches.

11. Find the area of the base of a cone if the radius is 11 inches.

C. *Solve these reading problems.*

12. An upright silo has the shape of what geometric solid?

13. All six sides of the most holy place in the tabernacle measured 10 cubits by 10 cubits. What was the shape of the most holy place?

14. The tabernacle itself was 30 cubits long, 10 cubits wide, and 10 cubits high. The tabernacle had the shape of what geometric solid?

15. The hopper of a feed bin has a circular base and narrows to a point. What is its shape?

16. Fifty tracts cost $1.75. Find the unit price to the nearest tenth of a cent.

17. The total cost of four children's books is $8.50. Find the unit price to the nearest tenth of a cent.

REVIEW EXERCISES

D. Find the missing numbers on this table for making a circle graph. *(Lesson 118)*

Number of Fruit Trees in the Gehmans' Orchard				
Type of Tree	*Number*	*Fraction*	*Decimal*	*Degrees*
Apple	30	**18.**		
Peach	20	**19.**		
Pear	10	**20.**		
Cherry	15	**21.**		
Totals	75	$\frac{75}{75}$	1.000	360°

E. Find the circumferences of circles having these diameters. Use $\frac{22}{7}$ for pi in Exercises 22 and 23. *(Lesson 112)*

22. 42"   **23.** 7"   **24.** 12 cm   **25.** 15 cm

F. Use a compass to draw these geometric designs. *(Lesson 110)*

26. Begin with a circle having a 3" diameter, and make a regular hexagon.

27. Begin with a circle having a $2\frac{1}{2}$" diameter, and make an equilateral triangle.

G. Find the unit prices to the nearest tenth of a cent. *(Lesson 102)*

28. 8 grapefruits for $2.00   **29.** 12 oz. evaporated milk for $0.59

H. Find the missing part in each exercise. *(Lesson 89)*

30. sales = $225
rate = 9%
commission = _____

31. sales = $375
rate = 14%
commission = _____

32. sales = $175
commission = $14
rate = _____

33. rate = 6%
commission = $14.40
sales = _____

I. Solve these multiplication problems. *(Lesson 60)*

34. 14.7 × 3.1   **35.** 0.8 × 0.15

123. Surface Area of Rectangular Solids

In finding the area of a plane figure such as a square or circle, you work with only one surface because these figures have no thickness. A geometric solid is different because it does have thickness, and it has more than one side. The areas of all the sides combined is the **surface area** of the solid. Knowing how to find surface area is useful when painting a geometric solid or covering it in some other way.

The surface area of a rectangular solid is the total area of its six sides. Because a rectangular solid has three pairs of congruent sides, its surface area is found by using the following steps. These steps are the basis for the formula introduced below.

1. Multiply the length times the width (lw) to find the area of the base. Because the top is congruent to the base, twice the area of the base ($2 \times l \times w$, or $2lw$) equals the total area of the base and the top.

2. Multiply the width times the height (wh) to find the area of the front side. Because the front and back sides are congruent, twice the area of the front side ($2wh$) equals the total area of the front and back sides.

3. Multiply the length by the height (lh) to find the area of the left or right side. Because the sides are congruent, twice the area of one side ($2lh$) equals the area of the left and right sides together.

4. Add the three answers obtained in the steps above. Notice that each of the three dimensions was multiplied with each of the other two, and that each of the products was doubled. Study the boxes below. The symbol a_s means "area of a surface."

Memorize this formula for the surface area of a rectangular solid.

$$a_s = 2lw + 2wh + 2lh$$

Example A

Find the surface area of this rectangular solid.

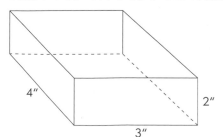

	a_s	=	$2lw$	+	$2wh$	+	$2lh$
	a_s	=	$2(4 \times 3)$	+	$2(3 \times 2)$	+	$2(4 \times 2)$
	a_s	=	$2(12)$	+	$2(6)$	+	$2(8)$
	a_s	=	24	+	12	+	16
	a_s	=	52 square inches				

Because all the sides of a cube are congruent, its total surface area is six times the area of one of the sides. The area of one side of a cube is found by squaring the length of one edge (e^2), so the surface area of a cube is six times as much, or $6e^2$.

Memorize this formula for the surface area of a cube.

$$a_s = 6e^2$$

Example B

Find the surface area of this cube.

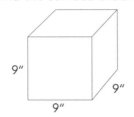

$$a_s = 6e^2$$
$$a_s = 6(9 \times 9)$$
$$a_s = 6(81)$$
$$a_s = 486 \text{ square inches}$$

CLASS PRACTICE

Find the surface areas of rectangular solids having these dimensions.

a. $l = 5''$
   $w = 4''$
   $h = 3''$

b. $l = 9''$
   $w = 6''$
   $h = 5''$

c. $l = 12$ cm
   $w = 9$ cm
   $h = 8$ cm

d. $l = 3.2$ m
   $w = 2.2$ m
   $h = 2$ m

Find the surface areas of cubes having these dimensions.

e. $e = 6''$ f. $e = 15''$ g. $e = 13$ cm   h. $e = 17$ cm

WRITTEN EXERCISES

A. Find the surface areas of rectangular solids with these dimensions by writing the missing numbers.

Dimensions	$2lw$	+	$2wh$	+	$2lh$	=	a_s
$l = 5''$ $w = 4''$ $h = 3''$	1. ____		2. ____		3. ____		4. ____
$l = 9''$ $w = 7''$ $h = 7''$	5. ____		6. ____		7. ____		8. ____
$l = 14$ cm $w = 12$ cm $h = 6$ cm	9. ____		10. ____		11. ____		12. ____
$l = 20$ cm $w = 15$ cm $h = 10$ cm	13. ____		14. ____		15. ____		16. ____

B. Find the surface areas of rectangular solids having these dimensions.

17. $l = 11''$
   $w = 9''$
   $h = 5''$

18. $l = 8'$
   $w = 7'$
   $h = 15'$

19. $l = 25$ cm
   $w = 16$ cm
   $h = 12$ cm

20. $l = 55$ cm
   $w = 55$ cm
   $h = 35$ cm

C. Find the surface areas of these cubes.

21. $e = 5''$
    22. $e = 7''$
    23. $e = 18$ cm
    24. $e = 25$ cm

25. $e = 28''$
    26. $e = 35''$
    27. $e = 80$ cm
    28. $e = 90$ cm

D. Solve these reading problems.

29. The Bolls are painting all the surfaces of their basement, which measures 44 feet by 32 feet by 8 feet. What is the surface area of the basement?

30. Mother is wrapping the book *All on a Mountain Day* to give the neighbor children. The box in which she is placing the book measures $10'' \times 8'' \times 2''$. What is the surface area of the box?

31. A cube of ice with 4-inch edges was placed in fruit drink to keep it cold. What was the surface area of the cube?

32. Father is building a crate with 40-inch edges. He is planning to fill it with clothing to send to a country that was stricken by an earthquake. Find the surface area of the crate.

33. One day Roseann picked 21 quarts of sugar peas. The next day she picked 24 quarts. To the nearest whole percent, what was the rate of increase?

34. A cow's average milk production increased from 60 pounds per day in one lactation to 65 pounds per day in the next. To the nearest whole percent, what was the rate of increase?

REVIEW EXERCISES

E. Identify these geometric figures. *(Lessons 107, 122)*

35.
   36.
   37.
   38.

F. Find the rate of increase or decrease. Label your answers. *(Lesson 90)*

	Original Price	New Price		Original Price	New Price
39.	$25.00	$28.00	40.	$16.00	$24.00
41.	$18.00	$14.40	42.	$35.00	$24.50

G. Write these decimals, using words. *(Lesson 54)*

43. 0.211
           44. 0.079

124. Surface Area of Cylinders

The surface area of a cylinder consists of two circular bases and a rectangular side. Finding the area of each surface and adding the amounts together gives the total surface area of a cylinder. To find the area of one circular base, use the formula $a = \pi r^2$. Because the two bases are congruent, the areas of both are found by doubling the area of one base ($2\pi r^2$). Finding the area of the rectangular side is the same as finding the area of a rectangle. The width of the rectangle is the height of the cylinder (h). The length of the rectangle is the circumference of the base. When the radius of the base is known, find the circumference by multiplying two times the radius times pi ($2\pi r$). Multiply that product by the height of the cylinder to find the lateral surface area ($2\pi rh$).

$$a_s = 2\pi r^2 + 2\pi rh$$
$$a_s = 2 \times 3.14 \times 2 \times 2$$
$$+ 2 \times 3.14 \times 2 \times 8$$
$$a_s = 25.12 + 100.48$$
$$a_s = 125.6 \text{ sq. in.}$$

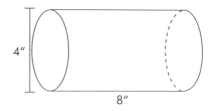

Combining the two formulas produces the formula shown below. The formula is not hard to memorize, for the two parts are nearly the same.

> **Memorize this formula for the surface area of a cylinder.**
> $$a_s = 2\pi r^2 + 2\pi rh$$

Example A	**Example B**
Find the surface area of a cylinder having a base with a radius of 3 inches and a height of 5 inches.	Find the surface area of cylinder having a base with a radius of 7 inches and a height of 12 inches.
$a_s = 2\pi r^2 + 2\pi rh$	$a_s = 2\pi r^2 + 2\pi rh$
$a_s = 2 \times 3.14 \times 3 \times 3$	$a_s = 2 \times 3.14 \times 7 \times 7$
$\qquad + 2 \times 3.14 \times 3 \times 5$	$\qquad + 2 \times 3.14 \times 7 \times 12$
$a_s = 56.52 + 94.2$	$a_s = 307.72 + 527.52$
$a_s = 150.72 \text{ sq. in.}$	$a_s = 835.24 \text{ sq. in.}$

CLASS PRACTICE

Find the surface area of cylinders having these dimensions.

  a. $r = 2''$; $h = 6''$ **b.** $r = 5''$; $h = 9''$ **c.** $r = 6''$; $h = 18''$

WRITTEN EXERCISES

A. *Do this exercise.*

1. Write the formula for finding the surface area of a cylinder.

B. *Find the surface areas of cylinders with these dimensions by writing the missing numbers.*

Dimensions	$2\pi r^2$	+	$2\pi rh$	=	a_s
$r = 3''$ $h = 4''$	2. _____		3. _____		4. _____
$r = 2''$ $h = 5''$	5. _____		6. _____		7. _____
$r = 4''$ $h = 10''$	8. _____		9. _____		10. _____
$r = 5$ m $h = 12$ m	11. _____		12. _____		13. _____
$r = 6$ m $h = 15$ m	14. _____		15. _____		16. _____

C. *Find the surface areas of these cylinders.*

17. $r = 8$ cm
    $h = 10$ cm

18. $r = 12$ cm
    $h = 30$ cm

19. $r = 10'$
    $h = 70'$

20. $r = 15''$
    $h = 40''$

D. *Solve these reading problems*

21. What is the surface area of a soup can if the radius is 1.5 inches and the height is 4 inches?

22. What is the surface area of a gasoline can if the radius is 6 inches and the height is 14 inches?

23. Delbert is painting a cylindrical fuel tank that has a radius of 2 feet and a height of 8 feet. What is the surface area being painted?

24. An air tank with a radius of 30 inches and a height of 144 inches holds air with a pressure of 100 pounds per square inch. What is the total pressure in pounds against the inside surface of the tank?

25. What is the surface area of a box measuring 14 inches by 10 inches by 8 inches?

26. What is the surface area of a cube with 9-inch edges?

REVIEW EXERCISES

E. *Write the following formulas.* (Lesson 123)

27. The formula for the surface area of a cube.

28. The formula for the surface area of a rectangular solid.

F. *Identify the geometric solids described.* (Lesson 122)

29. The three dimensions are equal.

30. The surface area consists of two circles and a rectangle.

31. The base is a circle, and the lateral surface narrows to a point.

32. The six sides are three pairs of congruent rectangles.

G. *Find the areas of parallelograms having these dimensions.* (Lesson 114)

33. $b = 12''$
   $h = 11''$

34. $b = 12.7$ m
   $h = 8.9$ m

H. *Draw these angles.* (Lesson 108)

35. a 50° angle

36. a 125° angle

I. *Solve these percent problems mentally.* (Lesson 91)

37. 40% of 45 = _____

38. 12 is 25% of _____

J. *Round these decimals as indicated.* (Lesson 55)

39. 0.4171 *(hundredth)*

40. 0.5953 *(tenth)*

125. Volume of Rectangular Solids

The length of your classroom is measured in feet or meters. But feet and meters can measure only the length of an object. They cannot measure the area of your classroom floor because it has two dimensions. Such a surface is measured in square feet or square meters.

Neither units of length nor units of area can measure the capacity or **volume** of your classroom. Volume has three dimensions: length, width, and height. Capacity or volume is measured in **cubic units** such as cubic feet or cubic meters. These express the total space occupied by something.

The term *cubic* shows that a unit has to do with the volume of an object. A cubic foot is equal to the space occupied by a 1-foot cube, a cubic meter is equal to the space occupied by a 1-meter cube, and so forth. The volume of a cubic meter does not need to have the shape of a cube; it only needs to take up the same amount of space.

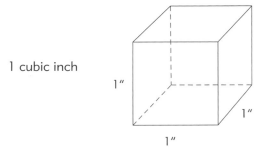

Following are the most common English and metric units of volume, along with their abbreviations. Notice that the exponent 3 is used in the metric system to indicate that a unit has length, width, and height.

Common English Units of Volume		Common Metric Units of Volume	
cubic inch	(cu. in.)	cubic millimeter	(mm^3)
cubic foot	(cu. ft.)	cubic centimeter	(cm^3)
cubic yard	(cu. yd.)	cubic meter	(m^3)
cubic mile	(cu. mi.)	cubic kilometer	(km^3)

To find the volume of a rectangular solid, multiply the area of the base times the height. Because the area of the base is found by multiplying the length times the width, the volume is found by multiplying all three dimensions: length, width, and height.

> **Memorize this formula for the volume of a rectangular solid.**
> $$v = lwh$$

Example A	Example B
Find the volume of a rectangular solid with these dimensions.	Find the volume of a room with these dimensions.
length = 14 feet	length = 4.2 m
width = 12 feet	width = 3.6 m
height = 8 feet	height = 2.4 m
$v = lwh$	$v = lwh$
$v = 14 \times 12 \times 8$	$v = 4.2 \times 3.6 \times 2.4$
$v = 1,344$ cu. ft.	$v = 36.288$ m³

CLASS PRACTICE

Find the volumes of these rectangular solids.

a. l = 5 in.
  w = 4 in.
  h = 6 in.

b. l = 25 in.
  w = 18 in.
  h = 16 in.

c. l = 35 cm
  w = 30 cm
  h = 25 cm

d. l = 25 m
  w = 14 m
  h = 5 m

WRITTEN EXERCISES

A. Find the volumes of these rectangular solids.

1. l = 4 in.
  w = 3 in.
  h = 2 in.

2. l = 5 in.
  w = 4 in.
  h = 3 in.

3. l = 9 cm
  w = 6 cm
  h = 4 cm

4. l = 9 m
  w = 9 m
  h = 8 m

5. l = 12 ft.
  w = 10 ft.
  h = 9 ft.

6. l = 16 ft.
  w = 14 ft.
  h = 8 ft.

7. l = 18 m
  w = 16 m
  h = 4 m

8. l = 22 m
  w = 12 m
  h = 9 m

9. l = 26 in.
  w = 22 in.
  h = 26 in.

10. l = 40 in.
  w = 25 in.
  h = 19 in.

11. l = 17 yd.
  w = 14 yd.
  h = 16 yd.

12. l = 18 yd.
  w = 15 yd.
  h = 13 yd.

13. l = 85 in.
  w = 42 in.
  h = 45 in.

14. l = 68 cm
  w = 51 cm
  h = 57 cm

15. l = 90 m
  w = 75 m
  h = 40 m

16. l = 90 yd.
  w = 50 yd.
  h = 35 yd.

B. Solve these reading problems

17. Brother Harvey has a rectangular classroom measuring 25 feet by 22 feet by 8 feet. What is the volume of the room?

18. The Martins' basement measures 48 feet by 28 feet by 7 feet. What is the volume?

19. Father went to a flood-stricken area to help with clean-up and repairs. From the basement of one house, he helped to pump out six feet of water. The basement measured 50 feet by 26 feet. Water weighs 62.4 pounds per cubic foot. How many pounds of water were in the basement?

20. Another house had collapsed. The house was rectangular, measuring 48 feet by 28 feet. If the water in the house reached a depth of 4 feet, what was its weight when the house collapsed? (Water weighs 62.4 pounds per cubic foot.)

21. The people who had lived in the house were rescued by helicopter. The blade of the helicopter made a circular sweep with a 25-foot radius. What was the area that the blade covered in one revolution?

22. If a trapezoid has bases of 10 inches and 12 inches, and its height is 17 inches, what is its area?

If thy brother be waxen poor, and fallen in decay with thee; then thou shalt relieve him: yea, though he be a stranger, or a sojourner; that he may live with thee.

Leviticus 25:35

REVIEW EXERCISES

C. Give the following formulas. See if you can write them without looking back. *(Lessons 123–124)*

23. The surface area of a cylinder.

24. The surface area of a rectangular solid.

25. The surface area of a cube.

26. The volume of a rectangular solid.

D. Find the surface areas of these geometric solids. *(Lessons 123, 124)*

27. *rectangular solid*
    $l = 7''$
    $w = 5''$
    $h = 6''$

28. *cube*
    $e = 11''$

29. *cube*
    $e = 12''$

30. *cylinder*
    $r = 4''$
    $h = 12''$

E. Find the areas of these planes. *(Lessons 116, 117)*

31. *circle*
    $r = 5''$

32. *circle*
    $r = 9$ cm

33. *trapezoid*
    $h = 5''$
    $b_1 = 4''$
    $b_2 = 8''$

34. *trapezoid*
    $h = 9''$
    $b_1 = 7''$
    $b_2 = 11''$

F. Change these fractions to decimals. You will not need to divide further than the ten-thousandths' place. *(Lesson 56)*

35. $\frac{13}{20}$

36. $\frac{11}{40}$

37. $\frac{5}{16}$

38. $\frac{13}{16}$

126. Volume of Cubes

A **cube** is a special kind of rectangular solid because all its edges have the same length. Its volume is also found by multiplying the length, width, and height. But since all three of these are equal, the term **edge** is used to refer to the dimensions. The volume of a cube is found by multiplying edge × edge × edge, or $e \times e \times e$.

When the same number is used as a factor three times, the third power of the number is obtained. Such a factor is said to be **cubed**, and it is expressed by using the exponent 3. Therefore, the expression $e \times e \times e$ can be simplified as e^3. The symbol e^3 is read "*e* cubed."

Memorize this formula for the volume of a cube.

$$v = e^3$$

Example A	**Example B**
Find the volume of a cube having 5-inch edges.	Find the volume of a cube with 23-centimeter edges.
$v = e^3$	$v = e^3$
$v = 5 \times 5 \times 5$	$v = 23 \times 23 \times 23$
$v = 125$ cu. in.	$v = 12{,}167$ cm^3

CLASS PRACTICE

Find the volumes of cubes having these dimensions.

  a. $e = 6$ in.   **b.** $e = 12$ ft.   **c.** $e = 16$ cm   **d.** $e = 25$ m

WRITTEN EXERCISES

  A. *Find the volumes of cubes having these dimensions.*

  1. $e = 2$ in.   **2.** $e = 3$ ft.   **3.** $e = 9$ cm   **4.** $e = 10$ m

  5. $e = 13$ in.   **6.** $e = 15$ ft.   **7.** $e = 18$ cm   **8.** $e = 20$ m

  9. $e = 22$ in.   **10.** $e = 26$ ft.   **11.** $e = 30$ cm   **12.** $e = 45$ m

13. $e = 50$ in.   **14.** $e = 60$ ft.   **15.** $e = 75$ cm   **16.** $e = 90$ m

  B. *Solve these reading problems.*

17. What is the volume of a cubic cedar closet with 8-foot edges?

18. One large toy block is a cube with edges of 7.5 centimeters. What is its volume?

19. A feed bin is an 11-foot cube. At 35 pounds per cubic foot, how many pounds of feed can the bin hold?

20. The Martins' cistern is a cube with 7-foot dimensions. At 62.4 pounds per cubic foot, how many pounds of water can the cistern hold?

21. In a hospital, two intersecting hallways form an 80° angle. What type of angle is that?

22. One week it rained four days. Write as a decimal the part of the week that was rainy. Round the decimal to the nearest thousandth.

Sing unto the Lord . . .

who prepareth rain for the earth, who maketh grass to grow upon the mountains.   Psalm 147:7, 8

REVIEW EXERCISES

C. Write the formulas indicated. *(Lessons 123–125)*

23. surface area of a cube

24. surface area of a rectangular solid

25. volume of a rectangular solid

26. surface area of a cylinder

D. Find the volumes of rectangular solids having these dimensions. *(Lesson 125)*

27. $l = 4'$
    $w = 3'$
    $h = 8'$

28. $l = 8$ m
    $w = 5$ m
    $h = 3$ m

29. $l = 25''$
    $w = 16''$
    $h = 15''$

30. $l = 32$ cm
    $w = 25$ cm
    $h = 18$ cm

E. Find the surface area of cylinders having these dimensions. *(Lesson 124)*

31. $r = 3''$
    $h = 10''$

32. $r = 4''$
    $h = 11''$

F. Name the geometric figures described below. *(Lessons 108, 122)*

33. Any figure with three dimensions.

34. A figure whose six sides are squares.

35. A 90° angle

36. A 125° angle

G. Express each fraction as a decimal to the nearest thousandth. *(Lesson 57)*

37. $\frac{3}{7}$

38. $\frac{10}{11}$

39. $\frac{11}{15}$

40. $\frac{13}{18}$

127. Volume of Cylinders

When you multiply lwh to find the volume of a rectangular solid, the first multiplication (lw) yields the area of the base. Multiplying that area times the height gives the volume of the rectangular solid. Thus, the formula could also be stated as $v = Bh$. (The capital B means "the **area** of the base.")

The formula $v = Bh$ can also be used to find the volume of a cylinder, as well as any geometric solid with vertical sides. First find the area of the base, and then multiply that area times the height. For the base of a cylinder, you must use the formula for the area of a circle.

volume of cylinder = area of circular base × height

$$v \qquad = \qquad \pi r^2 \qquad \times \quad h, \qquad \text{or } v = \pi r^2 h$$

> **Memorize this formula for the volume of a cylinder.**
> $$v = \pi r^2 h$$

Example A

Find the volume of a cylinder if the base has a radius of 4 inches and the height is 10 inches.

$$v = \pi r^2 h$$
$$v = 3.14 \times 4 \times 4 \times 10$$
$$v = 502.4 \text{ cu. in.}$$

Example B

Find the volume of a cylinder if the base has a radius of 10 meters and the height is 15 meters.

$$v = \pi r^2 h$$
$$v = 3.14 \times 10 \times 10 \times 15$$
$$v = 4{,}710 \text{ m}^3$$

CLASS PRACTICE

Find the volumes of cylinders having these dimensions.

a. $r = 2''$
  $h = 6''$

b. $r = 4'$
  $h = 15'$

c. $r = 12$ cm
  $h = 40$ cm

d. $r = 15$ m
  $h = 45$ m

WRITTEN EXERCISES

A. Find the volumes of cylinders having these dimensions.

1. $r = 3''$
  $h = 5''$

2. $r = 5''$
  $h = 8''$

3. $r = 6$ cm
  $h = 15$ cm

4. $r = 8$ cm
  $h = 20$ cm

5. $r = 9'$
  $h = 15'$

6. $r = 10'$
  $h = 9'$

7. $r = 12'$
  $h = 30'$

8. $r = 16'$
  $h = 40'$

9. $r = 15$ cm
  $h = 40$ cm

10. $r = 3$ m
  $h = 18$ m

11. $r = 30'$
  $h = 30'$

12. $r = 25'$
  $h = 30'$

B. Solve these reading problems.

13. A cylindrical fuel tank has a radius of 2 feet and a height of 8 feet. What is its volume?

14. If a silo has a radius of 10 feet and a height of 64 feet, what is its volume?

15. A horizontal fuel tank is a cylinder with a radius of 3 feet and a length (height) of 10 feet. At 7.5 gallons per cubic foot, how many gallons can the fuel tank hold?

16. A cylindrical water tank has a radius of 4 feet and a length of 12 feet. At 7.5 gallons per cubic foot, how many gallons of water can the tank hold?

17. What is the volume of a rectangular feed bin that measures 6 feet by 6 feet by 10 feet?

18. What is the volume of a rectangular feed bin whose dimensions are 8 feet, 8 feet, and 12 feet?

REVIEW EXERCISES

C. Write the formulas. *(Lessons 123–127)*

19. surface area of a cylinder

20. volume of a cylinder

21. volume of a cube

22. surface area of a cube

23. volume of a rectangular solid

24. surface area of a rectangular solid

D. Find the volumes of geometric solids having these dimensions. *(Lessons 125, 126)*

25. *rectangular solid*
$l = 15''$
$w = 12''$
$h = 10''$

26. *rectangular solid*
$l = 20$ m
$w = 18$ m
$h = 7$ m

27. *cube*
$e = 22''$

28. *cube*
$e = 18$ cm

E. Find the surface areas of geometric solids having these dimensions. *(Lesson 123)*

29. *rectangular solid*
$l = 16''$
$w = 14''$
$h = 10''$

30. *rectangular solid*
$l = 22$ m
$w = 15$ m
$h = 8$ m

31. *cube*
$e = 24''$

32. *cube*
$e = 16$ cm

F. Classify these triangles according to their angles. *(Lesson 109)*

33. angle $a = 50°$
angle $b = 65°$
angle $c = 65°$

34. angle $d = 30°$
angle $e = 40°$
angle $f = 110°$

G. Solve these problems. *(Lesson 58)*

35. $3.7 + 2.65 + 4.004 + 0.0017$

36. $14 + 7.075 + 6.89 + 2.0231$

128. Volume of Cones

A cone is similar to a cylinder in that it is round with a circular base. There is also a similarity between the volume of a cone and that of a cylinder. The volume of a cone is $\frac{1}{3}$ as much as that of a cylinder with the same dimensions. So instead of memorizing an altogether new formula for the volume of a cone, you need only to add $\frac{1}{3}$ to the formula for the volume of a cylinder.

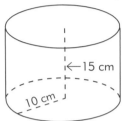

Cylinder: $v = \pi r^2 h$

Cone: $v = \frac{1}{3}\pi r^2 l$

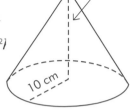

> **Memorize this formula for the volume of a cone.**
>
> $v = \frac{1}{3}\pi r^2 h$

Note carefully that the height of a cone is not the measure of the sloping side. It is the perpendicular measure from the center of the base to the point of the cone.

Remember that the formula for the volume of a cylinder could be stated as $v = Bh$. (B means area of the base.) Therefore, another way to state the volume of a cone is $v = \frac{1}{3}Bh$.

Example A	**Example B**
Find the volume of a cone if the radius of the base is 2 inches and the height is 5 inches.	Find the volume of a cone if the base has a radius of 12 centimeters and the height is 16 centimeters.
$v = \frac{1}{3}\pi r^2 h$	$v = \frac{1}{3}\pi r^2 h$
$v = \frac{1}{3} \times 3.14 \times 2 \times 2 \times 5$	$v = \frac{1}{3} \times 3.14 \times 12 \times 12 \times 16$
$v = 3.14 \times (2 \times 2 \times 5) \times \frac{1}{3}$	$v = (\frac{1}{3} \times 12) \times 3.14 \times (12 \times 16)$
$v = (3.14 \times 20) \div 3$	$v = 4 \times 3.14 \times 192$
$v = 20.93$ cu. in.	$v = 2,411.52$ cm³

Since factors can be multiplied in any order, it is helpful to group them together in a way that makes computation as simple as possible. In Example A, the factors $2 \times 2 \times 5$ are grouped together because they can be multiplied mentally, and the multiplication by $\frac{1}{3}$ (dividing by 3) is done last. In Example B, the factors $\frac{1}{3} \times 12$ are grouped together because the result is the whole number 4. You could also solve Example B by doing the division last, like this: $3.14 \times 12 \times 12 \times 16 = 7,234.56$, and $7,234.56 \div 3 = 2,411.52$. But the method shown is much simpler.

CLASS PRACTICE

Find the volumes of cones having these dimensions.

a. $r = 3''$
    $h = 7''$

b. $r = 5'$
    $h = 15'$

c. $r = 12$ cm
    $h = 20$ cm

d. $r = 24$ m
    $h = 45$ m

WRITTEN EXERCISES

A. Find the volumes of cones having these dimensions.

1. $r = 2''$
   $h = 9''$

2. $r = 4''$
   $h = 6''$

3. $r = 6$ cm
   $h = 12$ cm

4. $r = 9$ cm
   $h = 20$ cm

5. $r = 8'$
   $h = 12'$

6. $r = 7'$
   $h = 15'$

7. $r = 10'$
   $h = 30'$

8. $r = 11'$
   $h = 21'$

9. $r = 15$ cm
   $h = 50$ cm

10. $r = 14$ m
    $h = 24$ m

11. $r = 20'$
    $h = 30'$

12. $r = 24'$
    $h = 30'$

B. Solve these reading problems.

13. What is the volume of a conical (cone-shaped) cup that has a radius of 1.5 inches and a depth of 6 inches?

14. A conical food strainer has a radius of 3.5 inches and a depth (height) of 8.5 inches. What is its volume? Round to the nearest cubic inch.

15. The conical hopper of a feed bin has a radius of 8 feet and a depth of 9 feet. What is the volume?

16. A conical pile of stones at a stone quarry is 50 feet wide (diameter) and 21 feet high. What is the volume?

17. The town of Elizabeth has a cylindrical water reservoir with a radius of 30 feet and a height of 25 feet. What is the volume of the reservoir?

18. If a cube has 9-foot edges, what is its volume?

REVIEW EXERCISES

C. Find the volumes of geometric solids having these dimensions.
(Lessons 126, 127)

19. *cylinder*
    $r = 4''$
    $h = 10''$

20. *cylinder*
    $r = 6$ cm
    $h = 12$ cm

21. *cube*
    $e = 14''$

22. *cube*
    $e = 16$ cm

D. Find the surface areas of cylinders having these dimensions. *(Lesson 124)*

23. $r = 3''$
    $h = 12''$

24. $r = 5''$
    $h = 15''$

E. Use a compass to construct these geometric designs. *(Lesson 110)*

25. Draw a hexagon inside a circle with a 3″ diameter.

26. Draw an equilateral triangle inside a circle with a $3\frac{1}{2}$″ diameter.

F. Solve these multiplication and division problems by moving the decimal points. *(Lesson 59)*

27. $34.25 \div 100$

28. 0.3415×10

29. 15.59×100

30. $4.717 \times 1,000$

31. $42.27 \div 10$

32. $4,213.2 \div 1,000$

129. Working With Graphs: Drawing Circle Graphs

Preparing a circle graph is a two-part procedure. The first part, presented in Lesson 118, is to calculate the degrees in each sector of the graph. The second part is to actually construct the circle graph.

Calculating the Degrees for Each Sector

Following are the steps for calculating the degrees in each sector of a circle graph.

1. Write a fraction showing what part of the entire circle each sector will be. The numerator should be the number of items in that sector, and the denominator should be the total number of items that the graph represents.

2. Change each fraction found in step 1 to a decimal. Round the decimal to the nearest thousandth. This shows what part of the entire circle each sector should be.

3. To find the number of degrees in each sector, multiply 360 by the decimal found in step 2.

Parts of Joseph's Life				
Part	*No. of Years*	*Fraction*	*Decimal*	*Degrees*
At home in Canaan	17	$\frac{17}{110}$	0.155	56°
Slave and prisoner in Egypt	13	$\frac{13}{110}$	0.118	42°
Ruler in Egypt before family came	9	$\frac{9}{110}$	0.082	30°
In Egypt with family	71	$\frac{71}{110}$	0.645	232°
Totals	110	$\frac{110}{110}$	1.000	360°

Constructing a Circle Graph

Now that the degrees are calculated, you are ready to make the circle graph. Use the following steps.

1. Draw a circle with a 2-inch radius.

2. Draw a radius in the circle to use as a starting point.

3. Using the calculated degrees, draw an angle for the first sector. Use the second side of this angle as the base for the next angle. Continue around the circle until all the sectors are drawn.

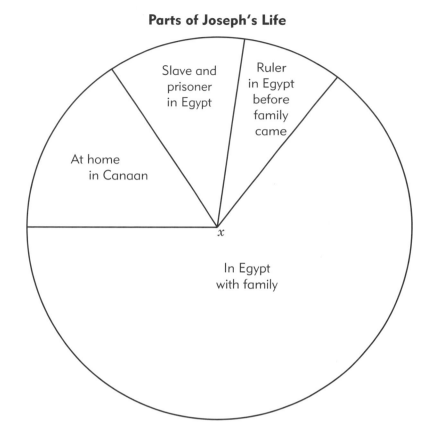

Parts of Joseph's Life

The last sector will be what is left when all the other sectors are drawn. Its size should be close to the number of degrees calculated for the last sector. Place a small x in the last sector to show that it is the last one completed.

4. Write the appropriate label in each sector.
5. Write a title for the graph.

CLASS PRACTICE

Complete the table showing the number of psalms in each of the five books of Psalms.

Psalms in the Five Books of Psalms							
Book	*No. of Psalms*	*Fraction*		*Decimal*		*Degrees*	
I	41	a.		b.		c.	
II	31	d.		e.		f.	
III	17	g.		h.		i.	
IV	17	j.		k.		l.	
V	44	m.		n.		o.	
Totals	150	p.		q.		r.	

Prepare a circle graph with the degrees you calculated in the table above.

WRITTEN EXERCISES

A. Copy and complete the table titled "Books in the Old and New Testaments."

Books in the Old and New Testaments				
	No. of Books	*Fraction*	*Decimal*	*Degrees*
O.T.	39	$\frac{39}{66}$	1.	2.
N.T.	27	$\frac{27}{66}$	3.	4.
Totals	66	$\frac{66}{66}$	5.	6.

B. Use the degrees calculated in Part A to make a circle graph.
This will be exercises 7–10.

C. Copy and complete this table.

Provinces and Territories of Canada by Regions				
Region	*No. of Items*	*Fraction*	*Decimal*	*Degrees*
Atlantic Provinces	4	$\frac{4}{12}$	11.	12.
Ontario and Quebec	2	$\frac{2}{12}$	13.	14.
Prairie Provinces	3	$\frac{3}{12}$	15.	16.
British Columbia	1	$\frac{1}{12}$	17.	18.
North (Territories)	2	$\frac{2}{12}$	19.	20.
Totals	12	$\frac{12}{12}$	21.	22.

D. Use the degrees calculated in Part C to make a circle graph.
This will be exercises 23–29.

E. Solve these reading problems.

30. A cone-shaped pile of feed has a radius of 12 feet and a height of 12 feet. What is its volume?

31. A conical pile of coal in a coal bin had a radius of 4 feet and a height of 6 feet. What was its volume?

32. One coal bin has the shape of a five-foot cube. Coal weighs about 80 pounds per cubic foot. If the bin is filled to capacity, how many pounds of coal are in it?

33. Air weighs about 0.08 pound per cubic foot. At that rate, how many pounds of air would be in an empty coal bin the shape of a 5-foot cube?

34. One week Father sent out bills amounting to $495.78 for carpentry work. His expenses that week were $125.48. What was his profit?

35. The following week the bills he sent totaled $435.67. His expenses were $65.49. What was his profit?

In all labour there is profit.

Proverbs 14:23

REVIEW EXERCISES

F. *Write the formulas. (Lessons 123–128)*

36. surface area of a rectangular solid

37. surface area of a cylinder

38. volume of a cylinder

39. volume of a cone

G. *Find the volume of each geometric solid. (Lessons 125–128)*

Rectangular Solid	*Cylinder*	*Cylinder*	*Cone*
40. l = 25 cm w = 15 cm h = 12 cm	41. r = 3″ h = 9″	42. r = 30 cm h = 50 cm	43. r = 20 cm h = 60 cm

H. *Calculate the profit or loss in each case. Label your answers profit or loss. (Lesson 96)*

44. income: $335.50
    expenses: $175.20

45. income: $450
    expenses: $532

130. Reading Problems: Drawing a Sketch

When you have a reading problem to solve, it is important that you can visualize the details. Drawing a simple sketch is sometimes helpful in seeing how the details fit together. This is especially true if the problem relates to area or distance. Notice how the sketch on page 377 helps in finding the solution for the reading problem in the box. Would you have solved the problem correctly without the sketch?

A church auditorium is 70 feet long. The front bench is 18 feet from the front of the auditorium. The distance from the front of one bench to the front of the next bench is $3\frac{1}{2}$ feet. The benches are 2 feet wide, and there is a $4\frac{1}{2}$-foot space behind the back bench. How many benches are on each side of the auditorium?

To draw a sketch for a reading problem, use the following steps.

1. Picture the problem and sketch it, using simple but neat shapes. Be sure to include all the necessary information from the problem. If the problem relates to distance, it is helpful to draw the sketch approximately to scale. The example on page 377 is drawn to the scale of 1" = 10'.
2. Write the information given in the problem where it belongs on the sketch.
3. Solve the problem. Make sure your answer agrees with the sketch.

CLASS PRACTICE

Draw a sketch for each problem. Then use your sketch to solve the problem.

a. Sandra hung 3 tablecloths on the line. She fastened each one with 4 clothespins. Wherever the tablecloths overlapped, she used one clothespin for both cloths. How many clothespins did she need?

b. Louise is setting the table for visitors that are coming to Sunday dinner. The table is 18 feet long. Sandra is placing plates at 2-foot intervals along both sides of the table, beginning 2 feet from each end. She is also placing two plates at each end of the table. How many plates does Louise need?

c. Marion is marking places to set fence posts for a 200-foot fence. The posts will be 20 feet apart. How many posts will be needed?

d. The foundation of a new church building is 2 feet wide. The inside measurement is 40 feet by 80 feet. What is the outside perimeter of the foundation?

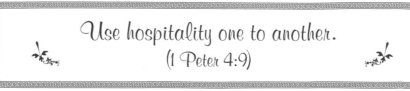

Use hospitality one to another.
(1 Peter 4:9)

Scale 1″ = 10′

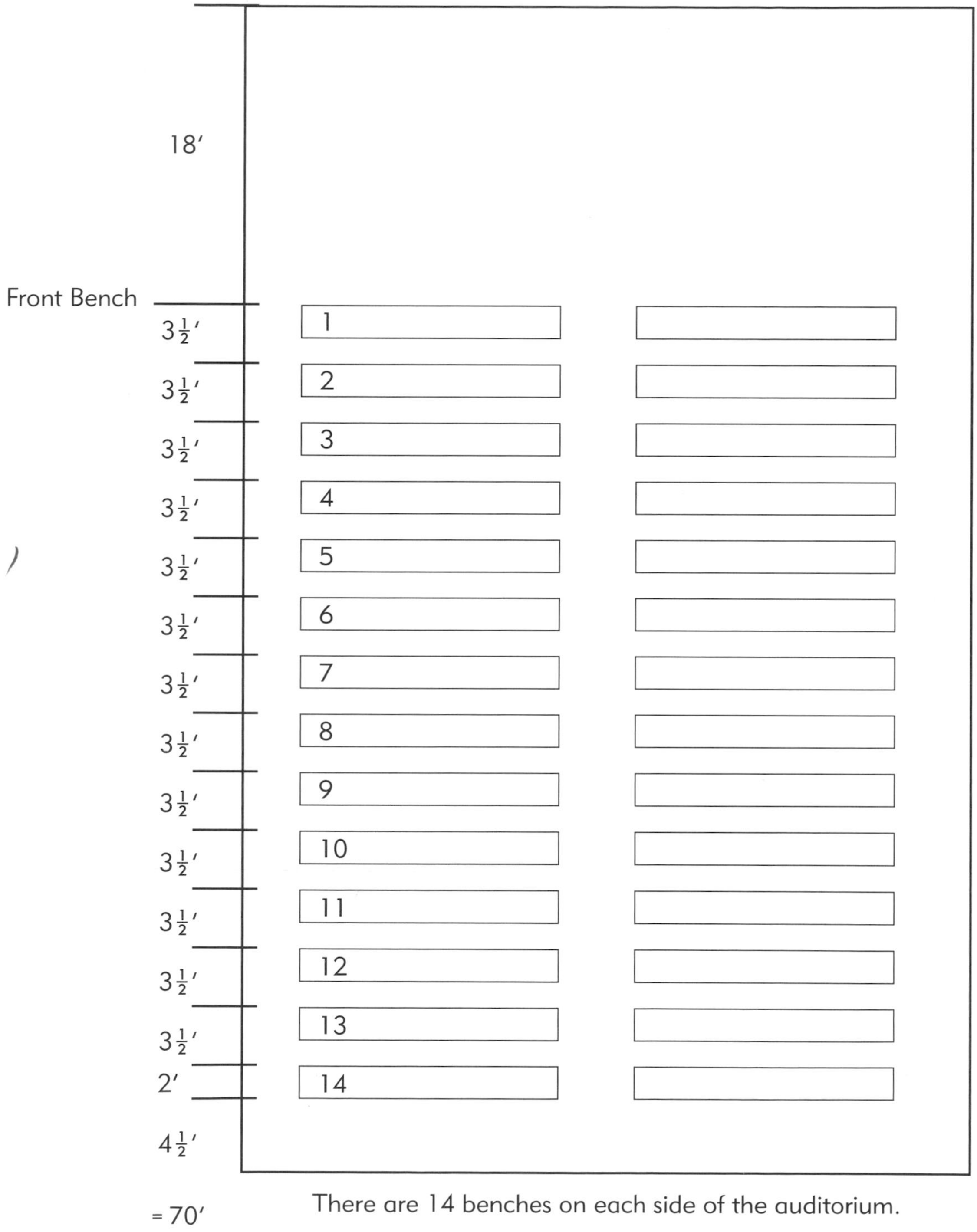

18′

Front Bench

$3\frac{1}{2}′$ 1

$3\frac{1}{2}′$ 2

$3\frac{1}{2}′$ 3

$3\frac{1}{2}′$ 4

$3\frac{1}{2}′$ 5

$3\frac{1}{2}′$ 6

$3\frac{1}{2}′$ 7

$3\frac{1}{2}′$ 8

$3\frac{1}{2}′$ 9

$3\frac{1}{2}′$ 10

$3\frac{1}{2}′$ 11

$3\frac{1}{2}′$ 12

$3\frac{1}{2}′$ 13

2′ 14

$4\frac{1}{2}′$

= 70′

There are 14 benches on each side of the auditorium.

WRITTEN EXERCISES

A. *Make a simple, neat sketch for each reading problem. Then use your sketch to solve the problem.*

1. Brother Allen is remodeling an old house. He plans to lay new linoleum in the kitchen, which measures 16 feet by 14 feet. One corner has a built-in rectangular cupboard that measures $2\frac{1}{2}$ feet by 4 feet. The area under this cupboard will not need linoleum. How many square feet of linoleum will Brother Allen use?

2. Brother Allen plans to put carpet on the living room floor, which is a rectangle measuring 15 feet by 14 feet. In one corner of the room is a triangular area for the wood stove; this area has a base of 10 feet and a height of 5 feet. How many square feet of carpet will Brother Allen use?

3. Brother Allen plans to mount an 8-foot shelf on one wall of the living room. The shelf will have one support at each end and one at every other wall stud in between. The studs are 16 inches apart. How many supports will Brother Allen need?

4. The rail fence along the front of the property needs to be replaced. There are 9 upright posts, each joined to the next one by 2 rails. How many rails will be needed?

5. The Beilers have a rectangular garden measuring 90 feet by 80 feet. This includes a 2-foot border on all four sides, which is unplanted. How many square feet do they plant?

6. How many square feet do the Beilers leave unplanted? (Use the facts and the sketch from problem 5.)

7. A rectangular pasture measuring 120 feet by 100 feet is enclosed with an electric fence. The posts of the fence are 20 feet apart. How many fence posts are needed for the entire meadow?

8. Stephen is planning to plant arborvitae bushes along one boundary of his family's property as a privacy hedge. He will plant the bushes 4 feet apart. How many bushes will he need if the first and last ones are 44 feet apart?

9. Sarah hung 18 pieces of clothes on two clotheslines. She hung 9 pieces on each line, using 1 clothespin between each 2 pieces of clothing and 1 at each end. How many clothespins did she use in all?

10. Father and Michael were putting siding on the barn, and Michael nailed the bottom edge. He put one nail in the middle of each sheet and one at each edge. The sheets overlapped, so he used only one nail to fasten two edges. How many nails did Michael use to fasten 5 sheets of siding?

REVIEW EXERCISES

B. Write the formulas. *(Lessons 123–128)*

11. surface area of a rectangular solid

12. surface area of a cube

13. surface area of a cylinder

14. volume of a rectangular solid

15. volume of a cube

16. volume of a cylinder

17. volume of a cone

C. Find the missing numbers for this table. *(Lesson 129)*

Students in Grades 6 and 7 at the Milltown Mennonite School				
Grades	*Students*	*Fraction*	*Decimal*	*Degrees*
Grade 6	11	$\frac{11}{26}$	**18.**	**19.**
Grade 7	15	$\frac{15}{26}$	**20.**	**21.**
Totals	26	$\frac{26}{26}$	**22.**	**23.**

D. Find the volumes of cones having these dimensions. *(Lesson 128)*

24. $r = 5''$
    $h = 18''$

25. $r = 8''$
    $h = 24''$

E. Find the circumferences of circles having these sizes. *(Lesson 112)*

26. $d = 12''$

27. $d = 19$ cm

F. Calculate the profit or loss as a percent of sales. *(Lesson 97)*

28. sales: $180   profit: $21.60

29. sales: $250   profit: $22.50

G. Multiply mentally by using common fractions. *(Lesson 61)*

30. 0.25 of 28

31. 0.8 of 45

32. $0.66\frac{2}{3}$ of 27

H. Write these numbers, using words. *(Lesson 1)*

33. 4,005,171

34. 2,000,050,000,000

131. Chapter 10 Review

A. Write the formula for each of these. Be sure you have the formulas memorized for the chapter test. *(Lessons 123–128)*

1. surface area of a rectangular solid

2. surface area of a cube

3. surface area of a cylinder

4. volume of a rectangular solid

5. volume of a cube

6. volume of a cylinder

7. volume of a cone

B. Name the geometric solids described below. *(Lesson 122)*

8. A figure that has one circular base and narrows to a point.

9. A figure with three pairs of congruent rectangles.

10. A figure that has two circular bases.

11. Any figure that has length, width, and height.

C. Find the surface areas of these geometric solids. *(Lessons 123, 124)*

Rectangular solids

12. $l = 8''$	**13.** $l = 9'$	**14.** $l = 17$ cm	**15.** $l = 25$ cm
$w = 5''$	$w = 6'$	$w = 15$ cm	$w = 15$ cm
$h = 3''$	$h = 5'$	$h = 12$ cm	$h = 13$ cm

Cubes

16. $e = 4''$	**17.** $e = 9''$	**18.** $e = 16$ cm	**19.** $e = 32$ cm

Cylinders

20. $r = 2$ cm	**21.** $r = 3$ cm	**22.** $r = 14'$	**23.** $r = 15''$
$h = 8$ cm	$h = 12$ cm	$h = 35'$	$h = 40''$

D. Find the volumes of these geometric solids. *(Lesson 125–128)*

Rectangular solids

24. $l = 7$ in.	**25.** $l = 8$ in.	**26.** $l = 19$ cm	**27.** $l = 19$ m
$w = 4$ in.	$w = 5$ in.	$w = 16$ cm	$w = 19$ m
$h = 6$ in.	$h = 4$ in.	$h = 14$ cm	$h = 18$ m
28. $l = 25$ in.	**29.** $l = 28$ cm	**30.** $l = 60$ m	**31.** $l = 90$ yd.
$w = 12$ in.	$w = 11$ cm	$w = 55$ m	$w = 50$ yd.
$h = 15$ in.	$h = 17$ cm	$h = 30$ m	$h = 45$ yd.

Cubes

32. *e* = 6 in.   **33.** *e* = 5 ft.   **34.** *e* = 12 cm   **35.** *e* = 17 m

36. *e* = 22 in.   **37.** *e* = 26 ft.   **38.** *e* = 48 cm   **39.** *e* = 80 m

Cylinders

40. *r* = 2″   **41.** *r* = 4″   **42.** *r* = 5 cm   **43.** *r* = 7 cm
      h = 7″   *h* = 9″   *h* = 18 cm   *h* = 30 cm

44. *r* = 10′   **45.** *r* = 20′   **46.** *r* = 25′   **47.** *r* = 45′
      h = 25′   *h* = 5′   *h* = 40′   *h* = 60′

Cones

48. *r* = 6 cm   **49.** *r* = 3 m   **50.** *r* = 9′   **51.** *r* = 8′
      h = 10 cm   *h* = 12 m   *h* = 15′   *h* = 12′

52. *r* = 10″   **53.** *r* = 12″   **54.** *r* = 24 cm   **55.** *r* = 45 cm
      h = 24″   *h* = 20″   *h* = 50 cm   *h* = 60 cm

E. Find the missing numbers for this table. *(Lesson 129)*

Tribes in the Kingdoms of Judah and Israel				
Kingdom	*No. of Tribes*	*Fraction*	*Decimal*	*Degrees*
Israel	10	$\frac{10}{12}$	**56.**	**57.**
Judah	2	$\frac{2}{12}$	**58.**	**59.**
Totals	12	$\frac{12}{12}$	**60.**	**61.**

F. Use the degrees calculated in Part E to make a circle graph.
This will be exercises 62–64. *(Lesson 129)*

G. Solve these reading problems. Draw sketches for numbers 65–68.

65. A basement wall 12 inches thick is built with concrete blocks. Its outside dimensions are 48 feet by 28 feet. What is the perimeter of the inside of the wall?

66. A silo with a diameter of 20 feet has a foundation that extends 2 feet outside the wall of the silo. What is the outside circumference of the foundation?

67. Two silos with diameters of 20 feet are standing 4 feet apart. They are built on a single foundation that extends 4 feet beyond their outside edges. How long is the foundation at the longest point?

68. The branches of two trees reach within 10 feet of each other. One tree has a 40-foot diameter and one has a 30-foot diameter. How far apart were the trees planted? Assume that both trees are perfectly round.

69. A silo has a diameter of 18 feet and a height of 50 feet. What is its volume?

70. Andrew is spraying flies in a room measuring 50 feet by 30 feet by 10 feet. If he wants to spray 6 seconds for every 1,000 cubic feet of volume, how long should he spray in this room? (A proportion may help.)

132. Chapter 10 Test

Chapter 11

Metric and Bible Measures

This was the dedication of the altar, in the day when it was anointed, by the princes of Israel: twelve chargers of silver, twelve silver bowls, twelve spoons of gold: each charger of silver weighing an hundred and thirty shekels, each bowl seventy: all the silver vessels weighed two thousand and four hundred shekels, after the shekel of the sanctuary.

(Numbers 7:84, 85)

133. Introduction to the Metric System

The English system of measures (Chapter 3) is still used in the United States and a few other countries. However, most countries of the world use the **metric system.** Because of its widespread use, the metric system is also called the International System of Units.

The metric system was developed by the French in the 1790s. No other system of measures has ever been as simple as the metric system. In this system there is one base unit for each type of measurement (such as length or weight); and all derived units have a decimal relationship to the base unit. The derived units have the name of the base unit as the root word, and a system of prefixes shows how each derived unit is related to the base unit. Below is a list of the base units and the abbreviations that you will study in this chapter. You will find it helpful to know these prefixes in order.

Type	**Base unit**		**Prefix**	**Abbreviation**	**Value**
length	meter		kilo-	k	1,000
weight	gram		hecto-	h	100
capacity	liter		deka-	dk	10
area	square meter			(base unit)	1
			deci-	d	0.1
			centi-	c	0.01
			milli-	m	0.001

The **meter** is the basic unit of length (linear measure). It is equal to about 3.28 feet or 39.4 inches. The meter is multiplied or divided by multiples of ten, and the units derived in this way are named by combining the six prefixes above with *meter*. Study the units in the box.

Metric Units of Length		
Unit	*Abbreviation*	*Value*
kilometer	km	1,000 m
hectometer	hm	100 m
dekameter	dkm	10 m
meter	m	1 m
decimeter	dm	0.1 m
centimeter	cm	0.01 m
millimeter	mm	0.001 m

Because the metric system is a decimal system (based on ten), converting from one unit to another is very simple. All multiplying and dividing is by powers of ten, such as 10, 100, and 1,000. Therefore, all conversions can be made by simply moving the decimal point as shown below.

Step 1: Decide which operation is needed. To change a larger unit to a smaller unit, multiply; to change a smaller unit to a larger unit, divide.

Step 2: Decide how many steps larger or smaller you want to change. The decimal point will be moved this number of places.

Step 3: Move the decimal point right to multiply and left to divide.

Number of steps	From larger to smaller unit	Move point to right...	From smaller to larger unit	Move point to left...
1 step	multiply by 10	1 place	divide by 10	1 place
2 steps	multiply by 100	2 places	divide by 100	2 places
3 steps	multiply by 1,000	3 places	divide by 1,000	3 places
4 steps	multiply by 10,000	4 places	divide by 10,000	4 places

---

Memorize these metric-English equivalents.

1 foot = 0.3 meter
1 meter = 3.28 feet

Example A

  2,534 m = _____ km

Step 1: Smaller to larger; divide.

Step 2: 3 steps larger; divide by 1,000.

Step 3: Move the decimal point 3 places to the left.

  2,534 m = 2.534 km

Example B

  47 m = _____ cm

Step 1: Larger to smaller; multiply.

Step 2: 2 steps smaller; multiply by 100.

Step 3: Move the decimal point 2 places to the right.

  47 m = 4,700 cm

CLASS PRACTICE

Measure these lines in millimeters.

a. ———————————

b. ————————————————————

Change these measures as indicated.

c. 80 cm = _____ m   d. 2.1 km = _____ m   e. 1.49 km = _____ cm

WRITTEN EXERCISES

A. *Measure these lines in millimeters.*

1. ⎯⎯⎯⎯

2. ⎯⎯⎯⎯⎯⎯⎯⎯⎯⎯

3. ⎯⎯⎯⎯⎯⎯

4. ⎯⎯⎯⎯⎯⎯⎯⎯⎯⎯⎯⎯⎯⎯⎯⎯⎯⎯⎯⎯

B. *Name the unit that is next larger in sequence.*

5. meter   6. centimeter   7. millimeter   8. dekameter

C. *Name the unit that is next smaller in sequence.*

9. kilometer   10. decimeter   11. meter   12. hectometer

D. *Write the abbreviations for these units.*

13. meter   14. kilometer   15. millimeter   16. dekameter

E. *Change these measures.*

17. 1.5 m = _____ cm

18. 5.7 mm = _____ cm

19. 575 m = _____ km

20. 0.15 km = _____ m

21. 28,000 cm = _____ m

22. 2.77 km = _____ m

23. 1.2 km = _____ mm

24. 565,000 cm = _____ km

F. *Solve these reading problems.*

25. A church parking lot is a quadrilateral with all sides of unequal length. The sides measure 50 meters, 30 meters, 40 meters, and 80 meters. What is the perimeter of the parking lot in kilometers?

26. The Masts' house and barn are 72 meters apart. How many centimeters is that?

27. The Frys have tires of size 235/75R15 on their van. In such a code, the 235 indicates the width of the tread in millimeters. How many centimeters is that?

28. In the tire size 235/75R15, the 75 means that the sidewall is 75% as high as the tread is wide. If the tread is 235 millimeters wide, how high is the sidewall? Express the answer to the nearest whole centimeter.

29. The interior of one 8-passenger van forms a rectangular solid measuring about 12.5 feet by 5.5 feet by 4 feet. To the nearest cubic foot, how much space is planned for each passenger?

30. A school parking lot forms a parallelogram with a base of 80 feet and a height of 50 feet. At $1.15 per square foot, what would it cost to pave the parking lot?

REVIEW EXERCISES

G. Make a circle graph based on the following facts.
This will be exercises 31–33. *(Lesson 129)*

Composition of the Earth's Surface

	Decimal	Degrees
Water	0.708	255°
Land	0.292	105°

H. Find the volumes of rectangular solids having these dimensions. *(Lesson 125)*

34. $l = 12'$
$w = 10'$
$h = 28'$

35. $l = 28'$
$w = 18'$
$h = 16'$

I. Find the areas of squares and parallelograms having these dimensions. *(Lesson 114)*

36. *square*
$e = 15''$

37. *square*
$e = 70$ cm

38. *parallelogram*
$b = 16'$
$h = 15'$

39. *parallelogram*
$b = 21$ m
$h = 19$ m

J. Find the simple interest. *(Lesson 99)*

40. $p = \$3,500$
$r = 7\%$
$t = 5$ yr.

41. $p = \$9,250$
$r = 7\%$
$t = 4$ yr.

K. Write a ratio in simplest form for each statement. *(Lesson 67)*

42. The Masts till 50 acres of their 65-acre farm.

43. David milked 5 cows for every 9 that Father milked.

L. Round each number to the place indicated. *(Lesson 3)*

44. 42,356,789 *(million)*

45. 12,783,323 *(hundred thousand)*

134. Metric Units of Weight

The **gram** is the base unit of weight in the metric system. A gram is very small; it is less than $\frac{1}{28}$ ounce. Because the gram is such a small unit, the kilogram (1,000 grams) is the metric unit of weight used most frequently. One kilogram equals about 2.2 English pounds.

Metric Units of Weight		
Unit	*Abbreviation*	*Value*
metric ton	MT	1,000 kg
kilogram	kg	1,000 g
hectogram	hg	100 g
dekagram	dkg	10 g
gram	g	1 g
decigram	dg	0.1 g
centigram	cg	0.01 g
milligram	mg	0.001 g

Six of these units are based directly on the gram, and their names are formed by using the metric prefixes with *gram*. The metric ton is an exception; it is equal to 1,000 kilograms. This unit is about 200 pounds greater than the 2,000-pound English ton used in the United States.

Converting units of weight follows the same method that you studied in Lesson 133. Because the metric system is a decimal system, changing from one unit to another can be done by simply moving the decimal point. The steps are the same as those in Lesson 133.

Step 1: Decide which operation is needed. To change a larger unit to a smaller unit, multiply; to change smaller unit to a larger unit, divide.

Step 2: Decide how many steps larger or smaller you want to change. The decimal point will be moved this number of places.

Step 3: Move the decimal point right to multiply and left to divide.

Example A	**Example B**
243 g = _____ kg	47 kg = _____ g
Step 1: Smaller to larger; divide.	Step 1: Larger to smaller; multiply.
Step 2: 3 steps larger; divide by 1,000.	Step 2: 3 steps smaller; multiply by 1,000.
Step 3: Move the decimal point 3 places to the left.	Step 3: Move the decimal point 3 places to the right.
243 g = 0.243 kg	47 kg = 47,000 g

> **Example C**   4,550 kg = _____ MT   4,550 kg = 4.55 MT

When changing kilograms to metric tons, divide by 1,000 because there are 1,000 kilograms in a metric ton. To divide by 1,000, move the decimal point three places to the left (Example C).

> **Example D**   37.5 MT = _____ kg   37.5 MT = 37,500 kg

When changing metric tons to kilograms, multiply by 1,000. To multiply by 1,000, move the decimal point three places to the right (Example D).

> **Memorize these metric-English equivalents.**
> 1 pound = 0.45 kilogram
> 1 kilogram = 2.2 pounds

CLASS PRACTICE

Change these measures.

a. 1.7 kg = _____ g

b. 3,890 g = _____ kg

c. 45,700 kg = _____ MT

d. 3.75 MT = _____ kg

e. 35.6 kg = _____ g

f. 17,190 g = _____ kg

WRITTEN EXERCISES

A. Write the abbreviation of the next larger unit in the sequence.

1. mg   2. dkg   3. g   4. cg

B. Write the abbreviation of the next smaller unit in the sequence.

5. kg   6. cg   7. dkg   8. g

C. Change these measures.

9. 250 mg = _____ g

10. 3.5 kg = _____ g

11. 5.7 MT = _____ kg

12. 575 kg = _____ MT

13. 13.7 kg = _____ g

14. 12,560 kg = _____ MT

15. 17.82 g = _____ mg

16. 49 g = _____ kg

17. 26 g = _____ mg

18. 0.75 MT = _____ kg

19. 2.3 kg = _____ mg

20. 420,000 mg = _____ kg

D. Solve these reading problems.

21. Elam sold some rabbits with the following weights: 950 grams, 990 grams, 1,050 grams, and 1,130 grams. What was their total weight in kilograms?

22. God has placed many necessary vitamins and minerals in fruit. A banana may contain 3.7 grams of potassium. How many milligrams is that?

23. A typical banana also contains 260 milligrams of phosphorus. How many grams is that?

24. An orange may contain 410 milligrams of calcium. How many grams would be in a dozen oranges?

25. A cylindrical pitcher having an inside radius of 6 centimeters is filled to a depth of 20 centimeters with orange juice. How much juice is that in cubic centimeters?

26. Find the simple interest on $800 at 7% interest for 75 days.

REVIEW EXERCISES

E. Change these linear measures. *(Lesson 133)*

27. 4 m = _____ cm

28. 152 mm = _____ m

29. 5.67 km = _____ m

30. 5,460 m = _____ km

F. Calculate the volumes of cylinders having these dimensions. *(Lesson 127)*

31. $r = 5''$
    $h = 17''$

32. $r = 9$ cm
    $h = 30$ cm

G. Find the areas of triangles having these dimensions. *(Lesson 115)*

33. $b = 12''$
    $h = 9''$

34. $b = 19$ m
    $h = 14$ m

H. Find the simple interest. *(Lesson 100)*

35. $p = \$500$
    $r = 6\%$
    $t = 60$ days

36. $p = \$900$
    $r = 8\%$
    $t = 150$ days

I. Solve these proportions. *(Lesson 68)*

37. $\frac{4}{18} = \frac{n}{27}$

38. $\frac{24}{18} = \frac{n}{30}$

J. Write these as Arabic numerals. *(Lesson 4)*

39. $\overline{\text{CDXI}}$

40. $\overline{\text{CM}}$

135. Metric Units of Capacity

In the English system, units of capacity are in two groups: dry measure and liquid measure. But the metric system has only one unit for both dry and liquid measure. This unit is the **liter**. The liter is a little larger than the English quart. Study the metric units in the box. Notice that the derived units have the same prefixes as those used with other metric units.

Metric Units of Capacity		
Unit	*Abbreviation*	*Value*
kiloliter	kl	1,000 l
hectoliter	hl	100 l
dekaliter	dkl	10 l
liter	l	1 l
deciliter	dl	0.1 l
centiliter	cl	0.01 l
milliliter	ml	0.001 l

Memorize these metric-English equivalents.

1 liquid quart = 0.95 liter
1 liter = 1.06 liquid quarts

To convert from one unit of capacity to another, use the same method as that given in Lesson 133.

Step 1: Decide which operation is needed. To change a larger unit to a smaller unit, multiply; to change a smaller unit to a larger unit, divide.

Step 2: Decide how many steps larger or smaller you want to change. The decimal point will be moved this number of places.

Step 3: Move the decimal point right to multiply and left to divide.

Example A	**Example B**
37.65 l = _____ ml	40,000 ml = _____ kl
Step 1: Larger to smaller; multiply.	Step 1: Smaller to larger; divide.
Step 2: 3 steps smaller; multiply by 1,000.	Step 2: 6 steps larger; divide by 1,000,000.
Step 3: Move the decimal point 3 places to the right.	Step 3: Move the decimal point 6 places to the left.
37.65 l = 37,650 ml	40,000 ml = 0.04 kl

392   *Chapter 11   Metric and Bible Measure*

CLASS PRACTICE

Change these measures.

a. 3.4 l = _____ kl

b. 5.45 kl = _____ ml

c. 7.1 l = _____ ml

d. 4,350,000 ml = _____ kl

WRITTEN EXERCISES

A. Write the name of the next larger unit.

1. dl

2. dkl

3. cl

4. hl

B. Write the abbreviation of the next smaller unit.

5. kl

6. dl

7. l

8. dkl

C. Change these measures.

9. 4.65 l = _____ ml

10. 151.3 ml = _____ l

11. 2,121 l = _____ kl

12. 29.31 kl = _____ l

13. 98 ml = _____ l

14. 3,059 l = _____ kl

15. 49 ml = _____ l

16. 785 l = _____ kl

17. 4.1 kl = _____ ml

18. 340,500 ml = _____ kl

19. 2,144,500 ml = _____ kl

20. 3.009 l = _____ ml

D. Solve these reading problems. Write proportions for 25 and 26.

21. Mother bought a two-liter bottle of ginger ale to make fruit punch slush for the school picnic. How many milliliters did she get?

22. Father bought a bottle of hydrogen peroxide for the first-aid cabinet at school. If the bottle contained 473 milliliters, what part of a liter of peroxide was in it?

23. The Clearview Fire Department has a tanker that can hold 8.5 kiloliters of water and a pump that can deliver 1,000 liters per minute. How long does it take the pump to fill the empty tanker?

24. Brian read about a helicopter used as a flying ambulance. Its fuel consumption was 396 liters of fuel per hour at a cruising speed of 288 kilometers per hour. How many liters of fuel did the helicopter use per kilometer? Calculate the answer to the thousandths' place.

25. The ratio for comparing miles per hour to feet per second is about 2:3. What is the speed in miles per hour of an automobile traveling 81 feet per second?

26. Conversely, the ratio for comparing feet per second to miles per hour is about 3:2. If an airplane is traveling at 450 miles per hour, how many feet per second is it traveling?

REVIEW EXERCISES

E. *Change these measures.* *(Lessons 133, 134)*

27. 7,525 g = _____ kg

28. 3.211 kg = _____ g

29. 4.155 MT = _____ kg

30. 4.5 m = _____ cm

F. *Find the volumes of cones having these dimensions.* *(Lesson 128)*

31. $r = 4''$
$h = 6''$

32. $r = 7$ cm
$h = 12$ cm

G. *Find the areas of trapezoids having these dimensions.* *(Lesson 116)*

33. $h = 12''$
$b_1 = 9''$
$b_2 = 15''$

34. $h = 16$ m
$b_1 = 13$ m
$b_2 = 19$ m

H. *Find the total interest if it is compounded annually.* *(Lesson 101)*

35. $p = \$200$
$r = 5\%$
$t = 2$ yr.

36. $p = \$500$
$r = 6\%$
$t = 2$ yr.

I. *Copy and solve these addition problems.* *(Lesson 5)*

37.
```
   41,171
   35,398
   42,616
   87,645
 + 32,009
```

38.
```
  $5,684.21
   2,717.89
 + 3,453.78
```

136. Metric Units of Area

The metric units of area, like the English units, are based on units of length. The most common units of area are shown in the box. Each name except *hectare* contains the name of the linear unit on which it is based.

Common Metric Units of Area		
Unit	*Abbreviation*	*Value*
square kilometer	km²	1,000,000 m² *or* 100 ha
hectare	ha	10,000 m²
square meter	m²	1 m² *or* 10,000 cm²
square centimeter	cm²	0.0001 m²

The **hectare** is the metric unit for measuring tracts of land. This unit is equal to a square that measures 100 meters by 100 meters, or 1 square hectometer. The word *hectare* means "100 ares." (*Are* may be pronounced like *air* or *are*.) One are is equal to a square 10 meters by 10 meters, or 1 square dekameter. But the are is too small to be of much practical value, so the hectare is most commonly used. One hectare is equal to about 2.5 acres.

Because metric units of area are not related to each other by tens, changing metric units of area is different from the steps used in the last few lessons.

> To change a larger unit to a smaller unit, multiply the number of larger units by the number of smaller units in the larger unit.
>
> To change a smaller unit to a larger unit, divide the number of smaller units by the number of smaller units in the larger unit.

Example A

A desktop has an area of 3,000 square centimeters. What is its area in square meters?

A smaller unit is being changed to a larger unit. Divide the number of square centimeters by 10,000 because there are 10,000 square centimeters in a square meter.

$$3,000 \text{ cm}^2 \div 10,000 = 0.3 \text{ m}^2$$

Example B

A wildlife refuge contained 4.8 square kilometers of land. How many hectares did it contain?

A larger unit is being changed to a smaller unit. Multiply the number of square kilometers by 100 because there are 100 hectares in 1 square kilometer.

$$100 \times 4.8 \text{ km}^2 = 480 \text{ ha}$$

> **Memorize these metric-English equivalents.**
>
> 1 acre = 0.4 hectare
> 1 hectare = 2.5 acres

CLASS PRACTICE

Change these measures.

a. 3.2 m² = _____ cm²   b. 0.45 km² = _____ ha   c. 5,600 cm² = _____ m²

d. 1.55 ha = _____ m²   e. 3.12 m² = _____ cm²   f. 2,012 ha = _____ km²

WRITTEN EXERCISES

A. *Write the abbreviations for these units.*

1. square centimeter   2. square meter

3. hectare   4. square kilometer

B. *Change these measures.*

5. 15,500 cm² = _____ m²   6. 2.35 ha = _____ m²

7. 0.46 ha = _____ m²   8. 75 ha = _____ km²

9. 4.22 m² = _____ cm²   10. 2.12 m² = _____ cm²

11. 11.7 ha = _____ m²   12. 7.15 km² = _____ ha

13. 22,100 m² = _____ ha   14. 25.3 m² = _____ cm²

15. 25 ha = _____ km²   16. 0.79 ha = _____ m²

17. 55,000 m² = _____ ha   18. 3.28 m² = _____ cm²

19. 7 ha = _____ km²   20. 0.035 km² = _____ ha

C. *Solve these reading problems. Write proportions for 25 and 26.*

21. One plot of land covers 32,400 square meters. What is its area in hectares?

22. The cover of Father's Bible has an area of 494 square centimeters. What is the area in square meters?

23. The Millers' garden is a rectangle measuring 40 meters by 30 meters. What is its area in hectares?

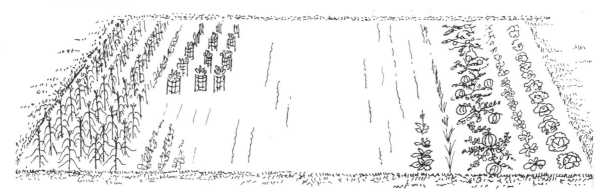

24. If a rectangular township measures 12 kilometers by 10 kilometers, how many hectares does it contain?

25. On a trip to Bible school, Marcus's parents drove 2 hours at 50 miles per hour for every 3 hours they drove 55 miles per hour. They drove a total of 15 hours. How many hours did they drive 55 miles per hour?

26. Jason is mixing oil and gasoline for a chain saw with a two-cycle engine. The ratio of gasoline to oil is 16 to 1. If Jason uses 2 gallons of gasoline, how much fuel mixture will he have in all?

REVIEW EXERCISES

D. Change these measures. *(Lessons 133–135)*

27. 1.4 l = _____ ml

28. 35.5 l = _____ kl

29. 14.5 cm = _____ mm

30. 3,145 m = _____ km

31. 179 g = _____ kg

32. 4.5 MT = _____ kg

E. Find the areas of circles having these sizes. *(Lesson 117)*

33. r = 7 cm

34. r = 8 in.

F. Find the unit prices to the nearest tenth of a cent. *(Lesson 102)*

35. 144 pencils for $15.48

36. 144 cap erasers for $8.28

G. Solve these addition problems mentally. *(Lesson 6)*

37. 48 + 37

38. 76 + 58

39. 57 + 94

40. 78 + 64

137. Adding and Subtracting Compound Measures

Many problems encountered in life involve addition or subtraction of compound measures. A butcher weighs meat in pounds and ounces; a surveyor records directions as degrees, minutes, and seconds; a carpenter measures by feet and inches, and the teacher times quizzes in minutes and seconds. In many cases, individual measurements need to be combined or compared with each other.

Most metric units are related to each other by tens. Therefore, calculating with metric units and with English units is not done in the same way. In this lesson you will work first with English measures and then with metric measures.

Adding Compound English Measures

To add compound English measures, use the following steps.

1. Add each unit separately.
2. Simplify the answer by converting as many smaller units as possible into larger units. In Example A, 16 inches is changed to 1 foot 4 inches and added to the 7 feet for a total of 8 feet 4 inches.

```
Example A
      3 feet    7 inches
    + 4 feet    9 inches
      7 feet   16 inches = 8 ft. 4 in.
```

Subtracting Compound English Measures

To subtract compound English measures, use the following steps.

1. Subtract each unit separately. If borrow-ing is required, borrow 1 from the next larger unit; then convert the 1 into the correct number of smaller units.
2. Subtract each unit separately. In Example B, 1 minute is borrowed from 9 minutes, changed to 60 seconds, and added to the 20 seconds already there.

```
Example B
    8                 80 (60 + 20)
    9 minutes         20 seconds
  - 4 minutes         35 seconds
    4 minutes         45 seconds
```

Adding and Subtracting Metric Measures

To add or subtract metric measures, use the following steps.

1. Change all units to the unit desired for the answer.
2. Add or subtract as indicated. Carry or borrow just as you do when adding or subtracting other decimals.

Example C

Add 25 liters and 475 milliliters. Express the answer in liters.

Step 1: 475 ml = 0.475 l

Step 2: 25 l + 0.475 l = 25.475 l

Example D

Find the difference between 2 metric tons and 1,760 kilograms. Express the answer in kilograms.

Step 1: 2 MT = 2,000 kg

Step 2: 2,000 kg – 1,760 kg = 240 kg

CLASS PRACTICE

Solve these addition and subtraction problems.

a.   4 ft. 3 in.
     + 2 ft. 11 in.

b.   8 gal. 2 qt.
     + 4 gal. 3 qt.

c.   6 wk. 4 days
     – 2 wk. 5 days

d.   12 hr. 20 min.
     – 9 hr. 40 min.

e. 12 cm + 114 mm = _____ mm

f. 2.3 kg + 750 g = _____ kg

g. 4 kl – 90 l = _____ kl

h. 14 km – 995 m = _____ m

WRITTEN EXERCISES

A. Add these English measures.

1.   4 ft. 9 in.
     + 2 ft. 9 in.

2.   3 yd. 1 ft.
     + 2 yd. 2 ft.

3.   7 min. 35 sec.
     + 9 min. 40 sec.

4.   3 lb. 4 oz.
     + 5 lb. 7 oz.

B. Subtract these English measures.

5.   7 ft. 3 in.
     – 1 ft. 7 in.

6.   7 hr. 10 min.
     – 2 hr. 40 min.

7.   9 bu. 1 pk.
     – 2 bu. 2 pk.

8.   8 yr. 5 mo.
     – 3 yr. 10 mo.

C. Add or subtract these metric measures. Answer in the indicated units.

9. 14 cm + 15 mm = _____ cm

10. 195 g + 1.1 kg = _____ g

11. 3,250 kg + 1.05 MT = _____ MT

12. 550 l + 7.5 kl = _____ l

13. 3 kg – 535 g = _____ kg

14. 1.2 km – 750 m = _____ m

15. 5 MT – 750 kg = _____ MT

16. 35 kl – 950 l = _____ l

D. Solve these problems.

17.   3 wk. 5 days
   + 4 wk. 6 days

18.   7 qt.
   – 2 qt. 1 pt.

19. 13 m – 72 cm = _____ m

20. 2 kg – 670 g = _____ g

E. Solve these reading problems.

21. A train engineer had the following schedule.

Meadville to Mount Stevens . . . . .1 hr. 22 min.
Stop at Mount Stevens . . . . .5 min.
Mount Stevens to Crooked Lane . . . . .43 min.
Stop at Crooked Lane . . . . .15 min.
Crooked Lane to Ross's Junction . . . . . . .2 hr. 35 min.

What was the total time from Meadville to Ross's Junction?

22. The Burkholders were dividing a 25-pound pack of hamburger into smaller portions to freeze. After they wrapped a portion weighing 3 pounds 5 ounces, how much of the 25-pound pack remained?

23. Sarah was comparing the weights of two boxes of cereal. The larger box weighed 0.425 kilogram and the smaller box 340 grams. In kilograms, what was the difference between the two weights?

24. If a tract of land has 14,500 square meters, how many hectares are in it?

25. One evening the Metzlers picked sour cherries at a nearby orchard. Their containers weighed 11 ounces, 13 ounces, 1 pound 10 ounces, and 1 pound 11 ounces. When the containers were filled, the weights were 11 pounds 9 ounces, 10 pounds 2 ounces, 13 pounds 4 ounces, and 12 pounds. How many pounds of cherries did they pick?

Go to the ant, thou sluggard;
consider her ways,
and be wise:
which having no guide,
overseer, or ruler,
provideth her meat
in the summer,
and gathereth her food
in the harvest.
(Proverbs 6:6–8)

26. A group of ministers flew to a mission in Guatemala. The flight from Washington, D.C., to Miami, Florida, took 2 hours 40 minutes. From Miami to Guatemala City, it took 3 hours 25 minutes. How much longer was the second flight than the first?

REVIEW EXERCISES

F. **Complete these by memory.** *(Lessons 133–136)*

27. 1 ft. = _____ m   **28.** 1 m = _____ ft.   **29.** 1 kg = _____ lb.

30. 1 qt. = _____ *l*   **31.** 1 ha = _____ a.   **32.** 1 lb. = _____ kg

G. **Change these measures.** *(Lesson 136)*

33. 2.2 km² = _____ ha   **34.** 15,000 m² = _____ ha

H. **Find the missing numbers on this table for making a circle graph.** *(Lesson 118)*

Verses per Chapter in 2 Timothy				
Chapter	*No. of Verses*	*Fraction*	*Decimal*	*Degrees*
1	18	$\frac{18}{83}$	**35.**	
2	26	$\frac{26}{83}$	**36.**	
3	17	$\frac{17}{83}$	**37.**	
4	22	$\frac{22}{83}$	**38.**	
Totals	83	$\frac{83}{83}$	1.000	360°

I. **Solve these subtraction problems.** *(Lesson 7)*

39. 48,201
         − 29,434

40. $3,515.71
         − 1,786.49

138. Multiplying and Dividing Compound Measures

Sometimes it is necessary to multiply or divide measures. As with addition and subtraction, metric measures are handled differently from English measures.

Multiplying Compound English Measures

To multiply compound English measures, use the following steps.

1. Multiply each unit separately.

2. Simplify the answer by converting as many smaller units as possible to larger units. In Example A, 35 inches can be expressed as 2 feet 11 inches and added to the 15 feet for a total of 17 feet 11 inches.

Example A

$$
\begin{array}{r}
3 \text{ ft.} \quad 7 \text{ in.} \\
\times \quad 5 \\
\hline
15 \text{ ft.} \quad 35 \text{ in.} \quad = 17 \text{ ft. } 11 \text{ in.}
\end{array}
$$

Dividing Compound English Measures

To divide compound English measures, use the following steps.

1. Divide the amount of the larger unit.

2. If there is a remainder, change it to the smaller unit.

3. Add the remainder to the smaller unit.

4. Divide the smaller unit.

5. If there is a remainder, express it as a fraction in lowest terms.

Example B

$$
\begin{array}{r}
2 \text{ yd.} \quad 1\frac{1}{3} \text{ ft.} \\
6\overline{)14 \text{ yd.} \quad 2 \text{ ft.}} \\
\underline{12} \\
2 \text{ yd.} \quad = \quad 6 \text{ ft.} \\
\underline{8 \text{ ft.}} \\
\underline{6 \text{ ft.}} \\
2 \text{ ft.}
\end{array}
$$

Multiplying or Dividing Metric Measures

To multiply or divide metric measures, use these steps.

1. Change all units to the unit desired for the answer.

2. Multiply or divide as indicated. Solve the problem just as you do when working with any decimals.

Example C

$8 \times 6\,l \; 60 \text{ ml} = \underline{\quad\quad} l$

Step 1: $6\,l \; 60 \text{ ml} = 6.060\,l$

Step 2:
$$
\begin{array}{r}
6.06\,l \\
\times \quad 8 \\
\hline
48.480\,l
\end{array}
$$

Example D

$7 \text{ m } 45 \text{ cm} \div 6 = \underline{\quad\quad} \text{ cm}$

Step 1: $7 \text{ m } 45 \text{ cm} = 745 \text{ cm}$

Steps 2 and 3:
$$
\begin{array}{r}
124\frac{1}{6} \text{ cm} \\
6\overline{)745 \text{ cm}}
\end{array}
$$

CLASS PRACTICE

Change these measures.

a. 4 m 25 cm = _____ m

b. 17 km 95 m = _____ km

c. 7 MT 650 kg = _____ kg

Solve these problems.

d. 9 × 4 ft. 5 in. = _____

e. 8 × 6 gal. 2 qt. = _____

f. 8 × 3 kl 740 l = _____ l

g. 12 ft. 6 in. ÷ 5 = _____

h. 14 km 500 m ÷ 6 = _____ m

i. 25 kl 800 l ÷ 12 = _____ kl

WRITTEN EXERCISES

A. Solve these problems involving English measures.

1. 5 ft. 9 in.
   × 7

2. 7 wk. 5 days
   × 9

3. 9 lb. 11 oz.
   × 6

4. 3)4 ft. 6 in.

5. 5)7 lb. 8 oz.

6. 8)6 yd. 2 ft.

B. Change these metric measures as indicated.

7. 14 kg 430 g = _____ kg

8. 4 l 75 ml = _____ ml

9. 12 m 27 mm = _____ m

10. 25 cm 7 mm = _____ mm

11. 28 kl 110 l = _____ kl

12. 1 km 675 m = _____ km

C. Solve these problems involving metric measures.

13. 7 × 17 MT 600 kg = _____ MT

14. 12 × 12 kl 400 l = _____ kl

15. 15 × 9 km 78 m = _____ m

16. 9 × 12 km 420 m = _____ m

17. 16 kg 700 g ÷ 10 = _____ kg

18. 15 m 620 mm ÷ 4 = _____ mm

19. 22 kl 442 l ÷ 14 = _____ kl

20. 46 m 95 mm ÷ 15 = _____ m

D. Solve these reading problems.

21. An iceberg is a huge piece of ice that breaks off an ice field and floats away. Less than $\frac{1}{7}$ of an iceberg is visible above the surface of the water. If an iceberg towers 305 feet 7 inches above the water and its total height is 8 times as much, what is the total height of the iceberg from the bottom to the top?

22. Fred was stocking shelves at the store where he worked. He wheeled a cart carrying 3 cases of cereal out of the storeroom. Each case contained six boxes, and each box contained 1 pound 5 ounces of cereal. What was the total weight of the cereal?

23. Jane weeded five rows of corn in 2 hours 25 minutes. What was her average time per row?

24. Marlin dug a hole for a clothesline post that was 2 meters 64 centimeters long. The post was four times as long as the hole was deep. What was the depth of the hole in meters?

25. The clothesline post (problem 24) had a crossbeam that was 1 meter 35 centimeters shorter than the upright post. How long was the crossbeam in centimeters?

26. From the Israelite Feast of Firstfruits until Pentecost was 7 weeks 1 day, and from the Feast of Trumpets until the Feast of Tabernacles was 14 days (Leviticus 23). How many days closer together were the Feast of Trumpets and the Feast of Tabernacles than the Feast of Firstfruits and Pentecost?

REVIEW EXERCISES

E. *Solve these addition and subtraction problems.* *(Lesson 137)*

27.
```
   4 lb. 7 oz.
 + 5 lb. 9 oz.
```

28.
```
   15 ft.  6 in.
 + 12 ft.  9 in.
```

29.
```
   5 qt.  2 cups
 - 1 qt.  3 cups
```

30.
```
   5 lb.  4 oz.
 - 2 lb.  9 oz.
```

F. *Change these measures.* *(Lessons 133–136)*

31. 1.4 m = _____ mm

32. 145 mg = _____ g

33. 175 ml = _____ *l*

34. 1.47 km^2 = _____ ha

G. *Complete the following chart.* *(Lesson 72)*

35.

Fraction	Decimal	Percent
$\frac{23}{25}$		

36.

Fraction	Decimal	Percent
	0.14	

H. *Do these subtractions mentally.* *(Lesson 8)*

37. 52 – 17   38. 82 – 35   39. 73 – 37   40. 91 – 14

139. Converting Between Metric and English Measures

Because metric and English measures are both widely used, it is sometimes necessary to change a measure in one system to its equivalent in the other system. The tables below give the approximate relationships of some English and metric units in common use.

Metric to English	English to Metric
Length	*Length*
1 cm = 0.39 in.	1 in. = 2.54 cm
1 m = 39.4 in.	1 ft. = 0.3 m
1 m = 3.28 ft.	1 mi. = 1.61 km
1 km = 0.62 mi.	*Weight*
Weight	1 oz. = 28.3 g
1 g = 0.035 oz.	1 lb. = 0.45 kg
1 kg = 2.2 lb.	*Capacity*
Capacity	1 qt. = 0.95 *l*
1 *l* = 1.06 qt. (liquid)	1 tbsp. = 15 ml
Area	*Area*
1 ha = 2.5 a.	1 a. = 0.4 ha
1 km² = 0.39 sq. mi.	1 sq. mi. = 2.59 km²

The following steps explain how to make conversions between English and metric measures.

1. Determine which table to use. If a metric measure is being changed to an English measure, use the "Metric to English" table. If an English measure is being changed to a metric measure, use the "English to Metric" table.

2. Find the proper equivalent on the table, and multiply it by the number of the original measure.

3. Label the product with the label of the unit to which the measure is being converted.

Example A	Example B
5 ft. = _____ m	55 g = _____ oz.
Step 1: Feet to meters; use the English-to-metric table.	Step 1: Grams to ounces; use the metric-to-English table.
Step 2: 1 ft. = 0.3 m 5 × 0.3 = 1.5	Step 2: 1 g = 0.035 oz. 55 × 0.035 = 1.925
Step 3: 5 ft. = 1.5 m	Step 3: 55 g = 1.925 oz.

Metric-English Equivalents to Be Memorized	
Metric to English	**English to Metric**
Length 1 m = 3.28 ft.	*Length* 1 ft. = 0.3 m
Weight 1 kg = 2.2 lb.	*Weight* 1 lb. = 0.45 kg
Capacity 1 *l* = 1.06 qt. (liquid)	*Capacity* 1 qt. = 0.95 *l*
Area 1 ha = 2.5 a.	*Area* 1 a. = 0.4 ha

CLASS PRACTICE

Change these measures.

a. 6 in. = _____ cm   b. 6 *l* = _____ qt.   c. 25 ha = _____ a.

d. 12 sq. mi. = _____ km² e. 14 oz. = _____ g   f. 4 tbsp. = _____ ml

WRITTEN EXERCISES

A. *Change these measures.*

1. 7 m = _____ ft.

2. 28 g = _____ oz.

3. 22 in. = _____ cm

4. 7 qt. = _____ *l*

5. 58 sq. mi. = _____ km²

6. 8 tbsp. = _____ ml

7. 16 cm = _____ in.

8. 25 *l* = _____ qt.

9. 18 ha = _____ a.

10. 35 kg = _____ lb.

11. 46 lb. = _____ kg

12. 48 a. = _____ ha

13. 1.6 m = _____ in.

14. 44 ft. = _____ m

15. 82 km = _____ mi.

16. 12 oz. = _____ g

17. 25 kg = _____ lb.

18. 35 mi. = _____ km

19. 18 in. = _____ cm

20. 1.7 m = _____ in.

B. *Solve these reading problems.*

21. The Weber family received a letter from their cousins who live at a mission station in Ghana. The letter stated that Dwight, a two-year-old, weighed 15.5 kilograms. What was his weight in pounds?

22. The letter also stated that every second Sunday, Uncle Stanley's travel to another congregation 85 kilometers from their home. How many miles is it to the other congregation?

23. One Sunday morning, the 85-kilometer trip took Uncle Stanley's $1\frac{1}{2}$ hours. What was the average speed in kilometers per hour?

24. Uncle Stanley's live on a 38-hectare plot of land. How many acres is that?

25. Eighty-five percent of Uncle Stanley's 38-hectare plot is wooded. How many hectares of land are wooded?

26. Uncle Stanley's wrote that when their electric generator was out of service, they needed to haul their water in 15-liter buckets. To the nearest tenth of a gallon, how many gallons of water did the buckets contain?

REVIEW EXERCISES

C. *Solve these division problems.* *(Lesson 138)*

27. $15\overline{)2.745 \text{ m}}$ **28.** $16\overline{)7.984 \text{ } l}$

29. $4\overline{)7 \text{ lb.   4 oz.}}$ **30.** $7\overline{)5 \text{ bu. 1 pk.}}$

D. *Change these measures.* *(Lessons 133–136)*

31. 8.313 km = _____ m   **32.** 1,717 kg = _____ MT

33. 1,717 ml = _____ l **34.** 27,500 ha = _____ km²

E. *Write the name of each geometric solid described below.* *(Lesson 122)*

35. It has two circular bases and a rectangular side.

36. It has six congruent sides.

F. *Solve these percentage problems.* *(Lesson 73)*

37. 16% of 38   **38.** 71% of 66

G. *Do these multiplications. Label each part of the problems.* *(Lesson 12)*

39.   458 _____
        × 317 _____

40.   652 _____
        × 278 _____

140. Changing From Celsius to Fahrenheit Temperature

The metric scale for measuring temperature is the **Celsius** scale. On this scale, water freezes at 0° and boils at 100°. The freezing and boiling points of water are 100° apart on the Celsius scale.

In the English system, the Fahrenheit scale is used to measure temperature. This scale is not based on the freezing and boiling points of water. Rather, water freezes at 32° and boils at 212°. Each degree Fahrenheit is only $\frac{5}{9}$ as large as each degree Celsius.

Comparisons of Celsius and Fahrenheit Temperatures		
	Celsius	Fahrenheit
Freezer	– 18°	0°
Freezing point of water	0°	32°
Room temperature	21°	70°
Body temperature	37°	98.6°
Highest outdoor temperature on record	58°	136°
Boiling point of water	100°	212°

The United States uses Fahrenheit temperatures, but Canada and many other nations use Celsius temperatures. Therefore, it is useful to know how to change temperatures from one scale to the other. The formula for changing degrees Celsius to degrees Fahrenheit is $F = \frac{9}{5} C + 32$. This formula is applied by using the steps below.

Step 1: Multiply the degrees Celsius by $\frac{9}{5}$.

Step 2: Add 32 to the product found in Step 1.

Step 3: Label the sum of Step 2 as degrees Fahrenheit (°F).

Use this formula to change degrees Celsius to degrees Fahrenheit.
$$F = \frac{9}{5} C + 32$$

Example A	**Example B**
$45°C = $ _____ °F	On a pleasant day in February, the temperature was 15°C. What was the temperature on the Fahrenheit scale?
$F = \frac{9}{5} \times 45° + 32°$	$F = \frac{9}{5} \times 15° + 32°$
$F = 81° + 32°$	$F = 27° + 32°$
$F = 113°F$	$F = 59°F$

CLASS PRACTICE

Calculate these temperatures to the nearest whole degree.

   a. 5°C = _____ °F   **b.** 85°C = _____ °F   **c.** 22°C = _____ °F   **d.** 46°C = _____ °F

WRITTEN EXERCISES

A. Change these Celsius temperatures to Fahrenheit, to the nearest whole degree.

  1. 10°C = _____ °F   **2.** 20°C = _____ °F

  3. 30°C = _____ °F   **4.** 40°C = _____ °F

  5. 25°C = _____ °F   **6.** 35°C = _____ °F

  7. 45°C = _____ °F   **8.** 55°C = _____ °F

  9. 75°C = _____ °F   **10.** 90°C = _____ °F

11. 65°C = _____ °F   **12.** 95°C = _____ °F

13. 16°C = _____ °F   **14.** 27°C = _____ °F

15. 7°C = _____ °F   **16.** 14°C = _____ °F

17. 32°C = _____ °F   **18.** 26°C = _____ °F

19. 48°C = _____ °F   **20.** 52°C = _____ °F

B. Solve these reading problems.

21. One summer afternoon the temperature was 36° Celsius. What was the Fahrenheit temperature to the nearest whole degree?

22. Doris had a fever of 38° Celsius. What was her temperature on the Fahrenheit scale?

23. One afternoon when the members of the Summitville congregation distributed tracts, the temperature was 12° Celsius. What was the Fahrenheit temperature to the nearest whole degree?

24. The township where the congregation distributed tracts had an area of 3.4 square miles. How many square kilometers is that to the nearest tenth of a square kilometer?

25. Brother Marvin calculated that he walked 3.4 kilometers distributing tracts along his assigned route. How many miles did he walk, to the nearest tenth of a mile?

26. One February morning at daybreak, the temperature was 2° Celsius. By noon it had increased by 15° Celsius. What was the Fahrenheit temperature at noon, to the nearest whole degree?

REVIEW EXERCISES

C. *Change these measures. You should know the answers to numbers 27–29 by memory.* (*Lessons 133–136*)

27. 1 m = _____ ft.

28. 1 l = _____ qt.

29. 1 ha = _____ a.

30. 15 ha = _____ km²

31. 2.8 MT = _____ kg

32. 448 ml = _____ l

D. *Find the surface areas of these figures.* (*Lesson 123*)

33. *rectangular solid*
    $l = 12''$
    $w = 10''$
    $h = 5''$

34. *rectangular solid*
    $l = 25$ cm
    $w = 20$ cm
    $h = 15$ cm

35. *cube*
    $e = 4'$

36. *cube*
    $e = 27$ cm

E. *Find the new prices to the nearest cent. Include both the amount of increase or decrease and the new price in each answer.* (*Lesson 74*)

37. $18.00 increased by 15%

38. $16.00 decreased by 35%

F. *Estimate the products. You need not find the exact answers.* (*Lesson 14*).

39. 4,582
     × 380

40. 6,492
     × 3,840

141. Changing From Fahrenheit to Celsius Temperature

In Lesson 140 you worked with the formula for changing from Celsius to Fahrenheit temperatures. This lesson teaches you the reverse: how to change from Fahrenheit to Celsius temperatures. The formula is $C = \frac{5}{9}(F - 32)$, and it is applied by using the following steps.

Step 1: Subtract 32° from the Fahrenheit temperature.

Step 2: Multiply $\frac{5}{9}$ times the difference found in Step 1.

Step 3: Label the product of Step 2 as degrees Celsius (°C).

> Use this formula to change degrees Fahrenheit to degrees Celsius.
> $$C = \frac{5}{9}(F - 32)$$

Example A	Example B
59°F = _____ °C $C = \frac{5}{9} \times (59° - 32°)$ $C = \frac{5}{9} \times 27°$ $C = \frac{5}{\cancel{9}_1} \times \frac{\cancel{27}^{3°}}{1} = \frac{15°}{1}$ $C = 15°C$	One morning when Mother took Dale's temperature, it was 103°F. What was the temperature on the Celsius scale? Round to the nearest tenth of a degree. $C = \frac{5}{9} \times (103° - 32°)$ $C = \frac{5}{9} \times \frac{71°}{1} = \frac{355°}{9} = 9\overline{)355°}\;39.44$ $C = 39.4°$

CLASS PRACTICE

Calculate these temperatures to the nearest whole degree.

a. 68°F = _____ °C   b. 75°F = _____ °C   c. 39°F = _____ °C

Calculate these temperatures to the nearest tenth of a degree.

d. 44°F = _____ °C   e. 60°F = _____ °C   f. 92°F = _____ °C

WRITTEN EXERCISES

A. Calculate these temperatures to the nearest whole degree.

1. 41°F = _____ °C   2. 50°F = _____ °C

3. 86°F = _____ °C   4. 113°F = _____ °C

5. 104°F = _____°C

6. 159°F = _____°C

7. 38°F = _____°C

8. 47°F = _____°C

9. 62°F = _____°C

10. 99°F = _____°C

11. 65°F = _____°C

12. 100°F = _____°C

B. Calculate these temperatures to the nearest tenth of a degree.

13. 72°F = _____.°C

14. 58°F = _____°C

15. 36°F = _____°C

16. 61°F = _____°C

17. 108°F = _____°C

18. 200°F = _____°C

19. 180°F = _____°C

20. 145°F = _____°C

C. Solve these reading problems.

21. One morning Brother Lamar, the janitor, found that the temperature was 18° Celsius when he arrived at church. By the time the service began, it had risen 2° Celsius. What was the temperature on the Fahrenheit scale at the beginning of the service?

22. During the worship service, the janitor noticed that the temperature had risen to 75°F. To the nearest whole degree, what was the temperature on the Celsius scale?

23. The highest temperature ever recorded in Iowa was 118°F on July 20, 1934. To the nearest whole degree, what was the temperature on the Celsius scale?

24. Marilyn's younger brother had a body temperature of 102°F. To the nearest tenth of a degree, what was his temperature on the Celsius scale?

25. The highest temperature ever recorded in North America was observed on July 10, 1913, when the temperature reached 134°F in Death Valley, California. To the nearest whole degree, what was the temperature on the Celsius scale?

26. Because of the high elevation of one mission station, the boiling point of water was 198°F. To the nearest whole degree, what was the boiling temperature on the Celsius scale?

REVIEW EXERCISES

D. *Change these Celsius temperatures to Fahrenheit temperatures, to the nearest whole degree. (Lesson 140)*

27. 60°C = _____ °F

28. 45°C = _____ °F

29. 10°C = _____ °F

30. 3°C = _____ °F

E. *Change these measures. (Lesson 139)*

31. 14 ft. = _____ m

32. 25 lb. = _____ kg

F. *Solve these problems. (Lesson 137)*

33. 7 kg + 225 g = _____ kg

34. 2 m – 45 cm = _____ cm

G. *Change these measures. You should know the answers to numbers 35 and 36 by memory. (Lessons 133–136)*

35. 1 a. = _____ ha

36. 1 lb. = _____ kg

37. 1.787 l = _____ ml

38. 3,222 cm = _____ m

H. *Draw these geometric figures. (Lesson 107)*

39. parallel lines AB and CD

40. perpendicular lines AB and CD

I. *Do these multiplications mentally. (Lessons 14, 15)*

41. 25 × 16

42. 60 × 50

43. 210 × 5

44. 14 × 45

142. Working With Bible Measures

The measures in the Bible are neither English nor metric; rather, they are measures that were used by the people of Bible lands. It is beneficial to be acquainted with the values of Bible measures so that we can better understand the distances and amounts that are mentioned.

Most measures in Bible times were not standard units; different cities and nations often had different systems. For this reason, it is often difficult to know the exact value of a Bible measure in English or metric units. The following table shows some of the measures in the Bible and gives their approximate English and metric equivalents.

Bible Measure	English Equivalent	Metric Equivalent
Length		
1 finger	$\frac{3}{4}$ inch	1.9 centimeters
1 span	.9 inches	23 centimeters
1 cubit	18 inches	46 centimeters
1 cubit	$1\frac{1}{2}$ feet	0.46 meter
1 fathom	6 feet	1.8 meters
1 furlong	606 feet	184.7 meters
1 furlong	$\frac{1}{9}$ mile	0.18 kilometer
Weight		
1 shekel	$\frac{2}{5}$ ounce	11.3 grams
1 talent	75 pounds	34 kilograms
Liquid capacity		
1 hin	$5\frac{1}{3}$ quarts	5 liters
1 bath	8 gallons	30.3 liters
1 firkin	about 9 gallons	34 liters
1 homer	80 gallons	303 liters
Dry capacity		
1 omer	$2\frac{1}{2}$ quarts	2.8 liters
1 ephah	$3\frac{1}{4}$ pecks	28.2 liters
1 homer	8 bushels	282 liters

Some of the Bible measures above are also units in the English measuring system but are seldom used today. One of them, the English furlong, is about 54 feet longer than the Bible furlong.

The steps for changing Bible measures to English or metric measures are much like those used in Lesson 139 to change English and metric measures.

1. Write the correct ratio from the table as the first ratio of a proportion, with each part correctly labeled. Also write those labels at the same place in the second ratio of the proportion. Write the number of the unit to be converted beside the correct label in the second ratio, and write n for the missing number.

2. Cross multiply, and then divide the product by the third fact in the proportion. (Division is not needed if the third fact is 1.) Label your answer with the word beside n in the second ratio.

Example A

During the storm when Paul was on his journey to Rome, the sailors sounded for the water depth and found it to be 20 fathoms (Acts 27:28). What was its depth in feet?

Step 1: 1 fathom = 6 feet

$$\frac{\text{fathoms}}{\text{feet}} \quad \frac{1}{6} = \frac{20}{n} \quad \frac{\text{fathoms}}{\text{feet}}$$

Step 2: 6 × 20 = 120 ft.

(120 ÷ 1 = 120)

Example B

After Jesus' resurrection, two of His followers unknowingly spoke with Him as they walked from Jerusalem to Emmaus, a distance of about threescore furlongs (Luke 24:13). What is this distance in miles?

Step 1: 1 furlong = $\frac{1}{9}$ mile

$$\frac{\text{furlongs}}{\text{miles}} \quad \frac{1}{\frac{1}{9}} = \frac{60}{n} \quad \frac{\text{furlongs}}{\text{miles}}$$

Step 2: $\frac{1}{9} \times 60 = 6\frac{2}{3}$ miles

$(6\frac{2}{3} \div 1 = 6\frac{2}{3})$

CLASS PRACTICE

Solve these problems.

a. Acts 1:12 states that the distance from Jerusalem to the Mount of Olives is a Sabbath day's journey. The Jewish rabbis placed the distance of a Sabbath day's journey at 2,000 cubits. How many feet is that? How many meters?

b. The golden nails used in the temple weighed 50 shekels (2 Chronicles 3:9). What was the weight of the nails in ounces? In grams?

WRITTEN EXERCISES

A. *Solve these problems.*

1. The Old Testament Law stated that when the people of Israel were numbered, every man was to give half a shekel as an offering of atonement (Exodus 30:13). (a) What was this weight in ounces? (b) If the offering was a half shekel of silver, and if silver is worth $4.671 per ounce, what was the value of the offering in today's money?

2. The Queen of Sheba brought King Solomon a gift of 120 talents of gold (1 Kings 10:10). What was the weight of the gold in pounds? In kilograms?

3. The ark Noah built was 300 cubits long (Genesis 6:15). What was its length in feet? In meters?

4. The "holy city, new Jerusalem" that John saw was 12,000 furlongs long, 12,000 furlongs wide, and 12,000 furlongs high (Revelation 21:16). How long is 12,000 furlongs in miles? In kilometers?

5. The daily morning and evening burnt offerings included $\frac{1}{4}$ hin of beaten oil (Numbers 28:5). How many quarts of oil was that? How many liters?

One lamb . . . and a tenth part of an ephah of flour . . . mingled with the fourth part of an hin of beaten oil . . . . And the drink offering thereof shall be the fourth part of an hin for the one lamb.
—Numbers 28:4–7

6. King Hiram made 10 lavers of brass for the temple of the Lord (1 Kings 7:38). Each laver could hold 40 baths of water. How many gallons of water could it hold? How many liters?

7. When God sent quail into the Israelite camp, "he that gathered least gathered ten homers" of quail (Numbers 11:32). How much was that in bushels? In liters?

8. When a famine came because of Judah's sin, planting one homer of seed yielded one ephah of grain in the harvest (Isaiah 5:10). How much less was being harvested than had been planted? First express your answer in bushels and pecks; then express it in liters.

9. In the wedding at Cana, the six water pots that were filled with water could hold two or three firkins apiece (John 2:6). If their capacity was 2.5 firkins each, how many gallons of water in all were put into them? How many liters?

10. The molten sea that King Solomon made for the temple of the Lord could hold 3,000 baths (2 Chronicles 4:5). How many gallons of water was that? How many liters?

11. Goliath's coat of armor weighed 5,000 shekels of brass (1 Samuel 17:5). What was its weight in pounds? In kilograms?

12. The pillars that King Solomon made for the house of the Lord were four fingers thick (Jeremiah 52:21). What was their thickness in inches? In centimeters?

REVIEW EXERCISES

B. Calculate these temperatures to the nearest whole degree. *(Lessons 140, 141)*

13. 40°F = _____°C

14. 60°F = _____°C

15. 40°C = _____°F

16. 60°C = _____°F

C. Solve these multiplication and division problems. *(Lesson 138)*

17. 15 × 4 m 13 cm = _____ m

18. 28 × 7 kg 70 mg = _____ mg

19. $4\overline{)3\text{ ft.}\quad 6\text{ in.}}$

20. $6\overline{)8\text{ lb.}\quad 2\text{ oz.}}$

D. Change these measures. *(Lessons 133–136)*

21. 1.5 l = _____ ml

22. 4.5 m² = _____ cm²

23. 3,145 g = _____ kg

24. 2.1 km = _____ m

E. Identify the type of angle described. *(Lesson 108)*

25. 121°

26. 90°

F. Solve these divisions. Label each part of the problems. *(Lesson 16)*

27. $148\overline{)16,581}$

28. $175\overline{)61,116}$

143. Chapter 11 Review

A. Measure these lines to the nearest millimeter. *(Lesson 133)*

1. _____

2. _____

B. Name the next larger unit. *(Lessons 133–136)*

3. centigram   **4.** hectare   **5.** liter   **6.** milligram

C. Write the abbreviation for the next smaller unit. *(Lessons 133–136)*

7. m   **8.** cg   **9.** hl   **10.** dkg

D. Write the abbreviations for these units. *(Lessons 133–136)*

11. kilogram   **12.** centimeter   **13.** gram   **14.** square kilometer

E. Change these measures. *(Lessons 133–136)*

15. 2.12 km = _____ m

16. 6,271 cm = _____ m

17. 0.03 km = _____ m

18. 0.82 MT = _____ kg

19. 4.01 kg = _____ mg

20. 118,600 mg = _____ kg

21. 4.51 kl = _____ l

22. 23 ml = _____ l

23. 5,177 l = _____ kl

24. 215,000 ml = _____ kl

25. 4,500,000 mm = _____ km

26. 7.11 l = _____ ml

27. 91 ha = _____ km^2

28. 2.01 m^2 = _____ cm^2

29. 0.77 km^2 = _____ ha

30. 28 kg 380 g = _____ kg

31. 9 l 80 ml = _____ ml

32. 78 m 45 mm = _____ m

F. Solve these problems with compound measures. *(Lessons 137, 138)*

33.
    9 ft. 11 in.
   + 7 ft. 10 in.

34.
    7 lb. 9 oz.
   + 9 lb. 10 oz.

35.
    6 bu. 1 pk.
   − 2 bu. 3 pk.

36.
    9 hr.
  − 4 hr. 15 min.

37.
    2 lb. 14 oz.
    ×   9

38.
    2 hr. 25 min.
    ×   8

39. $6\overline{)18 \text{ ft.   9 in.}}$

40. $4\overline{)18 \text{ lb.   7 oz.}}$

41. 89 cm + 25 mm = _____ cm

42. 4,110 kg + 2.21 MT = _____ kg

43. 4.1 MT – 919 kg = _____ MT

44. 4.7 kl – 590 l = _____ kl

45. 7 × 5 l 78 ml = _____ ml

46. 7 × 16 km 35 m = _____ km

47. 15 kl 80 l ÷ 20 = _____ kl

48. 28 m 80 mm ÷ 12 = _____ mm

G. Change these measures. You should be able to do them by memory. *(Lessons 133–136)*

49. 1 ft. = _____ m

50. 1 kg = _____ lb.

51. 1 qt. = _____ l

52. 1 ha = _____ a.

53. 1 m = _____ ft.

54. 1 lb. = _____ kg

H. Change these measures. *(Lesson 139)*

55. 9 qt. = _____ l

56. 112 sq. mi. = _____ km²

57. 11 tbsp. = _____ ml

58. 95 kg = _____ lb.

59. 108 lb. = _____ kg

60. 94 a. = _____ ha

I. Find these temperatures to the nearest whole degree. *(Lessons 140, 141)*

61. 45°C = _____°F

62. 65°C = _____°F

63. 91°F = _____°C

64. 37°F = _____°C

65. 10°C = _____°F

66. 12°C = _____°F

67. 42°F = _____°C

68. 69°F = _____°C

J. Find these temperatures to the nearest tenth of a degree. *(Lessons 140, 141)*

69. 46°F = _____°C

70. 62°F = _____°C

71. 32°C = _____°F

72. 78°C = _____°F

K. Solve these reading problems. *(Lessons 139, 142)*

73. Brother Witmer teaches school in another state. One weekend while driving home, he drove 145 miles before he stopped to buy gas. After that, he drove another 225 miles until he arrived at home. How many kilometers did he travel in all?

74. Uncle David delivered two truckloads of feed one afternoon. The one load weighed 18,500 pounds. The other weighed eleven tons. How many kilograms more did the second load weigh than the first one?

75. One medicine dropper can hold 1 milliliter. How many droppers full of medicine are equal to 2 tablespoons?

76. Goliath's height was six cubits and a span (1 Samuel 17:4). How tall was he?

77. Haman offered to pay 10,000 talents of silver to have the law passed that condemned the Jews to be killed (Esther 3:9). At $4.69 per ounce, what would be the value of Haman's offer in today's money?

78. The height of the golden image that Nebuchadnezzar built was 60 cubits (Daniel 3:1). What was the height in meters?

144. Chapter 11 Test

Chapter 12

Introduction to Algebra

For a just man falleth seven times, and riseth up again:
but the wicked shall fall into mischief.
(Proverbs 24:16)

145. Introducing Algebraic Expressions

In previous years you learned to solve number sentences such as $3 + n = 14$ and $7 \times n = 35$. In both of these number sentences, the letter n represents an unknown number. The value of n is found by calculating with the numbers whose values are known.

Algebra is a branch of mathematics in which letters are used to represent unknown numbers. In algebra we can add, subtract, multiply, and divide without knowing the value of the numbers. These "letter numbers" are called **literal numbers**. (*Literal* means "letter.")

Just as algebra uses a new set of numbers (literal numbers), so it also uses some new signs to indicate mathematical operations. The + and – signs still mean addition and subtraction. But × is not used for multiplication because it is easily confused with the literal number x. Neither is the ÷ sign used for division.

Multiplication in algebra is indicated in two different ways. One way is to use a raised dot (·) instead of the × sign. By this method, the problem 14 times 4 is written $14 \cdot 4$.

A second way of showing multiplication is by placing no sign at all between two letters or between a number and a letter. You have already seen examples of this in formulas for area and volume. For example, the expression $4s$ means 4 times s, and lw means l times w.

Notice that in multiplying an arithmetic number like 4 and a literal number like s, the arithmetic number always comes first. The correct order is $4s$, not $s4$.

A variation of the second method involves the use of parentheses. It does not always work to indicate multiplication by writing two factors directly side by side, because that sometimes changes their value. For example, 4 times 6 cannot be written as 46, because that means "forty-six." In that case, parentheses are used to set off the second factor, such as 4(6) to indicate 4 times 6. Parentheses are also used when the result of another operation is to be multiplied by a certain number. For example, 6(2 + 3) means 6 times the sum of 2 and 3, or 6 times 5.

In algebra, division is generally indicated by writing the numbers in fraction form. Thus 25 divided by 10 is $\frac{25}{10}$, and x divided by 7 is $\frac{x}{7}$.

Letters, numbers, and signs of operations are used to write **algebraic** (ăl·jə·brā´ĭk) **expressions** that are used in calculations. Notice how the following mathematical operations are written as algebraic expressions.

Mathematical Operation	Algebraic Expression
Three plus nine	$3 + 9$
n added to 7	$7 + n$
4 more than 2	$2 + 4$
8 minus 3	$8 - 3$
12 less than 25	$25 - 12$
x times b	xb

Mathematical Operation	Algebraic Expression
7 times y	$7y$
a subtracted from b	$b - a$
The product of 7 and 12	$7 \cdot 12$
15 divided by a	$\dfrac{15}{a}$
3 more than 8 times n	$8n + 3$
The sum of 7 and 9 divided by 4	$\dfrac{7+9}{4}$

Example A	Example B
Write all the literal numbers in the algebraic expression $6abc$. Answer: abc.	Write the problem 4×5, using the appropriate multiplication sign. Because both factors are arithmetic numbers, a raised dot should be used. Answer: $4 \cdot 5$
Example C	**Example D**
Write the problem 3 times a times b, using the appropriate multiplication sign. Because there are two literal numbers and only one arithmetic number, no sign is needed. Answer: $3ab$	Write an algebraic expression, using the appropriate multiplication sign, to show 7 times the sum of 5 and 6. Because both factors are arithmetic numbers and another operation is to be done first, parentheses are needed. Answer: $7(5 + 6)$

CLASS PRACTICE

Write these phrases as algebraic expressions. Be sure to use the appropriate signs for multiplication.

a. Six less than 7
b. c multiplied by d
c. 3 times the sum of a and b
d. 4 more than c
e. 7 less than d
f. 6.2 times 5

Write these algebraic expressions in words.

g. $5d$
h. $\dfrac{i}{4}$
i. $5k - 7$

WRITTEN EXERCISES

A. *Write all the literal numbers in each of these algebraic expressions.*

1. $6d$
2. $4mn$
3. $\dfrac{5d}{k}$
4. $abcd$

B. Write these mathematical operations as algebraic expressions, using the appropriate signs for multiplication.

5. 14×6

6. 7 times c

7. Two times the sum of 4 and 5

8. $8 \times c \times d$

9. 5 times 7

10. $5 \times$ the sum of a and b

C. Write these mathematical operations in algebraic form.

11. Seven less than k

12. Five more than seven

13. The product of 8 and n

14. The sum of 4 and d divided by 6

15. d plus 8

16. 5 less than 4 times d

D. Write these algebraic expressions, using words.

17. $k - 6$

18. $6d$

19. $\frac{h}{6}$

20. $4(k + 3)$

E. Solve these reading problems.

21. To change kilograms to pounds, multiply 2.2 times the number of kilograms (k). Write an algebraic expression for finding the product of 2.2 and k.

22. To change miles to kilometers, multiply 1.61 times the number of miles (m). Write an algebraic expression for finding the product of 1.61 and m.

23. To change feet to yards, divide the number of feet (f) by 3. Write an algebraic expression showing f divided by 3.

24. God created the cricket to chirp faster as the temperature increases. On warm days, adding 37 to the number of chirps (c) in 15 seconds yields the approximate temperature in degrees Fahrenheit. Write an algebraic expression showing the sum of c and 37.

25. God's greatness is seen in the creation of the stars. The sun, our nearest star, has a diameter of 865,000 miles. The average diameter of the variable star Betelgeuse is 460 times the diameter of the sun. To the nearest million miles, what is the average diameter of Betelgeuse?

26. The vast size of God's creation is incomprehensible to man. The largest known star in the Milky Way is one of the binary stars Epsilon Aurigae, which has a diameter of about 2.15 billion miles. Using the table in Lesson 139, find the approximate diameter in billions of kilometers.

REVIEW EXERCISES

F. Find the answers to the nearest tenth of a degree. *(Lessons 140, 141)*

27. 28°C = _____°F   **28.** 36°C = _____°F

29. 55°F = _____°C   **30.** 84°F = _____°C

G. Change these measures, using the table in Lesson 139 if necessary.

31. 15 km = _____ mi.   **32.** 28 in. = _____ cm

H. Change these metric measures. *(Lessons 133–136)*

33. 25 cm = _____ mm   **34.** 355 ml = _____ *l*

I. Find the volumes of rectangular solids having these dimensions.
(Lesson 125)

35. l = 14 cm   **36.** l = 8.5 m
     w = 13 cm w = 6.2 m
     h = 11 cm h = 2.3 m

J. Solve these division problems, and check by casting out nines. *(Lesson 18)*

37. 75$\overline{)228,161}$ **38.** 415$\overline{)399,872}$

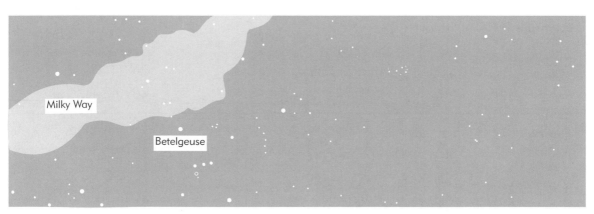

He is wise in heart, and mighty in strength . . . Which doeth great things past finding out; yea, and wonders without number.

Job 9:4–10

146. Using the Correct Order of Operations

To solve problems in algebra, we must **simplify** algebraic expressions by doing the calculations indicated. But it is very important that we use the correct **order of operations** when we do this. If the calculations are done in the wrong order, the result may not be correct even if all the work is done accurately.

In Example A below, the expression is simplified in two ways. Both sets of calculations are done accurately, but the results are different because of the order in which the operations are done.

Only one result in Example A is correct because a certain order has been established to simplify algebraic expressions. The rules for this order are listed below. When they are used to simplify any algebraic expression, there is only one possible result.

Memorize these rules for the order of operations.
1. Perform the operations within parentheses first.
2. Do multiplication and division in the order they appear.
3. Do addition and subtraction in the order they appear.

Example A	Simplify: $5 + 6 \cdot 7$	
	Wrong: $5 + 6 = 11$; $11 \cdot 7 = 77$	
	Right: $6 \cdot 7 = 42$; $42 + 5 = 47$	
Example B	Simplify: $2 + 6 \cdot 4$	
	Step 1: Not required.	
	Step 2: Do multiplication.	$2 + 24$
	Step 3: Do addition.	26 (result)
Example C	Simplify: $38 - 3(4 + 2)$	
	Step 1: Do operation in parentheses.	$38 - 3(6)$
	Step 2: Do multiplication.	$38 - 18$
	Step 3: Do subtraction.	20 (result)
Example D	Simplify: $8 + \frac{12}{4} - 2 \cdot 3$	
	Step 1: Not required.	
	Step 2: Do division and multiplication.	$8 + 3 - 6$
	Step 3: Do addition and subtraction.	5 (result)

CLASS PRACTICE

Write the number of the rule that applies to each statement.

   a. When simplifying the expression $7 + 3 \cdot 5$, first do $3 \cdot 5$.

   b. When simplifying the expression $4(5 - 3)$, first do $5 - 3$.

Simplify these expressions.

   c. $4 + 3 \cdot 5$

   d. $6(2 + 7)$

   e. $12 - \frac{15}{3} + 6 \cdot 5$

   f. $(6 + 8) - 3 \cdot 4$

   g. $4 + 5 - 2 \cdot 3$

   h. $20 - 3(8 - 4)$

WRITTEN EXERCISES

A. *Write the number of the rule that applies to each statement.*

   1. To simplify the expression $3 \cdot \frac{3}{4} \cdot 2$, first multiply $3 \cdot \frac{3}{4}$.

   2. To simplify the expression $3 + 6 \cdot 5$, first multiply $6 \cdot 5$.

   3. To simplify the expression $(3 + 4)5$, first add $3 + 4$.

   4. To simplify the expression $5 + 8 - 7$, first add $5 + 8$.

   5. To simplify the expression $2 \cdot 3 - 5$, first multiply $2 \cdot 3$.

   6. To simplify the expression $6 + 5 \cdot 2 + (3 - 2)$, first subtract $3 - 2$.

B. *Simplify these expressions.*

   7. $18 - 6 \cdot 3$

   8. $4 \cdot 5 - 1$

   9. $8 + \frac{12}{2} - 2 \cdot 3$

   10. $3(5 + 7)$

   11. $3 + 7 \cdot 3 - 6$

   12. $22 - 2(3 + 7)$

   13. $6(\frac{12}{4} - 3)$

   14. $6(2 + 7)$

   15. $30 - 7 \cdot 2 \cdot 2$

   16. $(5 + 1)(6 - 1)$

   17. $7(12 - 4)$

   18. $(30 - 2) - 2(3 \cdot 4)$

   19. $7(12 - 5) - 6$

   20. $14 - \frac{21}{7} + 3 \cdot 2$

C. *Solve each reading problem by first writing an algebraic expression. Then simplify the expression, using the rules for order of operations.*

   21. King Rehoboam reigned three years less than half as many years as King David. David reigned 40 years. How long did Rehoboam reign?

   22. King Josiah reigned two years less than three times as long as his son Zedekiah. Zedekiah reigned 11 years. How long did Josiah reign?

   23. Marian was helping to gather eggs on her uncle's farm. She filled two cases, each holding 30 dozen eggs, and there were 29 eggs left. How many eggs did she gather?

24. One of the chicken houses has 20 rows of cages with 45 chickens in each row. If Marian gathers 830 eggs from that house, how many chickens did not lay? (No chicken laid more than one egg.)

25. In 2 Kings 6:25 we read of a famine so severe that a donkey's head was sold for 80 pieces of silver. If these pieces weighed 1 shekel each, how many pounds did the silver weigh? (See Lesson 142.)

26. Ezekiel was instructed to drink one-sixth hin of water each day (Ezekiel 4:11). How much is that in liters?

REVIEW EXERCISES

D. Write these algebraic expressions in words. *(Lesson 145)*

27. $6a + 4$ **28.** $35 - \dfrac{k}{7}$

E. Write these phrases as algebraic expressions. *(Lesson 145)*

29. The product of 5 and k divided by n

30. The difference between 5 and d multiplied by 2

F. Change these measures as indicated. *(Lesson 142)*

31. 28 furlongs = _____ mi.   **32.** 45 homers (liquid) = _____ l

G. Solve these problems involving measures. *(Lesson 138)*

33.   4 ft. 7 in.
          $\underline{\times\quad 6\quad}$

34. 7 × 9 m 5 mm = _____ m

H. Find the volumes of cubes having these dimensions. *(Lesson 126)*

35. $e = 6$ m   **36.** $e = 22$ in.

I. Find the perimeters of polygons having these dimensions. *(Lesson 111)*

37. *square*   **38.** *rectangle*
     $s = 17''$ $l = 19''$
                                                           $w = 17''$

J. Find the average of each set of numbers. Express any remainder as a fraction. *(Lesson 19)*

39. 22, 24, 23, 28, 20   **40.** 51, 49, 48, 60, 45

147. Evaluating Expressions With Literal Numbers

Many algebraic expressions contain one or more literal numbers. In order to find the total value of such expressions, it is necessary to know the value of each literal number. Then the value of the algebraic expression can be found by substituting the literal numbers with their given values. Finding the value of algebraic expressions in this way is known as **evaluating** them.

To evaluate algebraic expressions with literal numbers, use the following steps.

Step 1: Rewrite the algebraic expression, replacing each literal number with its given value.

Step 2: Simplify the expression, following the rules for the order of operations in Lesson 146.

Example A

$a = 5$; $x = 2$; $y = 0.5$ Evaluate: $ax + y$

Step 1: Rewrite. $5 \cdot 2 + 0.5$

Step 2: Multiply. $10 + 0.5$

         Add. 10.5 (result)

Example B

$a = 5$; $n = 0.04$; $x = 2$; $y = 0.5$ Evaluate: $a - y(x + n)$

Step 1: Rewrite. $5 - 0.5(2 + 0.04)$

Step 2: Do operation in parentheses. $5 - 0.5(2.04)$

         Multiply. $5 - 1.02$

         Subtract. 3.98 (result)

CLASS PRACTICE

Evaluate these algebraic expressions by substituting the numerical value given for each literal number. Use number sentences in your calculations.

a. $36 - y$, if $y = 10$

b. $\dfrac{81}{m + 5}$, if $m = 4$

c. $(k - 2)(k + 2)$, if $k = 6$

d. $6a - \dfrac{12}{a}$, if $a = 2$

In whom are hid all the treasures of wisdom and knowledge.
Colossians 2:3

WRITTEN EXERCISES

A. *Evaluate these algebraic expressions by substituting the numerical value for each literal number. Use number sentences in your calculations.*

1. $\dfrac{23 - y}{2}$ $(y = 5)$

2. $22a$ $(a = 3)$

3. $41 + x$ $(x = 5)$

4. $3e + 5$ $(e = 6)$

5. $a - 7$ $(a = 12)$

6. $\dfrac{a + 22}{17}$ $(a = 12)$

7. $9 + s - 2 \cdot s$ $(s = 8)$

8. $f - 2 + 3 \cdot f$ $(f = 7)$

9. $3(x + 2) - 8$ $(x = 10)$

10. $\dfrac{14}{w} - 3 \cdot w$ $(w = 2)$

11. $\dfrac{6 - y}{2y}$ $(y = 3)$

12. $\dfrac{33}{x + 3 - x}$ $(x = 1)$

B. *Evaluate each expression by substituting the following numerical values for each literal number. Use number sentences in your calculations.*

$$a = 3 \qquad x = 4 \qquad y = 5$$

13. $21 + a$

14. $\dfrac{8}{9 - y}$

15. $\dfrac{14 + x}{2}$

16. $a(12 + x)$

17. $8(7 - x)$

18. $2(y + 3)$

19. $(y + x)(y + x)$

20. $(y + x)(y - x)$

C. *Solve these reading problems. Complete the algebraic expressions that are given for numbers 21–24.*

21. The Millers are planning to lay a new floor in their kitchen. If the kitchen measures 13 feet along each side, how much flooring do they need to buy?

$$s^2 = 13^2 = \underline{\hphantom{xxx}} \times \underline{\hphantom{xxx}} = \underline{\hphantom{xxx}}$$

22. Mr. Miller has several cylindrical vats in which he mixes solutions for tanning leather. The radius of one vat is 2 feet, and its height is 5 feet. What is the volume of the vat?

$$\pi r^2 h = \underline{\hphantom{xxx}} \times \underline{\hphantom{xxx}} \times \underline{\hphantom{xxx}} \times \underline{\hphantom{xxx}} = \underline{\hphantom{xxx}}$$

23. When the Moyer family moved to a mission in Paraguay, they shipped their belongings by sea container. The container was 20 feet long, 8 feet wide, and 8 feet high. What was the volume of the container?

$$lwh =$$

24. If the container traveled 8,750 miles from Toronto, Canada, to Asuncion, Paraguay in 75 days, what was the average distance traveled per day?

$$\dfrac{d}{t} =$$

25. The official language in Paraguay is Spanish, but an estimated 90% of the population commonly speaks Guaranì. In 1992, the population of Paraguay was estimated at 4,500,000. What is 90% of 4,500,000?

26. Although freedom of worship is promised to all faiths, Roman Catholicism is the official religion of Paraguay. If 95% of the population is Catholic, what percent is non-Catholic?

REVIEW EXERCISES

D. *Simplify these expressions, using the correct order of operations.* (*Lesson 146*)

27. $9 - 2 \cdot 2$

28. $6 + 3$

29. $4(6 - 2)$

30. $17 - 5(6 - 3)$

E. *Write an algebraic expression for each phrase.* (*Lesson 145*)

31. Five times the sum of 3 and k

32. Three less than the product of 4 and y

F. *Find the volumes of cylinders having these dimensions.* (*Lesson 127*)

33. $r = 3''$
   $h = 8''$

34. $r = 5$ cm
   $h = 19$ cm

G. *Solve these division problems mentally.* (*Lesson 20*)

35. $700 \div 25$

36. $3,400 \div 50$

37. $144 \div 18$

38. $900 \div 25$

148. Solving Equations by Addition and Subtraction

An **equation** is a number sentence with an equal sign between two sides that contain expressions of equal value. The problem $5 + 7 = 4 \cdot 3$ is an equation because both sides have a value of 12.

Because both sides of an equation are equal, an equation with a literal number can be solved to find the value of the literal number. For example, in the equation $x = 7 + 8$, we know that the value of x is 15 because $7 + 8 = 15$ and both sides of the equation must be equal.

Equations are seldom as easy to solve as the one given above and the ones studied in earlier lessons, because the literal number is not always by itself on one side of the equation. In the equation $n - 3 = 25 + 5$, n is not by itself. To solve such an equation, mathematical operations are used to get the literal number by itself on one side of the equation. These operations are governed by certain mathematical laws.

The mathematical laws used to solve equations state what can be done to an equation without changing its equality. One of these laws is the **addition axiom,** which states that the same number can be added to both sides of an equation. For example, in the equation $7 = 7$, you can add 4 to each side and the equation is still true. The equation is now $7 + 4 = 7 + 4$, or $11 = 11$.

The addition axiom can be used to solve equations when an arithmetic number is subtracted from a literal number. Adding the same number being subtracted from the literal number results in the literal number being by itself on one side of the equation.

The Addition Axiom

The same value can be added to both sides of an equation without changing its equality. This axiom is used to remove a number being subtracted from a literal number.

Example A	Example B
$n - 9 = 28$	$n - 12 = 32$
$n - 9 + 9 = 28 + 9$	$n - 12 + 12 = 32 + 12$
$n = 37$	$n = 44$

The **subtraction axiom** is similar to the addition axiom. It states that the same number can be subtracted from both sides of an equation without changing its equality.

The subtraction axiom can be used to solve equations when an arithmetic number is added to the literal number. If the number being added to the literal number is subtracted from both sides of the equation, it will remove the arithmetic number from the side of the equation that has the literal number.

The Subtraction Axiom

The same value can be subtracted from both sides of an equation without changing its equality. This axiom is used to remove a number being added to a literal number.

Example C	**Example D**
$n + 9 = 28$	$n + 12 = 32$
$n + 9 - 9 = 28 - 9$	$n + 12 - 12 = 32 - 12$
$n = 19$	$n = 20$

Solving equations usually involves several calculations, and often the addition or subtraction axiom is only one of those calculations. To solve an equation that requires more than one calculation, follow the steps listed below. **Your aim in solving an equation is to get the literal number by itself on one side and its value on the other side.**

Step 1: Simplify the expression on the side of the equation that does not have a literal number.

Step 2: Eliminate any mathematical operation on the side of the equation that has the literal number, by using the operation that is opposite.

    a. If a number is being subtracted from the literal number, use the addition axiom.

    b. If a number is being added to the literal number, use the subtraction axiom.

Step 3: Simplify the side of the equation that does not have the literal number. You should now have the solution. State the answer in algebraic form, with the literal number, an equal sign, and the answer.

Step 4: Check your answer by substituting it for the literal number in the original equation. If the equation is true, the answer is correct.

Example E	**Example F**
$n - 14 = 5 - 3$	$x + 4 = \frac{36}{3}$
Step 1: $\quad n - 14 = 2$	Step 1: $\quad x + 4 = 12$
Step 2: $\quad n - 14 + 14 = 2 + 14$	Step 2: $\quad x + 4 - 4 = 12 - 4$
Step 3: $\quad n = 16$	Step 3: $\quad x = 8$
Step 4: $\quad 16 - 14 = 5 - 3$	Step 4: $\quad 8 + 4 = \frac{36}{3}$
$\quad\quad 2 = 2$	$\quad\quad 12 = 12$
Because $16 - 14 = 2$ and $5 - 3 = 2$, the answer is correct.	Because $8 + 4 = 12$ and $36 \div 3 = 12$, the answer is correct.

CLASS PRACTICE

First state which axiom you will use to get the literal number by itself on one side. Then solve the equation.

a. $n + 12 = 3 \cdot 5$

b. $k + 8 = 18 - 3$

c. $m - 5 = 16 + 8$

d. $25 - 7 = x - 5$

e. $25 \cdot 4 = d + 70$

f. $\frac{42}{6} = n - 12$

WRITTEN EXERCISES

A. State which axiom should be used to get the literal number by itself on one side.

1. $y + 7 = 23$

2. $m - 3 = 21$

3. $z - 12 = 3 \cdot 5$

4. $z - 6 = \frac{72}{6}$

5. $4 \cdot 8 = m + 16$

6. $\frac{20}{4} = d - 5$

B. Solve these equations by using the addition axiom.

7. $t - 12 = 3 \cdot 5$

8. $a - 15 = 14 - 6$

9. $b - 7 = \frac{80}{5}$

10. $b - 3 = \frac{49}{7}$

C. Solve these equations by using the subtraction axiom.

11. $c + 8 = 2 \cdot 7$

12. $e + 14 = 30 - 5$

13. $f + 12 = \frac{96}{8}$

14. $g + 15 = 19 + 7$

D. Use the correct axiom to solve each equation.

15. $a + 22 = 36$

16. $y - 15 = 40$

17. $t + 3 = 6 \cdot 8$

18. $n - 10 = 11 + 5$

19. $x + 5 = \frac{72}{9}$

20. $y - 15 = 20 + 7$

E. Solve these reading problems. Complete and solve the equations for numbers 21–24.

21. Methuselah lived m years. His father Enoch lived 604 years less than that. Enoch's life on the earth equaled 365 years. How long did Methuselah live?

$$m - \underline{} = \underline{}$$

22. Lamech lived l years. His son Noah lived 173 years more than Lamech. If Noah lived 950 years, how long did Lamech live?

$$l + \underline{} = \underline{}$$

23. God's greatness is seen in the different kinds of animals He created. There are b species of butterflies and moths on the earth, and there are 140,000 more species of beetles than there are of moths and butterflies. There are 250,000 species of beetles in all. How many species of moths and butterflies are there?

$$b + \underline{} = \underline{}$$

24. There are a species of algae. There are 20,000 fewer species of sponges than of algae. If there are 5,000 species of sponges, how many species of algae are there?

$$a - \underline{\hspace{1cm}} = \underline{\hspace{1cm}}$$

25. The conical hopper of a feed bin has a radius of 6 feet and a height of 8 feet. What is its volume?

26. Indian tribes living on the plains of North America often used conical tepees for their homes. If a tepee had a radius of 5 feet and a height of 12 feet, what was its volume?

REVIEW EXERCISES

F. Evaluate these expressions by using this substitution: $n = 3$. *(Lesson 147)*

27. $2n + 8$ 28. $\dfrac{15}{n} \cdot 2$ 29. $n(3 + 2)$ 30. $4n - 6$

G. Simplify these expressions, using the correct order of operations. *(Lesson 146)*

31. $3 + 2 \cdot 5 - 8$ 32. $6 \cdot 2 + 9 \cdot 3$

H. Find the answers to the nearest tenth of a degree. *(Lessons 140, 141)*

33. $92°C = \underline{\hspace{1cm}} °F$ 34. $92°F = \underline{\hspace{1cm}} °C$

I. Find the volumes of cones having these dimensions. *(Lesson 128)*

35. $r = 4''$ 36. $r = 9$ cm

  $h = 9''$ $h = 23$ cm

J. Find the areas of quadrilaterals having these dimensions. *(Lesson 114)*

37. *parallelogram*   38. *parallelogram*

  $b = 14''$ $b = 28$ cm

  $h = 9''$ $h = 22$ cm

39. *square*   40. *square*

  $s = 19''$ $s = 62$ cm

149. Solving Equations by Multiplication and Division

In Lesson 148 you learned that the addition axiom is used to remove a number being subtracted from a literal number. You also learned that the subtraction axiom is used to remove a number being added to a literal number. In this lesson you will learn axioms that are used when a literal number is multiplied or divided. These axioms are known as the multiplication axiom and the division axiom.

Like addition and subtraction, multiplication and division are opposite operations. The multiplication problem $2 \cdot 3 = 6$ pairs with the division problem $\frac{6}{3} = 2$. Because of this, we use the multiplication axiom if a literal number is divided and the division axiom if a literal number is multiplied.

The **multiplication axiom** states that both sides of an equation may be multiplied by the same number without changing the equality. Consider the equation $6 = 6$. If both sides are multiplied by 5, the equation becomes $5 \cdot 6 = 5 \cdot 6$. The equation is still true because both sides have an equal value, 30.

The multiplication axiom is used to solve equations when a literal number is divided by an arithmetic number. Multiplying both sides of the equation by the divisor will remove that number from the side of the equation where the literal number is.

The Multiplication Axiom

Both sides of an equation may be multiplied by the same number without changing the equality. This axiom is used to remove the number by which a literal number is being divided.

Example A	**Example B**
$\frac{n}{9} = 5$	$\frac{x}{6} = 12$
$\frac{n}{9} \cdot 9 = 5 \cdot 9$	$\frac{x}{6} \cdot 6 = 12 \cdot 6$
$n = 45$	$x = 72$
Check: $\frac{45}{9} = 5$	Check: $\frac{72}{6} = 12$
$5 = 5$	$12 = 12$

The **division axiom** is similar to the multiplication axiom. It states that both sides of an equation may be divided by the same number without changing the equality of the equation. Consider the equation $10 = 10$. If both sides are divided by 2, the equation becomes $\frac{10}{2} = \frac{10}{2}$. This equation is still true because both sides have an equal value, 5.

The division axiom is used to solve equations when a literal number is multiplied by an arithmetic number. Dividing both sides of the equation by that factor number will remove it from the side of the equation where the literal number is.

The Division Axiom

Both sides of an equation may be divided by the same number without changing the equality. This axiom is used to remove the number by which a literal number is being multiplied.

Example C	Example D
$9k = 54$	$12m = 144$
$\dfrac{9k}{9} = \dfrac{54}{9}$	$\dfrac{12m}{12} = \dfrac{144}{12}$
$k = 6$	$m = 12$
Check: $9 \cdot 6 = 54$	Check: $12 \cdot 12 = 144$
$54 = 54$	$144 = 144$

The same steps are applied to solving equations by these axioms as were presented in Lesson 148. Remember: Your aim in solving an equation is to get the literal number by itself on one side and its value on the other side.

Step 1: Simplify the expression on the side of the equation that does not have a literal number.

Step 2: Eliminate any mathematical operation on the side of the equation that has the literal number by using the operation that is opposite.

a. If a number is being subtracted from the literal number, use the addition axiom.

b. If a number is being added to the literal number, use the subtraction axiom.

c. If the literal number is being divided by a number, use the multiplication axiom.

d. If the literal number is being multiplied by a number, use the division axiom.

Note: The side with the literal number may require addition or subtraction as well as multiplication or division. In such a case, use the addition or subtraction axiom first. See Example F below.

Step 3: Simplify the side of the equation that does not have the literal number. You should now have the solution. State the answer in algebraic form, with the literal number, an equal sign, and the answer.

Step 4: Check your answer by substituting it for the literal number in the original equation. If the equation is true, the answer is correct.

Example E	Example F
$5n = \frac{45}{3}$	$4x + 2 = \frac{36}{2}$
Step 1: $5n = 15$	Step 1: $4x + 2 = 18$
Step 2: $\frac{5n}{5} = \frac{15}{5}$	Step 2: $4x + 2 - 2 = 18 - 2$
	$4x = 16$
	$\frac{4x}{4} = \frac{16}{4}$
Step 3: $n = 3$	Step 3: $x = 4$
Step 4: $5 \cdot 3 = \frac{45}{3}$	Step 4: $4 \cdot 4 + 2 = \frac{36}{2}$
$15 = 15$	$18 = 18$

CLASS PRACTICE

First tell which of the four axioms to use to get the literal number by itself on one side. Then solve the equation.

a. $4m = 160$ b. $n + 70 = 71$ c. $q - 6 = 35$ d. $\frac{p}{15} = 7$

WRITTEN EXERCISES

A. Write which of the four axioms you would use to get the literal number by itself on one side.

1. $q - 8 = 35$ 2. $\frac{r}{4} = 7 + 5$ 3. $s - 9 = 41$ 4. $6t = 78$

B. Solve these equations by using the multiplication axiom.

5. $\frac{u}{2} = 40 + 5$ 6. $\frac{v}{9} = 2 \cdot 7$ 7. $\frac{w}{7} = \frac{18}{6}$ 8. $\frac{x}{8} = 17 - 5$

C. Solve these equations by using the division axiom.

9. $4y = 36$ 10. $12z = 35 + 25$

11. $9a = 60 - 6$ 12. $7b = \frac{120}{2} + 3$

D. Solve these equations by using all four axioms as needed.

13. $c - 7 = 3 \cdot 5$ 14. $\frac{d}{7} = 25 - 8$

15. $8e = 9 \cdot 16$ 16. $f - 9 = 25 + 4$

17. $g + 7 = \frac{44}{4}$ 18. $5h = 72 - 17$

19. $\frac{i}{6} = 14(9 - 6)$ 20. $5n = 12 + 6 \cdot 3$

E. Solve these reading problems. Finish the equations for problems 21–24.

21. Mary was asked how many girls (g) were in the seventh grade. She replied that there were exactly 2 times as many boys as girls and that there were 12 boys. What was the number of girls?

_____ $g =$ _____

22. Brother Dwight charges $5 for a bushel of slightly bruised peaches. This is $3 less than his regular price (p) for a bushel. What is the regular price?

$p -$ _____ $=$ _____

23. Mr. Thompson told his son that if they were to put 35 more tons of hay in the barn, they would have 100 tons. What is the number of tons (t) already in the barn?

$t +$ _____ $=$ _____

24. Karen and her sisters spent a morning baking cookies (c). When they divided them into 10 piles, they had exactly 15 cookies on each pile. What number of cookies had they baked?

$\frac{c}{\_\_} = \_\_$

25. A church cemetery is triangular, having a base of 350 feet and a depth (height) of 300 feet. What is its area?

26. Adam lived to be 930 years old. In the United States, the average person lives about 8.1% as long as Adam did. What is the average life span in the United States? Round your answer to the nearest tenth of a year.

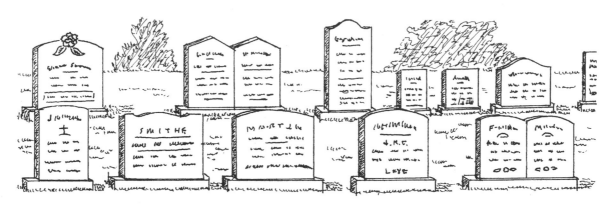

Then shall the dust return to the earth as it was: and the spirit shall return unto God who gave it.

Ecclesiastes 12:7

REVIEW EXERCISES

F. Solve these equations by using this substitution: $s = 6$. *(Lesson 147)*

27. $n = 3s + 7$ **28.** $n = \dfrac{s}{2} - 1$ **29.** $n = 3 \cdot 5 - s$ **30.** $n = 30 - 5s$

G. Write these phrases as algebraic expressions. *(Lesson 145)*

31. Three more than the product of seven and z

32. The product of three and n divided by the difference between six and m

H. Find the areas of triangles having these dimensions. *(Lesson 115)*

33. $b = 5$ in.   **34.** $b = 9$ cm
      $h = 7$ in. $h = 12$ cm

I. Solve these percent problems. *(Lesson 83)*

35. 117% of 60   **36.** 122% of 85

37. 228% of 120   **38.** 315% of 260

150. Reading Problems: Choosing the Correct Equation

Equations are useful for solving mathematical problems in many areas of life. Writing equations requires analyzing problems until they are thoroughly understood. And then when the equation is written, it can be solved by following one or more logical steps. So writing an equation has two benefits: it helps us to analyze a problem, and it provides a logical way to find the solution.

Writing equations to solve reading problems is basically the same as writing number sentences to solve reading problems, which you learned in grade 6. The facts stated in a reading problem need to be expressed as a number sentence or an equation before the problem can be solved.

In order to write a valid equation for a problem, you need to evaluate the problem and determine what operation or operations are needed. Following are some of the phrases that indicate the use of a specific mathematical operation.

Mathematical Operation	**Phrases That Indicate the Operation**
Addition	More than, added to, increased by, plus, greater than, larger than, the sum of
Subtraction	Less than, subtracted from, decreased by, minus, less than, smaller than, difference
Multiplication	Times multiplied by, times greater than, product of
Division	Divided by, the quotient of

Example A

A neighbor asked Mrs. Moser if she had fresh eggs to sell. Mrs. Moser looked into the cooler and replied, "If I can find 4 eggs to add to these eggs (e), we will have two dozen." How many eggs did Mrs. Moser have?

Solution: Addition is clearly indicated. If 4 eggs are added to a certain number (e), the total will be two dozen eggs (24).

(a certain number of eggs)	plus	(four more eggs)	equals	(two dozen eggs)
e	$+$	4	$=$	24

$$e + 4 = 24$$
$$e + 4 - 4 = 24 - 4$$
$$e = 20 \text{ eggs}$$

Check: $20 + 4 = 24$
$$24 = 24$$

Example B

Enos helped his father set out cauliflower plants. After planting 3 equal rows, they had only 6 plants left for the fourth row. They planted a total of 60 plants. How many plants did they set in each of the first three rows?

Solution: A certain number of plants (n) were planted in 3 rows, with 6 plants remaining for the fourth row. Because there were a certain number of plants in each of three rows, multiplication is used to find the total number in the three rows. Replacing the phrase "a certain number" with a literal number results in the following equation.

(3 rows of a certain number)	plus	(number remaining for fourth row)	equals	(total number of plants)
$3n$	$+$	6	$=$	60

$$3n + 6 = 60$$
$$3n + 6 - 6 = 60 - 6$$
$$3n = 54$$
$$\frac{3n}{3} = \frac{54}{3}$$
$$n = 18 \text{ plants}$$

Check:
$$3 \cdot 18 + 6 = 60$$
$$54 + 6 = 60$$
$$60 = 60$$

CLASS PRACTICE

Choose the correct equations, and find the solutions.

a. Grace bought two stamps of the same value and a 23¢ stamp. The stamps cost 81¢ in all. What was the value of each of the other two stamps?

    a. $n + 23 = 81$ **b.** $n - 23 = 81$ **c.** $2n + 23 = 81$ **d.** $n + 2 + 23 = 81$

b. Father told Louise that she was paying 2¢ more than 10 times what he paid to mail a letter when he was her age. She was paying 32¢. How much did it cost to mail a letter when Father was a boy?

    a. $10s + 2 = 32$ **b.** $10s - 2 = 32$ **c.** $\frac{32}{10} = s$ **d.** $32 - 2 = s$

WRITTEN EXERCISES

A. Write equations for these sentences.

1. A certain number times 5 plus 2 is equal to 47.

2. Six less than the product of six and c is equal to 48.

3. Subtract 2 from a number, and you get 15.

4. Divide 72 by a number, and you get 56.

5. Multiply a number by 4 and then add 12, and you get 24.

6. Multiply a number by 3 and then subtract 2, and you get 13.

B. Use the four axioms to solve these equations.

7. $n + 17 = 20$ **8.** $y - 12 = 4$

9. $6a = 24$ **10.** $\frac{m}{24} = 2$

11. $12s = 40 + 8$ **12.** $12 + m = 2 \cdot 10 - 5$

13. $s - 24 = \frac{36}{2}$ **14.** $3a = 24 - 3$

C. Solve these reading problems. For numbers 15–24, choose the correct equation and use it to solve the problem.

15. Marcus is 3 times as old as Dwight. Dwight is 6 years old. How old is Marcus? (m = Marcus's age)

    a. $3m = 6$ **b.** $3m - 3 = 6$ **c.** $m = 3 \cdot 6$ **d.** $\frac{m}{6} = 3$

16. Lucy is twice as old as Susan. Susan is 6 years old. How old is Lucy? (l = Lucy's age)

    a. $2 \cdot 6 = l$ **b.** $6 = 2l$ **c.** $\frac{6}{2} = l$ **d.** $\frac{l}{6} = 2$

17. David is six years less than three times Michael's age. David is 30 years old. How old is Michael? (m = Michael's age)

    a. $6m - 3 = 30$ **b.** $3m + 6 = 30$ **c.** $3m - 6 = 30$ **d.** $m = \frac{6 \cdot 5}{3}$

18. Ronald is five years more than twice Lewis's age. Ronald is 13 years old. How old is Lewis? (l = Lewis's age)

    a. $2l + 5 = 13$ **b.** $l = 2 \cdot 13 + 5$ **c.** $\frac{l}{2} - 5 = 13$ **d.** $\frac{13}{2} - 5 = l$

19. The number of eighth grade students is five less than 2 times the number of seventh grade students. There are 11 students in grade 8. How many students are in seventh grade? (s = number of seventh graders)

    a. $s + 5 = 11$ **b.** $2s - 5 = 11$ **c.** $11 - s = 5$ **d.** $2 \cdot 11 - 5 = s$

20. The number of students in school is 6 more than three times as many students as are in Brother Marvin's classroom. There are 15 students in Brother Marvin's classroom. How many students are in the entire school? (s = number of students in the school)

    a. $3s + 6 = 15$ **b.** $s = 3 \cdot 6 - 15$ **c.** $s = 3 \cdot 15 + 6$ **d.** $\frac{s}{15} = 3 \cdot 6$

21. Neil has 2 more than twice as many books as Keith. If Neil has 16 books, how many books does Keith have? (k = number of Keith's books)

    a. $2k + 2 = 16$ **b.** $2k - 2 = 16$ **c.** $\frac{k}{2} + 2 = 16$ **d.** $k = \frac{16}{2} - 2$

22. Leonard has 6 less than three times as many books as Clarence. If Clarence has 10 books, how many books does Leonard have? (l = number of Leonard's books)

    a. $3l - 6 = 10$ **b.** $3l + 6 = 10$ **c.** $\frac{l}{3} - 6 = 10$ **d.** $l = 3 \cdot 10 - 6$

23. Jacob and Esau were twins. When their father Isaac was 100 years old, the twins' combined ages plus twenty years equaled their father's age. How old were the twins when their father was 100 years old? (t = age of Esau or Jacob)

    a. $2t + 20 = 100$ **b.** $2t - 20 = 100$ **c.** $t + 20 = \frac{100}{2}$ **d.** $t = 2 \cdot 100 + 20$

24. Father is 3 inches less than twice as tall as Joseph. Joseph is 36 inches tall. How tall is Father? (f = Father's height)

    a. $3f - 2 = 36$ **b.** $2f + 3 = \frac{36}{2}$ **c.** $f = 2 \cdot 36 - 3$ **d.** $f = 2 - 3$

25. Abraham paid Ephron 400 shekels for the field and the cave in which he buried Sarah (Genesis 23:15, 16). What was the weight of this amount in English pounds?

26. An offering of $\frac{1}{10}$ bath of oil is described in Ezekiel 45:14. How many liters of oil is this to the nearest tenth of a liter?

REVIEW EXERCISES

D. Solve these equations. *(Lessons 148, 149)*

27. $3n + 5 = 20$

28. $z - 4 = 3 \cdot 7$

29. $\frac{n}{5} - 2 = 3$

30. $4y - 3 = 12 + 9$

E. Solve these problems, using the correct order of operations. *(Lesson 146)*

31. $n = 2 + 7 \cdot 3 - 6$

32. $n = 12 - 7 + 5 \cdot 6$

F. Change these measures. *(Lesson 142)*

33. 25 talents = _____ kg

34. 2 cubits 1 span 1 finger = _____ cm

G. Find the areas of trapezoids having these dimensions. *(Lesson 116)*

35. $b_1 = 22''$
    $b_2 = 18''$
    $h = 7''$

36. $b_1 = 29$ cm
    $b_2 = 25$ cm
    $h = 23$ cm

H. Solve these percent problems. *(Lesson 85)*

37. $\frac{1}{2}\%$ of 700

38. $\frac{3}{4}\%$ of 350

39. $1\frac{1}{2}\%$ of 200

40. $3\frac{1}{4}\%$ of 175

151. Reading Problems: Writing Equations

In Lesson 150 you practiced studying a reading problem and choosing an equation to match the facts in the problem. In this lesson you will practice writing your own equations and using them to solve problems.

The following steps are required to write and solve equations.

1. Decide what must be found in the reading problem.
2. Assign a literal number to the amount that is unknown.
3. Decide how the given facts relate to the unknown number. Identify the operations indicated in the problem.
4. Write an equation showing how the facts relate to the unknown number.
5. Solve the equation.
6. Check by substituting your answer for the unknown number in the equation.

Study the following problems and their equations, and observe how the equations were derived from the problems. Key phrases are in italics.

Example A

The present enrollment at the Hillcrest Mennonite School is 5 *less than* 2 *times* the enrollment of 10 years ago. If the present enrollment is 45, what was the enrollment 10 years ago?

Step 1: The enrollment 10 years ago must be found.

Step 2: Let e equal the enrollment 10 years ago.

Step 3: The present enrollment is 45. The enrollment 10 years ago relates to the present enrollment in that the present enrollment is 5 *less than* 2 *times* the enrollment (e) of 10 years ago, or $2e - 5$.

Step 4:

Twice the enrollment 10 years ago	less	5	is	the present enrollment
$2e$	$-$	5	$=$	45

Step 5: $2e - 5 = 45$
$$2e - 5 + 5 = 45 + 5$$
$$2e = 50$$
$$\frac{2e}{2} = \frac{50}{2}$$
$$e = 25 \text{ students}$$

Step 6: $2 \cdot 25 - 5 = 45$

Example B

An atom of zinc has 30 electrons. An atom of oxygen has 2 *more than* $\frac{1}{5}$ *as many* electrons as an atom of zinc. How many electrons does an atom of oxygen have?

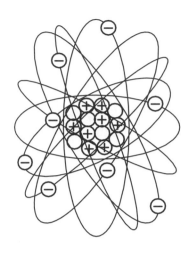

Step 1: The number of electrons in an atom of oxygen must be found.

Step 2: Let e equal the number of electrons.

Step 3: An atom of zinc has 30 electrons. The number of electrons in an atom of oxygen (e) relates to the number in zinc (30) in that it is 2 *more than* $\frac{1}{5}$ *as many*. Because $\frac{1}{5}$ of 30 is the same as 30 divided by 5, this is written $\frac{30}{5} + 2$.

Step 4:

one-fifth of 30	plus	2	equals	electrons in oxygen
$\frac{30}{5}$	$+$	2	$=$	e

Step 5: $\frac{30}{5} + 2 = e$

$\qquad$ $6 + 2 = e$

$\qquad\qquad$ $8 = e;\ \ e = 8$ electrons

Step 6: $\frac{30}{5} + 2 = 8$

CLASS PRACTICE

Use equations to solve these reading problems. Key phrases are in italics.

a. The age of Sarah's mother's is *3 years less than 3 times Sarah's age* (s). If Sarah's mother is 42, how old is Sarah?

b. There are *3 more than* $\frac{1}{3}$ *as many girls as boys* in grades 7–10. If there are 12 boys, how many girls (g) are there?

WRITTEN EXERCISES

A. *Write these key phrases as algebraic expressions.*

1. Five more than 3 times a

2. 7 less than $\frac{1}{2}$ of b

3. 4 times the sum of 6 and c

4. 9 more than 6 times d

5. 14 less than the product of 8 and e

6. 8 less than $\frac{1}{4}$ of f

B. *Write equations to solve these reading problems. Key phrases are in italics.*

7. Uncle Elam drives a delivery truck at a feed mill. Today he delivered *5 tons more than twice as much* dairy feed (*d*) as he did chicken feed. If he delivered 16 tons of chicken feed, how much dairy feed did he deliver?

8. On Tuesday evening, the Simsons planted *½ as many pounds of peas* (*p*) to sell at their market stand as they did corn. If they planted 15 pounds of corn, how many pounds of peas did they plant?

9. Mark went to the barn one morning and found that two sows each had a litter of pigs. One litter contained *3 more piglets than the other*. If there were 11 piglets in the larger litter, how many piglets were in the smaller litter (*s*)?

10. Lynette's parents bought her a pair of new shoes and a used jacket before school began in the fall. The cost of the shoes (*s*) was *3 dollars less than 9 times as much* as the jacket. If the jacket cost $2.50, how much did the shoes cost?

11. Three bundles of shingles are required to cover a square that is 100 square feet. If the cost of the shingles is $6.60 *per bundle*, what is the cost (*c*) per square?

12. The Old Testament priests retired from active service when they were *10 years less than twice as old* as when they began active service (Numbers 4:23). If they began service at the age of 30, at what age did they retire (*r*)?

13. David reigned at Hebron for 7 years before he moved his capital to Jerusalem (1 Kings 2:11). He reigned in Jerusalem *2 years less than 5 times as long* as he reigned in Hebron. How many years (*y*) did he reign at Jerusalem?

14. The number of days that King Ahasuerus showed the wealth of his kingdom to the rulers of the kingdom's 127 provinces was *2 less than 26 times more days* than the length of the final feast. The final feast was 7 days long. How long (*d*) did Ahasuerus show them his wealth?

REVIEW EXERCISES

C. Solve these equations. *(Lessons 148, 149)*

15. $3x = 30 - 3$

16. $y + 7 = 3 \cdot 8$

17. $\frac{z}{6} = 18 - 14$

18. $y + 8 = 6 \cdot 5 - 4$

D. Solve these equations by using this substitution: $a = 9$. *(Lesson 147)*

19. $n = 48 - 4a$

20. $\frac{n}{5} = a - 3$

E. Change these measures. *(Lesson 133)*

21. 15.2 km = _____ m

22. 78 cm = _____ m

F. Find the areas of circles having these sizes. *(Lesson 117)*

23. $r = 2''$

24. $r = 5$ cm

25. $r = 9$ in.

26. $r = 12$ m

G. Solve these percent problems. *(Lesson 86)*

27. 15 is 60% of _____

28. 21 is 70% of _____

---

152. Working With Exponents

Some mathematical processes require using the same number repeatedly as a factor. For example, the formula for finding the area of a square requires multiplying the length of one side (s) by itself. Also, finding the volume of a cube requires multiplying the length of one edge (e) by itself and then multiplying that product by e again.

As you learned in working with these geometric formulas, the simplest way to show that a number is to be multiplied repeatedly is to use an exponent. An **exponent** is a small raised number written to the right of another number to show how many times the other number is used as a factor. Examples A and B illustrate this with geometric formulas you have studied.

Example A	**Example B**
Area of a square = side × side or $s \cdot s$ or s^2	Volume of a cube = edge × edge × edge or $e \cdot e \cdot e$ or e^3

As you can see in Examples A and B, the exponent shows how many times a number, called the **base**, is used as a factor. For example, 3^4 means $3 \times 3 \times 3 \times 3$ and equals 81. In this example, 3 is the base and 4 is the exponent. This expression is read "three to the fourth power." The expression 5^2 is read "five to the second power" or "five squared," and 5^3 is read "five to the third power" or "five cubed."

Example C

2^2 is read "2 to the second power" or "2 squared." $2^2 = 4$
2^3 is read "2 to the third power" or "2 cubed." $2^3 = 8$
2^4 is read "2 to the fourth power." $2^4 = 16$

Example D

$4^1 = 4$
$4^2 = 4 \cdot 4 = 16$
$4^3 = 4 \cdot 4 \cdot 4 = 64$
$4^4 = 4 \cdot 4 \cdot 4 \cdot 4 = 256$

To find the value of a number that has an exponent, write a multiplication problem in which the base is a factor as many times as the number of the exponent. Then multiply to find the answer. Any number with an exponent of 1 is equal to the number itself.

CLASS PRACTICE

Simplify these expressions.

a. 5^3 b. 6^2 c. 8^4 d. 9^2

WRITTEN EXERCISES

A. Identify the bases and exponents as is shown in the example.

Example: 4^7 *Answer:* $b = 4, e = 7$

1. 3^2
2. 4^5
3. 5^7
4. 6^4
5. 7^{11}
6. 9^6

B. Simplify these expressions.

7. 2^5
8. 3^3
9. 4^3
10. 5^3
11. 6^4
12. 7^3
13. 11^2
14. 12^3
15. 14^1
16. 16^1
17. 25^2
18. 13^3
19. 16^2
20. 7^4
21. 5^4
22. 9^4
23. 121^1
24. 119^1

C. Solve these reading problems.

25. A square room has 14-foot sides. What is its floor area?

26. A cube has 35-centimeter edges. What is the volume?

27. How much greater is the volume of a 15-inch cube than that of a 14-inch cube?

28. One cube-shaped box has 20-inch edges, and another has 16-inch edges. What is the difference in their volumes?

29. Adam lived *30 years more than the square* of Christ's age when He began His earthly ministry. If Christ was 30 when he began His ministry, what was the age of Adam (a) when he died? Write an equation and solve it.

30. The *fourth power of 3 is 16 more* than the age of Enoch when Methuselah was born. How old was Enoch (e) when Methuselah was born? Write an equation and solve it.

REVIEW EXERCISES

D. Solve these equations. *(Lessons 148, 149)*

31. $n - 15 = \frac{45}{15}$
32. $3n - 2 = 12 + 4$
33. $\frac{n}{8} + 5 = 12 - 5$
34. $5n - 5 = 45$

E. Change these measures. *(Lessons 26, 134)*

35. 7.2 MT = _____ kg
36. 3,750 g = _____ kg
37. 6,200 lb. = _____ tons
38. 13 lb. = _____ oz.

F. Solve these percent problems. *(Lesson 87)*

39. 3 is 12% of _____
40. 18 is 15% of _____
41. 21 is 12% of _____
42. 24 is 80% of _____

153. Working With Square Roots

In Lesson 152 you saw that when a number is multiplied by itself, it is raised to the second power, or squared. This is shown by an exponent 2 after a number. The process opposite of squaring a number is finding what number squared equals the number being considered. Such a number is called the **square root** of the first number. For example, the square root of 25 is 5 because $5 \times 5 = 25$.

Just as the four basic operations have signs, so there is a sign for indicating the square root. The sign $\sqrt{}$ is the **radical sign.** The equation $\sqrt{144} = 12$ is read, "The square root of 144 is 12."

Following are some square roots that you should know because you know the multiplication and division facts up to the twelves. If you do not know any of these, be sure to memorize them.

Memorize these square roots.

$\sqrt{4} = 2$ $\sqrt{9} = 3$ $\sqrt{16} = 4$

$\sqrt{25} = 5$ $\sqrt{36} = 6$ $\sqrt{49} = 7$

$\sqrt{64} = 8$ $\sqrt{81} = 9$ $\sqrt{100} = 10$

$\sqrt{121} = 11$ $\sqrt{144} = 12$

A number whose square root is a whole number is known as a **perfect square.** The squares on the table above are all perfect squares. However, most numbers are not perfect squares. For those numbers, the square root is usually given as a decimal rounded to the nearest thousandth. Use the table on the facing page to find the square roots of the numbers 1–200. To use the table, first look in the column to the left and find the number whose square root you want to know. Then find its square root in the column to the right of that number.

Example A

Find the square root of 7.

Find 7 in the first column on the table. The square root, 2.646, is in the column to the right of 7.

$$\sqrt{7} = 2.646$$

Example B

Find the square root of 126.

Find 126 in the number column on the table. The square root, 11.225, is in the column to the right of 126.

$$\sqrt{126} = 11.225$$

TABLE OF SQUARE ROOTS

Number	Square Root	Number	Square Root	Number	Square Root	Number	Square Root
1	1.000	51	7.141	101	10.050	151	12.288
2	1.414	52	7.211	102	10.100	152	12.329
3	1.732	53	7.280	103	10.149	153	12.369
4	2.000	54	7.348	104	10.198	154	12.41
5	2.236	55	7.416	105	10.247	155	12.450
6	2.449	56	7.483	106	10.296	156	12.490
7	2.646	57	7.550	107	10.344	157	12.530
8	2.828	58	7.616	108	10.392	158	12.570
9	3.000	59	7.681	109	10.440	159	12.610
10	3.162	60	7.746	110	10.488	160	12.649
11	3.317	61	7.810	111	10.536	161	12.689
12	3.464	62	7.874	112	10.583	162	12.728
13	3.606	63	7.937	113	10.630	163	12.767
14	3.742	64	8.000	114	10.677	164	12.806
15	3.873	65	8.062	115	10.724	165	12.845
16	4.000	66	8.124	116	10.770	166	12.884
17	4.123	67	8.185	117	10.817	167	12.923
18	4.243	68	8.246	118	10.863	168	12.961
19	4.359	69	8.307	119	10.909	169	13.000
20	4.472	70	8.367	120	10.954	170	13.038
21	4.583	71	8.426	121	11.000	171	13.077
22	4.690	72	8.485	122	11.045	172	13.115
23	4.796	73	8.544	123	11.091	173	13.153
24	4.899	74	8.602	124	11.136	174	13.191
25	5.000	75	8.660	125	11.180	175	13.229
26	5.099	76	8.718	126	11.225	176	13.266
27	5.196	77	8.775	127	11.269	177	13.304
28	5.292	78	8.832	128	11.314	178	13.342
29	5.385	79	8.888	129	11.358	179	13.379
30	5.477	80	8.944	130	11.402	180	13.416
31	5.568	81	9.000	131	11.446	181	13.454
32	5.657	82	9.055	132	11.489	182	13.491
33	5.745	83	9.110	133	11.533	183	13.528
34	5.831	84	9.165	134	11.576	184	13.565
35	5.916	85	9.220	135	11.619	185	13.601
36	6.000	86	9.274	136	11.662	186	13.638
37	6.083	87	9.327	137	11.705	187	13.675
38	6.164	88	9.381	138	11.747	188	13.711
39	6.245	89	9.434	139	11.790	189	13.748
40	6.325	90	9.487	140	11.832	190	13.784
41	6.403	91	9.539	141	11.874	191	13.820
42	6.481	92	9.592	142	11.916	192	13.856
43	6.557	93	9.644	143	11.958	193	13.892
44	6.633	94	9.695	144	12.000	194	13.928
45	6.708	95	9.747	145	12.042	195	13.964
46	6.782	96	9.798	146	12.083	196	14.000
47	6.856	97	9.849	147	12.124	197	14.036
48	6.928	98	9.899	148	12.166	198	14.071
49	7.000	99	9.950	149	12.207	199	14.107
50	7.071	100	10.000	150	12.247	200	14.142

Even without a table, it is not hard to identify a perfect square whose square root is a two-digit number. If the last digit of the square is 2, 3, 7, or 8, the square root cannot be a whole number, because no number times itself ends in one of these digits. To find a whole number square root between 10 and 100, use the following steps.

1. Decide in which group of tens (the 10's, 20's, 30's, and so on) the square root will be. For example, a square between 100 (10 x 10) and 400 (20 x 20) will have a square root in the 10's. A square between 400 (20 x 20) and 900 (30 x 30) will have a square root in the 20's.

2. After the digit in the tens' place is determined, look at the last digit of the square to determine what digit is in the ones' place of the square root. By using the table below, you can narrow that digit to one or two possibilities.

3. If there are two possibilities, use trial and error to determine the correct square root.

Relationship between last digit of square root and its square	
Last digit of square	Last digit of square root
1	1 or 9
2	not a perfect square
3	not a perfect square
4	2 or 8
5	5
6	4 or 6
7	not a perfect square
8	not a perfect square
9	3 or 7
0	0

Example C

Find the square root of 324, which is a perfect square.

Step 1: The square is between 100 (10 × 10) and 400 (20 × 20). So the square root is in the 10's.

Step 2: The digit in the ones' place of the square is 4. So the digit in the ones' place of the square root is 2 or 8.

Step 3: Multiply 12 × 12 and 18 × 18.

$$\begin{array}{cc} 12 & 18 \\ \underline{12} & \underline{18} \\ 144 & 324 \end{array}$$ The square root is 18.

Example D

Find the square root of 2,209, which is a perfect square.

Step 1: The square is between 1,600 (40 × 40) and 2,500 (50 × 50). So the square root is in the 40's.

Step 2: The digit in the ones' place of the square is 9. So the digit in the ones' place of the square root is 3 or 7.

Step 3: Multiply 43 × 43 and 47 × 47.

$$\begin{array}{cc} 43 & 47 \\ \underline{\times 43} & \underline{\times 47} \\ 1,849 & 2,209 \end{array}$$ The square root is 47.

CLASS PRACTICE

Use the table to find these square roots.

a. $\sqrt{35}$ b. $\sqrt{48}$ c. $\sqrt{66}$ d. $\sqrt{97}$

Find the square roots by using the method shown in the lesson.

e. $\sqrt{289}$ f. $\sqrt{784}$ g. $\sqrt{1,444}$ h. $\sqrt{2,401}$

WRITTEN EXERCISES

A. Use the table to find these square roots.

1. $\sqrt{14}$ 2. $\sqrt{18}$ 3. $\sqrt{42}$ 4. $\sqrt{58}$ 5. $\sqrt{64}$

6. $\sqrt{71}$ 7. $\sqrt{78}$ 8. $\sqrt{83}$ 9. $\sqrt{91}$ 10. $\sqrt{96}$

B. Write these square roots by memory.

11. $\sqrt{121}$ 12. $\sqrt{81}$ 13. $\sqrt{25}$ 14. $\sqrt{100}$

C. Using the last table in the lesson, give the last digit in the square root of each of these perfect squares. Some will have two answers.

15. 2,304   16. 3,025   17. 9,604   18. 676

D. Find these square roots. The numbers are perfect squares.

19. $\sqrt{361}$ 20. $\sqrt{576}$ 21. $\sqrt{3,249}$ 22. $\sqrt{3,721}$

E. Solve these reading problems.

23. A square room has an area of 169 square feet. What is the length of one side of the room?

24. Another square room has an area of 196 square feet. What is the perimeter of the room?

25. A certain square field has an area of 2,500 square meters. What is the length of one side of the field?

26. The basement of a two-story house is a square with an area of 576 square feet. How long is each side of the house?

27. Rufus built a square pen with a perimeter of 120 feet. What is its area?

28. A square field has a perimeter of 2,000 feet. What is its area?

REVIEW EXERCISES

F. Solve these problems. *(Lesson 152)*

29. $3^2 =$ _____   **30.** $4^3 =$ _____   **31.** $6^4 =$ _____   **32.** $7^4 =$ _____

G. Write algebraic expressions for these phrases. *(Lesson 145)*

33. n divided by the sum of 3 and k

34. 5 added to the product of 6 and d

H. Change these measures. *(Lesson 27, 135)*

35. 575 ml = _____ l **36.** 2.2 kl = _____ l

37. 14 fl. oz. = _____ cups   **38.** 12 pk. = _____ qt.

I. Solve these percent problems. *(Lesson 88)*

39. $B = 53$ **40.** $P = 18$
   $R = 47\%$ $R = 45\%$
   $P =$ _____ $B =$ _____

154. Making a Table Based on a Formula

Sometimes a formula is used to construct a table for quick reference. Such a table shows the answers that are obtained when the literal numbers in the formula are replaced with various arithmetic numbers. For example, the table below is based on the formula for finding the circumference of a circle. To use the table, find the needed diameter in the first row and look directly below to find the circumference.

Formula: $c = \pi d$	**Circumferences of Circles With Diameters of 1"–8"**							
Diameter (d)	1"	2"	3"	4"	5"	6"	7"	8"
Circumference (c)	3.14"	6.28"	9.42"	12.56"	15.7"	18.84"	21.98"	25.12"

To complete a table, use the following steps:
1. Substitute the letter in the formula with the first number in the top row of the table, and calculate the result. Write the answer in the second row of the table immediately below the number used in the formula.
2. Repeat the process until the table is complete.

CLASS PRACTICE

Copy and complete the following table.

Formula: $p = 4s$	**Perimeters of Squares With Sides of 10–24 Millimeters**							
Side (s)	10 mm	12 mm	14 mm	16 mm	18 mm	20 mm	22 mm	24 mm
Perimeter (p)	a. ___	b. ___	c. ___	d. ___	e. ___	f. ___	g. ___	h. ___

WRITTEN EXERCISES

A. Copy and complete the following tables.

Formula: $a = s^2$	**Areas of Squares With Sides of 1–8 Meters**							
Side (s)	1 m	2 m	3 m	4 m	5 m	6 m	7 m	8 m
Area (a)	1 m²	4 m²	1. ___	2. ___	3. ___	4. ___	5. ___	6. ___

Formula: $c = 0.04s$	**Commissions on Sales at a Rate of 4%**							
Sales (*s*)	$100	$200	$300	$400	$500	$600	$700	$800
Commissions (*c*)	$4	$8	7. ___	8. ___	9. ___	10. ___	11. ___	12. ___

Formula: $F = \frac{9}{5}C + 32$	**Degrees Celsius Converted to Degrees Fahrenheit**							
Celsius	5°	10°	15°	20°	25°	30°	35°	40°
Fahrenheit	13. ___	14. ___	15. ___	16. ___	17. ___	18. ___	19. ___	20. ___

REVIEW EXERCISES

B. Solve these reading problems.

21. What is the volume of a cubical storage crate that measures 35 centimeters along each edge?

22. In the first recorded number of the children of Israel, the men in the tribe of Issachar numbered 400 more than 15 to the fourth power plus 15 to the third power. How many men were numbered in the tribe of Issachar?

23. A square pasture has an area of 5,776 square feet. What is the length of one side?

24. This same pasture has a smaller fenced-in square of 256 square feet. What is the perimeter of this smaller area?

The Lord is my shepherd; I shall not want.
He maketh me to lie down in green pastures.
Psalm 23:1, 2

25. One day Uncle Myron sold $525 worth of seed corn and earned a 7% commission. How much was the commission (c)? Write an equation and solve it.

26. Father sent a cow to market. The cow sold for $620, and the auctioneer charged $37.20 for the sale. What was the rate of commission (r)? Write an equation and solve it.

C. Find these square roots. The numbers are perfect squares. *(Lesson 153)*

27. $\sqrt{1,936}$ **28.** $\sqrt{3,721}$ **29.** $\sqrt{7,569}$ **30.** $\sqrt{8,836}$

D. Simplify these expressions. *(Lesson 152)*

31. 8^4 **32.** 9^4

E. Solve these problems, using the correct order of operations. *(Lesson 146)*

33. $n = 25 - 4 \cdot 3$ **34.** $n = 6 \cdot 5 - 4 \cdot 5$

F. Change these measures. *(Lessons 28, 136)*

35. 9.1 km² = _____ ha   **36.** 25,000 m² = _____ ha

37. 3 sq. mi. = _____ a.   **38.** 16 sq. yd. = _____ sq. ft.

G. Find the missing parts in these commission problems. *(Lesson 89)*

Sales	Rate	Commission		Sales	Rate	Commission
39. $8,000	5%	____		**40.** $7,000	____	$560.00

155. Making a Graph Based on a Formula

Sometimes a formula is illustrated with a line graph to make its effects easier to comprehend. The first thing to do in graphing a formula is to make a table as you did in Lesson 154. The completed table then provides all the data you need to construct a line graph. Following is the table shown in Lesson 154. Notice the steps used to put the data on a line graph. A line graph for this table is shown on the facing page.

Formula: $c = \pi d$	**Circumferences of Circles With Diameters 1"–8"**							
Diameter (d)	1"	2"	3"	4"	5"	6"	7"	8"
Circumference (c)	3.14"	6.28"	9.42"	12.56"	15.7"	18.84"	21.98"	25.12"

1. Write the numbers in the first row at regular intervals along the bottom of the line graph. Give these bottom numbers the same label as that used for the first row of the table.

2. Make an appropriate vertical scale at the left edge of the graph. Be sure to increase the numbers by regular intervals. The numbers should extend at least as high as the largest number in row 2 of the table. Give these numbers the same label as that used for the second row of the table.

3. Plot the numbers in the second row of the table on the graph. To determine where to put the dots, read the numbers in the second row of the table and use the scale on the graph. In the example graph, the first dot was placed a little higher than 3 inches because the diameter of a 1-inch circle is 3.14 inches. After all the dots are placed on the graph, draw a line to connect the dots.

4. Give the graph the same title that the table has.

CLASS PRACTICE

Construct a graph from this table.

Formula: $C = \frac{5}{9}(F - 32)$	**Degrees Fahrenheit Converted to Degrees Celsius**						
Fahrenheit (F)	40°	50°	60°	70°	80°	90°	100°
Celsius (C)	4°	10°	16°	21°	27°	32°	38°

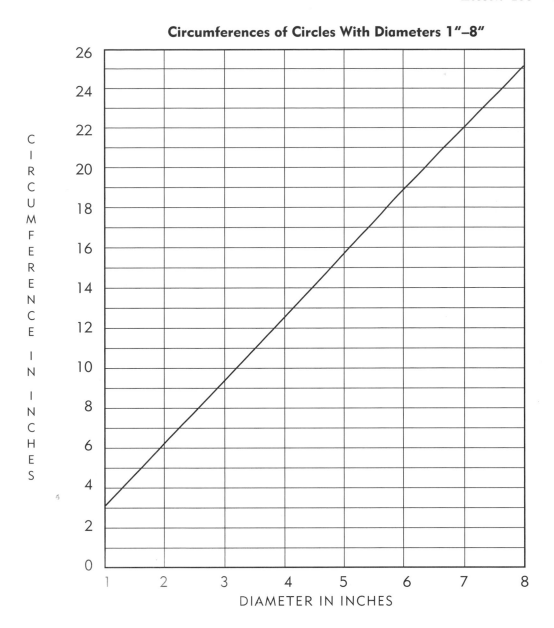

Circumferences of Circles With Diameters 1″–8″

WRITTEN EXERCISES

A. *Construct line graphs as indicated.*

1–11. Prepare a graph showing the commissions on the sales shown.

Formula: $c = 0.07s$	**Sales Commissions at the Rate of 7%**							
Sales (s)	$100	$150	$200	$250	$300	$350	$400	$450
Commissions (p)	$7.00	$10.50	$14.00	$17.50	$21.00	$24.50	$28.00	$31.50

12–21. Prepare a graph showing the lengths of the sides of squares with the perimeters given.

Formula: $s = \frac{p}{4}$	Lengths of Sides of Squares With Various Perimeters						
Perimeter (p)	20 in.	40 in.	60 in.	80 in.	100 in.	120 in.	140 in.
Side (s)	5 in.	10 in.	15 in.	20 in.	25 in.	30 in.	35 in.

22–28. Prepare a graph showing the areas of circles with the radii given.

Formula: $a = \pi r^2$	Areas of Circles With Radii of 1–6 Centimeters					
Radius (r)	1 cm	2 cm	3 cm	4 cm	5 cm	6 cm
Area (a)	3.14 cm²	12.56 cm²	28.26 cm²	50.24 cm²	78.5 cm²	113.04 cm²

REVIEW EXERCISES

B. Solve these reading problems.

29. The floor of a Sunday school room is a square with an area of 324 square feet. What is the perimeter of the room?

30. God gave the earth a great variety of creatures. It has been estimated that the number of species of beetles is equal to 500 squared. The total number of species of bees, ants, and wasps is estimated to equal 200 to the second power. How many more species of beetles is that than species of bees, ants, and wasps?

31. The beauty of the creation is enhanced by the music of various bird songs. Mockingbirds can imitate the songs of many other birds. During a ten-minute period, the number of different bird songs imitated by one mockingbird was two to the fifth power. How many bird songs were imitated?

32. Another marvel of creation is the way large numbers of ants live together in perfect order. Some scientists estimate that among the mound builders, the number of ants in the largest nests may be 100 to the fourth power. How many ants is that?

33. The large nests of these ants may be up to ten feet in diameter. What is the circumference of such a nest?

34. What is the volume of a conical ant mound if it has a radius of 5 feet and a height of 3 feet?

> Thou, even thou, art Lord alone;
> thou hast made heaven, the heaven of heavens, with all their host,
> the earth, and all things that are therein.
> Nehemiah 9:6

C. Find these square roots. *(Lesson 153)*

35. $\sqrt{256}$ **36.** $\sqrt{1,444}$ **37.** $\sqrt{3,249}$ **38.** $\sqrt{5,776}$

D. Solve these equations by using this substitution: $n = 5$. *(Lesson 147)*

39. $a = 27 - 5n$

40. $a = \frac{n}{10} \times 4$

E. Solve these problems. *(Lesson 137)*

41.
```
    4 lb.  7 oz.
  - 1 lb.  9 oz.
```

42.
```
    5 ft.  9 in.
  + 8 ft.  8 in.
```

43. 3 m + 250 cm = _____ cm

44. 6 kl + 46 l = _____ kl

F. Find the percent of increase or decrease. Label your answers. *(Lesson 90)*

	Original Price	New Price		Original Price	New Price
45.	$15.50	$18.60	**46.**	$22.00	$20.68

G. Change these measures. *(Lesson 29)*

47. 4.5 hr. = _____ min.

48. 12 centuries = _____ yr.

156. Introduction to Signed Numbers

Early in this book you learned about numbers up to trillions. However, numbers continue far beyond the trillions' place. In fact, numbers keep on going without end. In that way, they are like our great God, who never has an end.

The numbers you have worked with so far have had beginnings. The smallest of these numbers is zero, and in most cases it is not possible to have less than zero. It is not possible, for example, to own less than zero pencils or less than zero books.

In some situations, however, it is possible for numbers to have a value less than zero. This is true when zero is used as a reference point rather than as a number that means "nothing." Probably the most common example is a temperature scale. It is possible for the temperature to be less than zero or below zero. Just as the numbers greater than zero continue without end, so the numbers less than zero continue without end.

When working with some numbers greater than zero and some numbers less than zero, it is necessary to indicate on which side of zero a number belongs. This is done by using the positive sign (+) with numbers greater than zero and the negative sign (–) with numbers less than zero.

Numbers with these signs are known as **signed numbers.** Those greater than zero are **positive numbers,** and those less than zero are **negative numbers.** The number + 9 is read "positive nine." The number –9 is read "negative nine." Any number without a sign is assumed to be positive. Zero is neither positive nor negative, and is always written without a sign.

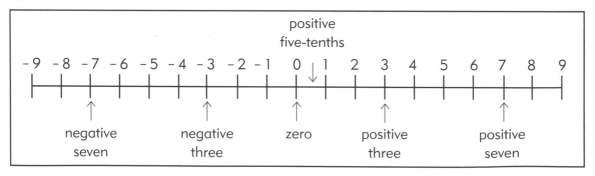

Consider the numbers + 5 and – 5. If the temperature increases five degrees (+ 5), the temperature has changed five degrees. If the temperature decreases five degrees (– 5), it has again changed 5 degrees. A + 5° change and a – 5° change are the same amounts of change, except that the changes are in opposite directions. Because the amount of change is 5 in both cases, both numbers have an **absolute value** of 5.

The absolute value of any number is the value of that number without the sign. Absolute value is represented by placing a vertical bar before and after the number. Thus, | – 5| is read, "the absolute value of negative five." That value is 5.

> Use signed numbers to show the following things.
>
> **Example A** A 10-degree drop in temperature: – 10°
>
> **Example B** A $50 profit: + $50
>
> **Example C** A $20 loss: – $20
>
> **Example D** An elevation of 75 feet below sea level: – 75 feet
>
> **Example E** Show that you mean the absolute value of + 14. | + 14|
>
> **Example F** Show that you mean the absolute value of – 9. | – 9|

CLASS PRACTICE

Write signed numbers to show these values.

 a. The elevation of the mountain is 3,458 feet above sea level.

 b. The elevation at the Zehr home is 55 feet lower than at the Wenger home.

 c. One winter day the temperature in Florida was 55° warmer than in Ontario.

Write the absolute value of these numbers.

 d. $|-19|$ e. $|-7|$ f. $|+14|$ g. $|+8|$ h. $|78|$

WRITTEN EXERCISES

A. *Write these numbers, using words.*

 1. + 15   2. – 7   3. 0

 4. – 8   5. + 2   6. – 3

B. *Write signed numbers to show the values indicated by these statements.*

 7. One night the temperature plunged 25 degrees.

 8. A mountain gap has an elevation of 715 feet above sea level.

 9. The elevation of Death Valley, California, is 282 feet below sea level.

 10. During the 1993 flood, the Mississippi River crested at 49.4 feet above the normal level.

 11. One morning the temperature was 6 degrees below zero.

 12. On one shipment of hogs, the Mohlers lost $12 per hog.

 13. On another shipment of hogs, the Mohlers made a profit of $11 per hog.

 14. One day the temperature rose 35 degrees.

C. *Write the absolute value of these numbers.*

 15. $|-2|$ 16. $|+7|$ 17. $|0|$ 18. $|-154|$ 19. $|688|$ 20. $|-43|$

D. Solve these reading problems.

21. The lowest elevation on earth is at the shore of the Dead Sea. There the elevation is 1,312 feet below sea level. Write this elevation as a signed number.

22. On February 21, 1918, the temperature rose 83 degrees Fahrenheit in twelve hours at Granville, North Dakota. Write this temperature change as a signed number.

23. On January 22, 1943, the temperature rose 34 degrees Fahrenheit in seven minutes in Kipp, Montana. Use a signed number to write this temperature change.

24. In Browning, Montana, the temperature dropped 100° Fahrenheit in a twenty-four hour period between January 23 and 24, 1916. Write this temperature change, using a signed number.

25. On January 10, 1911, the temperature dropped 47° Fahrenheit in fifteen minutes at Rapid City, South Dakota. Write the absolute value of the temperature change.

26. Rapid City, South Dakota, is in the Mountain Standard Time Zone. If it is 6:00 A.M. in Rapid City, what time is it in the Alaska Time Zone?

REVIEW EXERCISES

E. Copy and complete the tables, using the formulas given. *(Lesson 154)*

27. $d = 45t$

t	1	2	3	4	5	6
d						

28. $i = 0.04p$

p	$100	$200	$300	$400	$500	$600
i						

F. Simplify these expressions. *(Lesson 152)*

29. 12^3

30. 15^3

G. Solve these equations. *(Lessons 148, 149)*

31. $\frac{n}{2} - 5 = 2 + 5$

32. $6 \cdot 2 + 4 = 2n$

H. Solve these problems involving compound measures. *(Lesson 138)*

33. 2 yd. 2 ft.
       × 4

34. 7 lb. 9 oz.
       × 5

35. 3 m 15 cm × 6 = _____ cm

36. 7 kl 12 l × 9 = _____ kl

I. Solve these percent problems mentally. *(Lesson 91)*

37. 20% of 45 = _____

38. 12 is 25% of _____

39. 10 is _____% of 80

40. 80% of 35 = _____

J. Give the correct time in these time zones if it is 11:00 A.M. in the Mountain Time Zone. Use the map in Lesson 30.

41. Newfoundland Time Zone

42. Hawaii–Aleutian Time Zone

157. Adding Signed Numbers

The addition of signed numbers is different from the addition of counting (positive) numbers. When counting numbers are added, two positive numbers are combined and the result is a greater positive number. However, when signed numbers are added, their signs need to be considered.

Look at Example A below. In this problem we are beginning at -2 and adding a negative 4 to it. To add a **negative** 4 is to add a **decrease** of 4 to -2. Four less than -2 is -6.

Now consider Example B. In this problem we are beginning at $+2$ and adding a positive 4 to it. To add a **positive** 4 is to add an **increase** of 4 to $+2$. Four more than $+2$ is $+6$.

Now look at Example C. In this problem we are beginning at -3 and adding a positive 5 to it. To add a **positive** 5 is to add an **increase** of 5 to -3. Five more than -3 is $+2$.

It would be possible to draw number lines to calculate all addition of signed numbers; however, that would be cumbersome. The same results are obtained by applying one of two rules. Use Rule 1 for adding numbers with like signs. Use Rule 2 for adding numbers with unlike signs.

> **Rule 1:** To add numbers that have the same sign, add their absolute values. The sum has the same sign as that of the addends.

Example D	Example E	Example F
(Same as Example A)	(Same as Example B)	
$\begin{array}{r} -2 \\ +(-4) \\ \hline -6 \end{array}$	$\begin{array}{r} +2 \\ +(+4) \\ \hline +6 \end{array}$	$\begin{array}{r} -7 \\ +(-8) \\ \hline -15 \end{array}$
The signs are alike. Add $2+4$, and bring down the negative sign.	The signs are alike. Add $2+4$, and bring down the positive sign.	The signs are alike. Add $7+8$, and bring down the negative sign.

Rule 2: To add numbers that have opposite signs, ignore the signs and find the difference between the two absolute values. The answer has the same sign as that of the number with the larger absolute value.

Example G
(Same as Example C)
$$-3$$
$$+(+5)$$
$$+2$$

The signs are different; subtract 5 – 3. The answer is positive because the number with the larger absolute value (5) is positive.

Example H
$$-8$$
$$+(+4)$$
$$-4$$

The signs are different; subtract 8 – 4. The answer is negative because the number with the larger absolute value (8) is negative.

Example I
$$+8$$
$$+(-9)$$
$$-1$$

The signs are different; subtract 9 – 8. The answer is negative because the number with the larger absolute value (9) is negative.

CLASS PRACTICE

Add these signed numbers.

a. $+8$; $+(-2)$ b. $+7$; $+(+5)$ c. -4; $+(-2)$ d. -8; $+(+11)$ e. $+6$; $+(-8)$ f. -7; $+(+5)$

WRITTEN EXERCISES

A. Write the number that has the larger absolute value.

1. -5 or $+6$ 2. $+8$ or -9 3. -3 or -8 4. $+6$ or $+5$

B. Copy each sum, and give it the proper sign.

5. -3; $+(-8)$; 11   6. -8; $+(+6)$; 2   7. $+6$; $+(-3)$; 3   8. $+5$; $+(+12)$; 17   9. $+3$; $+(-3)$; 0   10. -2; $+(+8)$; 6

C. Add these signed numbers.

11. $+7$; $+(-8)$ 12. $+9$; $+(+3)$ 13. -3; $+(+8)$ 14. -9; $+(+4)$ 15. $+4$; $+(+7)$ 16. $+6$; $+(-5)$

17. -9; $+(-5)$ 18. -5; $+(+7)$ 19. -6; $+(+3)$ 20. $+7$; $+(+14)$ 21. -3; $+(-12)$ 22. -2; $+(+7)$

23. -9; $+(+11)$ 24. $+3$; $+(+7)$ 25. $+8$; $+(-6)$ 26. -15; $+(+14)$ 27. $+22$; $+(-9)$ 28. -47; $+(+35)$

D. ***Solve these reading problems, using signed numbers in problems 29–32. Show your work.***

29. At 7:30 A.M. on January 22, 1943, the temperature at Spearfish, South Dakota, was – 4°F. In the next two minutes, the temperature rose 49°F. What was the temperature at 7:32 A.M.?

30. At 9:00 A.M. that morning, the temperature in Spearfish was 54°F. In the next 27 minutes, the temperature dropped 58°F. What was the temperature at 9:27 A.M.?

31. The first five books of the Bible are thought to have been written by Moses about 1,500 years before Christ (– 1,500). Revelation, the last book of the Bible, is dated 1,595 years later. According to these figures, when was the last book of the Bible written? A positive number represents a year A.D.

32. Badwater Basin in Death Valley, California, has an elevation of 282 feet below sea level. Telescope Peak, west of Badwater Basin, is 11,327 feet higher. What is the elevation of Telescope Peak?

33. The highest temperature ever recorded in North America was observed at the Greenland Ranch weather station in Death Valley, California. This occurred on July 10, 1913, when the temperature reached 134°F. What was the temperature on the Celsius scale? Round your answer to the nearest tenth of a degree.

34. In the winter, the temperature in Death Valley rarely falls below 21°C. To the nearest whole degree, what temperature is that on the Fahrenheit scale?

REVIEW EXERCISES

E. ***Write a signed number for each situation.*** *(Lesson 156)*

35. 30 feet below sea level

36. $45 profit

37. 15 degrees below zero

38. $12 loss

F. ***Find these square roots.*** *(Lesson 153)*

39. $\sqrt{784}$

40. $\sqrt{5,929}$

G. ***Change these measures, using the tables in Lesson 139 if necessary.***

41. 14 qt. = _____ l

42. 92 km² = _____ sq. mi.

H. ***Find each temperature to the nearest tenth of a degree.*** *(Lessons 140, 141)*

43. 71°C = ____°F

44. 61°F = ____°C

I. ***Find the surface areas of cylinders having these dimensions.*** *(Lesson 124)*

45. $r = 2''$
$h = 5''$

46. $r = 5$ cm
$h = 20$ cm

158. Subtracting Signed Numbers

Subtracting is the operation used to find the difference between two numbers; it shows how far apart two numbers are. In Example A, 27° is 32° more than – 5°. In Example B, – 235 feet is 47 feet higher than · – 282 feet.

There is only one rule for subtracting signed numbers. To subtract signed numbers, change the sign of the subtrahend and add, using the rules for adding signed numbers.

There are two things to remember when applying this rule. First, change the subtraction sign to addition and the sign of the subtrahend to the opposite sign. Second, remember that you are now adding signed numbers; so apply the rules in Lesson 157.

> To subtract signed numbers, change the sign of the subtrahend and add according to the rules for adding signed numbers.

Example A	**Example B**
One morning the temperature was – 5°. By noon, the temperature was 27°. How much had the temperature risen?	Badwater Basin has an elevation of – 282 feet. The elevation of the Salton Sea is – 235 feet. How much higher is the Salton Sea than Badwater Basin?

Example A:
$$\begin{array}{r} + 27° \\ -(-5°) \end{array} \quad \text{Change sign and add.} \quad \begin{array}{r} + 27° \\ +(+5°) \\ \hline + 32° \end{array}$$

The temperature had risen 32°.

After the sign is changed, the numbers are added as you learned in Lesson 157. The addends have like signs, so they are added, and the positive sign is brought down.

Example B:
$$\begin{array}{r} - 235 \\ -(-282) \end{array} \quad \text{Change sign and add.} \quad \begin{array}{r} - 235 \\ +(+282) \\ \hline + 47 \end{array}$$

The Salton Sea is 47 feet higher than Badwater Basin.

The sign is changed, and the numbers are added as you learned in Lesson 157. These addends have unlike signs; so their absolute values are subtracted, and the positive sign is brought down because it is the sign of the number with the larger absolute value.

Example C	**Example D**
Subtract + 31 from – 6.	Subtract + 19 from + 14.

Example C:
$$\begin{array}{r} - 6 \\ -(+31) \end{array} \quad \text{Change sign and add.} \quad \begin{array}{r} - 6 \\ +(-31) \\ \hline - 37 \end{array}$$

– 6 is – 37 more (37 less) than + 31.

Example D:
$$\begin{array}{r} + 14 \\ -(+19) \end{array} \quad \text{Change sign and add.} \quad \begin{array}{r} + 14 \\ +(-19) \\ \hline - 5 \end{array}$$

+ 14 is – 5 more (5 less) than + 19.

CLASS PRACTICE

Subtract these signed numbers.

a. $+5$ $-(-3)$	b. $+7$ $-(+5)$	c. -5 $-(-9)$	d. -4 $-(+15)$	e. $+7$ $-(-3)$	f. -9 $-(+3)$

WRITTEN EXERCISES

A. *Subtract these signed numbers.*

1. $+4$
   $-(-7)$

2. $+8$
   $-(+6)$

3. -2
   $-(+3)$

4. -1
   $-(+1)$

5. $+4$
   $-(+3)$

6. $+4$
   $-(-4)$

7. -6
   $-(-2)$

8. -3
   $-(+7)$

9. -8
   $-(+9)$

10. $+9$
    $-(+12)$

11. -6
    $-(-15)$

12. -9
    $-(+4)$

13. -15
    $-(+13)$

14. $+9$
    $-(+9)$

15. $+2$
    $-(-2)$

16. -9
    $-(-4)$

17. $+31$
    $-(-8)$

18. -15
    $-(+32)$

19. $+12$
    $-(-15)$

20. -11
    $-(+7)$

21. $+9$
    $-(-4)$

22. -8
    $-(+5)$

23. -26
    $-(-38)$

24. $+25$
    $-(-40)$

B. *Solve these reading problems, using signed numbers in numbers 25–28. Show your work.*

25. One morning the temperature was $-22°$ Celsius. By noon, the temperature had risen to $-9°C$. What was the change in temperature?

26. Lewis had an income of $350 from sale of merchandise. His expenses were $440. What was his profit? (Give both numbers a positive sign and use the formula *profit = income – expense*. If the answer is negative, leave it as a negative number. A negative profit is a loss.)

27. Brother Marvin sent two shipments of steers to market. He made a profit of $60 per steer on one shipment, but he had a loss of $14 per steer on the second shipment. What was the difference in his earnings per steer on the two shipments? Express each number as a signed number before calculating.

28. The city of Jerusalem has an elevation of $+2{,}548$ feet. The surface of the Dead Sea, the lowest place on earth, has an elevation of $-1{,}312$ feet. What is the difference in elevations between Jerusalem and the Dead Sea?

29. Stanley is 3 years more than twice as old as Nelson. Stanley's age is 13 years. How old is Nelson (n)? Write an equation and solve it.

30. Mary is 2 years less than three times as old as Sandra. Mary is 13 years old. How old is Sandra (s)?

REVIEW EXERCISES

C. Add these signed numbers. *(Lesson 157)*

31.	32.	33.	34.
$+4$	-6	$+6$	-9
$+(-5)$	$+(-8)$	$+(+8)$	$+(+12)$

D. Write a signed number for each of these statements. *(Lesson 156)*

35. Moscow, Russia, is about $55°$ north of the equator. (North is considered a positive direction.)

36. Johannesburg, South Africa, is about $25°$ south of the equator. (South is considered a negative direction.)

E. Copy and complete these tables by using the formulas given. *(Lesson 154)*

37. $p = 2000t$

t	1	2	3	4	5	6
p						

38. $o = 16p$

p	1	2	3	4	5	6
o						

F. Solve these problems relating to distance, rate, and time. *(Lesson 32)*

39. $d = 220$ mi.
$r = 40$ m.p.h.
$t = \underline{\hspace{1cm}}$

40. $t = 7$ hr.
$r = 91$ m.p.h.
$d = \underline{\hspace{1cm}}$

41. $d = 680$ mi.
$t = 3$ hr.
$r = \underline{\hspace{1cm}}$

42. $t = 6.5$ hr.
$r = 38$ m.p.h.
$d = \underline{\hspace{1cm}}$

159. Multiplying and Dividing Signed Numbers

Signed numbers are multiplied and divided by the same rule, as indicated in the box. Study the rule and the examples below.

> If two numbers with like signs are multiplied or divided, the result is positive. If two numbers with unlike signs are multiplied or divided, the result is negative.

Example A	Example B	Example C
$\begin{array}{r} -7 \\ \times\,(+5) \\ \hline -35 \end{array}$	$\begin{array}{r} -6 \\ \times\,(-3) \\ \hline +18 \end{array}$	$\begin{array}{r} +5 \\ \times\,(+6) \\ \hline +30 \end{array}$
Example D	**Example E**	**Example F**
$-2\overline{)+20}\;\;^{-10}$	$-3\overline{)-18}\;\;^{+6}$	$+7\overline{)+35}\;\;^{+5}$

Following are several examples of cases when signed numbers are multiplied or divided.

Example G

The temperature dropped 3° (– 3°) per hour for 5 hours. What was the total temperature change?

$$+5\cdot(-3) = -15°$$

The temperature dropped 15° in 5 hours.

Example H

The temperature dropped 4° (– 4°) per hour for the last 3 hours. How much higher was the temperature three hours ago (– 3) than it is now? $-3\cdot(-4) = 12°$

The temperature was 12° higher three hours ago.

Example I

The temperature dropped 15° (– 15°) in 5 hours. What was the average temperature change per hour?

$$\frac{-15°}{+5} = -3°$$

The temperature changed – 3° per hour.

CLASS PRACTICE

Solve these problems involving signed numbers.

a.
$$+5 \\ \times (-3)$$

b.
$$+7 \\ \times (+5)$$

c.
$$-5 \\ \times (-9)$$

d. $-8\overline{)+24}$

e. $+6\overline{)-36}$

WRITTEN EXERCISES

A. Solve these problems.

1.
$$+4 \\ \times (-7)$$

2.
$$+8 \\ \times (+6)$$

3.
$$-2 \\ \times (+3)$$

4.
$$-1 \\ \times (+1)$$

5.
$$+4 \\ \times (+3)$$

6.
$$+4 \\ \times (-4)$$

7.
$$-6 \\ \times (-2)$$

8.
$$-3 \\ \times (+7)$$

9.
$$-8 \\ \times (+9)$$

10.
$$+9 \\ \times (+12)$$

11.
$$-6 \\ \times (-15)$$

12.
$$-9 \\ \times (+4)$$

13. $-3\overline{)+21}$ 14. $+5\overline{)+25}$ 15. $-4\overline{)-16}$ 16. $+7\overline{)-21}$ 17. $-6\overline{)-18}$

18. $+3\overline{)-27}$ 19. $-5\overline{)-20}$ 20. $+4\overline{)-20}$ 21. $-5\overline{)-25}$ 22. $+3\overline{)+15}$

B. Use signed numbers to solve these reading problems.

23. The descent of a certain stream is an average of 20 feet per mile. At that rate, what is the change in elevation 8 miles downstream from a given point?

24. A bathyscaph is a submersible vessel used for deep-sea exploration. Suppose a bathyscaph descends from the surface of the ocean at a rate of 75 feet per minute for 8 minutes. How far is it from the surface at the end of that time?

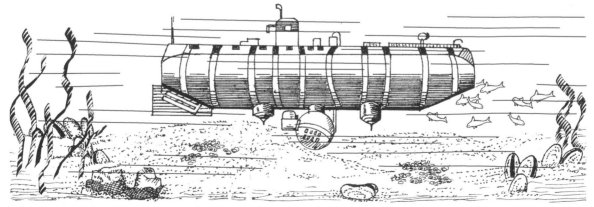

In his hand are the deep places of the earth.   *Psalm 95:4*

25. An airplane decreased its altitude 3,000 feet in 5 minutes. What was the average change in altitude per minute?

26. When Uncle David sold 45 hogs, his profit on each one was – $12 (a $12 loss). What was Uncle David's profit on the hogs?

27. A small store had a $75 profit one week and a $35 loss the next week. What was the difference between the profit and the loss?

28. The elevation of the Dead Sea is – 1,312 feet. If a person climbs 350 feet above the level of the Dead Sea, what is his elevation?

REVIEW EXERCISES

C. Solve these problems with signed numbers. *(Lessons 157, 158)*

29.   – 6
    + (– 8)

30.   – 4
    + (+ 8)

31.   + 6
    – (– 8)

32.   – 9
    – (+ 12)

D. Find each temperature to the nearest whole degree. *(Lessons 140, 141)*

33. 34°C = _____ °F

34. 48°F = _____ °C

E. Calculate the volumes of rectangular solids having these dimensions. *(Lesson 125)*

35. l = 16"
    w = 13"
    h = 11"

36. l = 41 cm
    w = 35 cm
    h = 20 cm

F. Identify each number as prime or composite. *(Lesson 37)*

37. 51

38. 53

39. 55

40. 57

160. Chapter 12 Review

A. *Write algebraic expressions for these phrases. (Lesson 145)*

1. Five more than t
2. Three less than the product of 3 and d
3. The product of 6 and d
4. k divided by 5, increased by five

B. *Solve these equations, using the correct order of operations. (Lesson 146)*

5. $d = (3 + 2)(4 - 3)$
6. $k = 7 + 7 \cdot 4 - 2$
7. $n = 4(13 - 6) + 8$
8. $x = 25 - \frac{15}{5} + 5 \cdot 6$

C. *Evaluate these algebraic expressions by substituting the numerical value given for each literal number. Use number sentences in your calculations. (Lesson 147)*

9. $a = \dfrac{15 + z}{4}$ $(z = 5)$
10. $b = 45y$ $(y = 7)$
11. $c = \dfrac{20 + x}{3x}$ $(x = 4)$
12. $d = \dfrac{40}{v + 2 \cdot w}$ $(v = 2;\ w = 3)$

D. *Solve these equations by using all four axioms as needed. (Lesson 148, 149)*

13. $e + 8 = 6 \cdot 4$
14. $\dfrac{f}{4} = 14 + 3$
15. $4g = 24 - 6$
16. $h - 2 = 14 \cdot 3$
17. $i - 9 = \frac{36}{9}$
18. $4j = 34 - 6$
19. $\dfrac{k}{5} = 12(8 - 3)$
20. $3l = 29 - 4 \cdot 5$

E. *Write equations for these statements. (Lesson 150)*

21. A certain number divided by 4 is equal to five less than the product of 3 and 2.
22. Four more than the product of eight and m is equal to 39.
23. Subtracting the product of 2 and 3 from a number equals 13.
24. Adding the product of 2 and k to a certain number equals 45.

F. *Simplify these expressions. (Lesson 152)*

25. 3^5 26. 2^8 27. 7^4 28. 9^3 29. 4^6 30. 27^2

G. *Use the table to find the square roots of these numbers. (Lesson 153)*

31. 165   32. 99   33. 111   34. 151

H. *Calculate the square roots of the following perfect squares. (Lesson 153)*

35. 441   36. 1,225   37. 3,969   38. 6,724

I. Copy and complete the following table. *(Lesson 154)*

Formula: $d = 52t$	Distances Traveled at 52 Miles per Hour							
Time (t)	1 hr.	2 hr.	3 hr.	4 hr.	5 hr.	6 hr.	7 hr.	8 hr.
Distance (d) in mi.	52	104	39. ___	40. ___	41. ___	42. ___	43. ___	44. ___

J. Prepare a graph as indicated. *(Lesson 155)*

45–54. Make a line graph showing the volumes of these cubes.

Formula: $v = e^3$	Volumes of Cubes With Selected Dimensions						
Edge (e) in cm	20	22	24	26	28	30	32
Volume (v) in cm³	8,000	10,648	13,824	17,576	21,952	27,000	32,768

K. Write signed numbers for these statements. *(Lesson 156)*

55. One morning the temperature rose 32 degrees.

56. The business suffered a loss of $2,000.

57. The airplane decreased its altitude by 550 feet.

58. The business made a profit of $250.

L. Do these computations with signed numbers. *(Lessons 157–159)*

59. $-5 + (-7)$ **60.** $+8 + (+9)$ **61.** $+3 + (-7)$ **62.** $-4 + (+9)$

63. $-9 - (-5)$ **64.** $+8 - (+11)$ **65.** $-7 - (-16)$ **66.** $-7 - (+7)$

67. $-4 \times (+6)$ **68.** $-5 \times (+3)$ **69.** $+2 \times (+7)$ **70.** $+5 \times (-3)$

71. $-3\overline{)-36}$ **72.** $+6\overline{)-24}$ **73.** $-8\overline{)+24}$ **74.** $+7\overline{)+49}$

M. Write the answers. *(Lessons 145, 156)*

75. Copy all the literal numbers in the expression $4a - bc + e$.

76. Copy all the literal numbers in the equation $3k - xy = m$.

77. Write the number -27 in words.

78. Write the number $+14$ in words.

N. Write equations to solve these reading problems. *(Lessons 150, 151)*

79. A car is traveling 60 feet per second. Each time a tire makes one revolution, it travels 6.25 feet. How many revolutions (r) does the tire make in one second?

80. A steer sold for $756. If the selling price was $0.72 per pound, find the weight of the steer in pounds (p).

81. Marla's grandmother is 3 years less than five times as old as Marla. Marla's grandmother is 62 years old. How old is Marla (m)?

82. Erla's father is 4 years less than three times as old as Erla. Erla's father is 41 years old. How old is Erla (e)?

83. One book in the Old Testament has one more chapter than the value of seven to the second power. How many chapters (c) does the book contain? What is the name of the book?

84. Another book in the Old Testament has two more chapters than four to the third power. How many chapters (c) does the book contain? What is the name of the book?

161. Chapter 12 Test

Chapter 13

Year-End Reviews

John to the seven churches which are in Asia: Grace be unto you, and peace, from him which is, and which was, and which is to come; and from the seven Spirits which are before his throne;

162. Review of Chapters 1 and 2: Numeration and Basic Mathematical Operations

A. Copy and solve these problems. Check your work as indicated.

Check addition by adding upward. Write the check answer above each problem.

1.	2.	3.	4.
2,672	31,275	264,763	356,148
6,825	27,137	784,858	862,828
4,722	63,273	+ 784,682	472,596
8,499	82,471		+ 536,472
6,343	85,486		
+ 8,562	+ 38,559		

5.	6.	7.	8.
$426.87	$3,612.91	3,567,871	$23,712.42
124.77	2,771.64	3,271,612	15,737.67
726.74	1,612.75	+ 4,712,673	+ 21,612.89
+ 812.34	+ 5,151.89		

Check subtraction by adding the subtrahend to the difference.

9.	10.	11.	12.
73,346	71,717	$147.75	$674.29
− 38,922	− 33,539	− 101.97	− 298.65

13.	14.	15.	16.
4,101,314	3,005,211	$25,565.82	$29,919.53
− 1,571,611	− 1,683,539	− 18,393.89	− 19,974.89

Check multiplication and division by casting out nines.

17.	18.	19.	20.
97	89	$4.89	$6.57
× 68	× 47	× 74	× 64

21.	22.	23.	24.
3,427	1,567	5,534	3,872
× 631	× 328	× 1,251	× 2,345

25. $7\overline{)8,649}$ 26. $9\overline{)7,815}$ 27. $45\overline{)23,151}$ 28. $72\overline{)44,454}$

29. $56\overline{)\$29.57}$ 30. $46\overline{)\$67.79}$ 31. $300\overline{)49,700}$ 32. $3,800\overline{)490,000}$

B. Solve problems 33–38 by horizontal computation, and write the answers one digit at a time. Solve problems 39 and 40 by short division.

33. 59,826 + 12,561

34. 32,454 + 16,575

35. 38,563 – 17,726

36. 82,315 – 36,723

37. 8 × 572

38. 6 × 693

39. 5)4,999

40. 7)9,835

C. Solve these problems mentally.

41. 4 + 6 + 6 + 7 + 4 + 5 + 5

42. 3 + 2 + 7 + 6 + 3 + 7 + 9

43. 46 + 39

44. 48 + 65

45. 76 – 47

46. 82 – 26

47. 24 × 35

48. 18 × 6

49. 36 × 25

50. 3 × 30 × 5 × 4

51. 216 ÷ 24

52. 350 ÷ 5

53. 900 ÷ 50

54. 800 ÷ 25

D. Write the answers for these exercises.

55. Using digits, write the number fifty billion, four million.

56. Using digits, write the number fourteen trillion, sixty-six billion, fifty thousand.

57. Write 44,689,000 as you would read it.

58. Write 6,000,050,000 as you would read it.

59. Write the value of the digit 4 in 23,457,275.

60. Write the value of the digit 6 in 46,217,800,000.

61. Round 747,300 to the nearest ten thousand.

62. Round 4,530,899,533 to the nearest hundred million.

63. Write 1,256, using Roman numerals.

64. Write 63,500, using Roman numerals.

65. Write MMXCIX, using Arabic numerals.

66. Write MCDX, using Arabic numerals.

67. Write the multiplicand in the problem at the right.

$$\begin{array}{r} 27 \\ \times\, 34 \\ \hline 918 \end{array} \qquad \begin{array}{r} 442 \\ 65\overline{)28{,}730} \end{array}$$

68. Write the quotient in the problem at the right.

69. Estimate the product of 696 × 48.

70. Estimate the product of 4,322 × 2,975.

71. Find the average of this set of numbers. 67, 71, 56, 82, 76

72. Find the average of this set of numbers. 95, 82, 78, 85, 81

73. Is 4,661 divisible by 3?

74. Is 16,668 divisible by 9?

E. *Refer to the graph to answer these questions.*

Number of Years in Three Major Divisions of Time	
Creation to Flood	Y Y Y Y Y Y Y Y Y Y Y Y Y Y Y Y Y
Flood to Christ's birth	Y Y Y Y Y Y Y Y Y Y Y Y Y Y Y Y Y Y Y Y Y Y Y Y
Christ's birth to present	Y Y Y Y Y Y Y Y Y Y Y Y Y Y Y Y Y Y Y Y Y

Y = 100 years

Source: *The Wonders of Bible Chronology*

75. How many years were between the Creation and the Flood?

76. How many years longer was the time from the Flood to Christ than from Christ to the present?

77. How many years were between the Flood and the birth of Christ?

78. How many years have passed from the Creation to the present?

F. *Solve these reading problems.*

79. God placed the planet Mars in orbit about 142,000,000 miles from the sun. The Earth is about 93,000,000 miles from the sun. How much farther from the sun is Mars than Earth?

80. The average temperature on Mars is considerably colder than on Earth. The average surface temperature on Earth is 72°F, but on Mars it is – 9°F. How much colder is the average temperature on Mars than the average temperature on Earth?

81. God created the earth with an atmosphere around it that supports life. This atmosphere has weight, which we call air pressure. At sea level, the atmosphere has pressure of about 14.7 pounds per square inch. At 3.5 miles above sea level, its pressure is about half as much. What is the atmospheric pressure at 3.5 miles above sea level?

82. The water God placed on the earth is another resource that supports life. The oceans, through evaporation, provide rain for the land. It has been estimated that when the sun shines on a square mile of ocean, as much as 5,435 tons of water will evaporate in an hour. How many pounds of water vapor is that?

83. God has given water the special property of expansion when it cools. At 4°C, water begins to expand. Because of this, ice floats rather than sinking. At what temperature Fahrenheit does water begin to expand?

84. The earth is nearly spherical in shape. Its circumference at the equator is 24,902.4 miles. Its circumference at the poles is 24,860.2 miles. How much smaller is its circumference at the poles than at the equator?

In the beginning God created the heaven and the earth.
Genesis 1:1

163. Review of Chapters 3 and 11: English and Metric Measure

A. Measure each line and write the measurement on your paper. Use English units for numbers 1 and 2, and metric units for 3 and 4.

1. _____

2. _____

3. _____

4. _____

B. Write the abbreviation for each unit of measure.

5. mile

6. bushel

7. tablespoon

8. fluid ounce

9. metric ton

10. kilometer

11. gram

12. square centimeter

C. Change these measures. In numbers 41–45, round all answers to the nearest whole degree.

13. 12 yd. = _____ ft.

14. 6 mi. = _____ ft.

15. 14 tons = _____ lb.

16. 256 oz. = _____ lb.

17. 23 pt. = _____ qt.

18. 130 mo. = _____ yr.

19. 6 days _____ hr.

20. 1,400 yr. = _____ centuries

21. 7 sq. yd. = _____ sq. ft.

22. 3 yr. 8 mo. = _____ yr.

23. 6 ft. 9 in. = _____ ft.

24. 8 lb. 4 oz. = _____ oz.

25. 3 pk. 6 qt. = _____ pk.

26. 2 cups 4 fl. oz. = _____ fl. oz.

27. 7 sq. yd. 6 sq. ft. = _____ sq. yd.

28. 515 cm = _____ m

29. 0.95 MT = _____ kg

30. 2,250 mg = _____ g

31. 120 ml = _____ l

32. 750 l = _____ kl

33. 8.5 l = _____ ml

34. 1.6 m^2 = _____ cm^2

35. 15 kg 275 g = _____ kg

36. 24 m 90 mm = _____ m

37. 225 sq. mi. = _____ km^2

38. 82 kg = _____ lb.

39. 75 a. = _____ ha

40. 70°C = _____ °F

41. 70°F = _____ °C

42. 40°C = _____ °F

43. 45°F = _____ °C

44. 50°F = _____ °C

45. 16°C = _____ °F

D. Solve these problems with compound measures.

46.   6 lb. 14 oz.
      + 8 lb. 15 oz.

47.   6 ft.
      − 3 ft. 4 in.

48.   3 hr. 15 min.
      ×   6

49. 8)‾26 ft. 4 in.

50. 4)‾20 lb. 6 oz.

51. 3,900 kg + 1.46 MT = _____ kg

52. 3.9 kl − 660 *l* = _____ kl

53. 18 km 80 m × 9 = _____ km

54. 65 m 40 mm ÷ 12 = _____ mm

E. Solve these problems mentally.

55. 25 ft. = _____ in.

56. 20 cups = _____ tbsp.

57. 360 sq. ft. = _____ sq. yd.

58. 1 ft. = _____ m

59. 1 m = _____ ft.

60. 1 a. = _____ ha

61. 1 kg = _____ lb.

62. 1 lb. = _____ kg

63. 1 pk. = _____ qt.

64. 1 sq. ft. = _____ sq. in.

F. Answer the following questions.

65. If it is 4:00 P.M. in the Central Time Zone, what time is it in the Alaska Time Zone?

66. If it is 11:00 A.M. in the Eastern Time Zone, what time is it in the Newfoundland Time Zone?

67. If 288 kilometers is traveled in 4.5 hours, what is the rate?

68. If a car travels at 70 kilometers per hour for 3.25 hours, what is the distance?

69. What is the unit next larger than the centimeter?

70. What is the unit next smaller than the kilogram?

G. Refer to the line graph to answer the following questions.

71. What was the average life expectancy in 1920?

72. What was the average life expectancy in 1960?

73. How much did the average life expectancy increase from 1920 to 1990?

74. How much did the average life expectancy increase from 1920 to 1950?

Life Expectancy in the United States

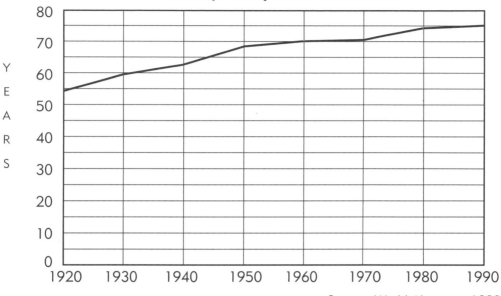

Source: *World Almanac, 1992*

H. Solve these reading problems.

75. One very warm summer afternoon, the temperature was 37°C. To the nearest whole degree, what was the temperature Fahrenheit?

76. One autumn afternoon, the temperature reached 65°F. To the nearest whole degree, what was the temperature Celsius?

77. The tabernacle included ten curtains that were each 28 cubits long (Exodus 26:2). What was the length of each curtain in feet?

78. The Weber family drove 650 miles one weekend to visit a new congregation. How many kilometers was that?

79. The province of Ontario has an area of 1,068,582 square kilometers. What is its area in square miles?

80. In Ruth 2:17, Ruth gleaned an ephah of barley one day in the field of Boaz. Ruth gleaned in the fields of Boaz until the end of the barley harvest. If she gleaned an ephah of barley each day for five days, how many liters of barley was that?

Thou shalt not wholly reap the corners of thy field, . . .

thou shalt leave them

for the poor and stranger.

Leviticus 19:9, 10

164. Review of Chapter 4: Fractions

A. *Identify each number as prime or composite. (Lesson 37)*

1. 31   **2.** 33   **3.** 35   **4.** 37

B. *Divide by primes to find the prime factors of these composite numbers. (Lesson 37)*

5. 24   **6.** 50   **7.** 80   **8.** 64

C. *Find the greatest common factor (g.c.f.) of each pair of numbers. (Lesson 38)*

9. 9, 12   **10.** 16, 24   **11.** 18, 45   **12.** 34, 85

D. *Find the lowest common multiple (l.c.m.) of each pair of numbers. (Lesson 39)*

13. 6, 9   **14.** 12, 15   **15.** 14, 16   **16.** 15, 20

E. *Do these exercises on the terms used with fractions. (Lesson 40)*

17. Write the fraction $\frac{3}{4}$, and label its two parts.

18. The number $\frac{7}{5}$ is an example of a/an _____ fraction.

19. The number $1\frac{17}{20}$ is an example of a/an _____ number.

20. The number 68 is an example of a/an _____ number.

F. *Reduce these fractions to lowest terms. (Lesson 41)*

21. $\frac{12}{15}$ **22.** $\frac{28}{42}$ **23.** $\frac{18}{51}$ **24.** $\frac{38}{95}$

G. *Copy and compare these fractions, using the "greater than" and "less than" symbols. (Lesson 41)*

25. $\frac{7}{9}$ _____ $\frac{3}{4}$ **26.** $\frac{7}{12}$ _____ $\frac{5}{8}$

H. *Solve by multiplying mentally. (Lesson 44)*

27. $\frac{1}{3}$ of 33   **28.** $\frac{1}{7}$ of 56   **29.** $63 \times \frac{4}{9}$ **30.** $56 \times \frac{7}{8}$

I. *Find the reciprocals of these numbers. (Lesson 47)*

31. $\frac{4}{16}$ **32.** $\frac{7}{13}$ **33.** $\frac{21}{4}$ **34.** 40

J. *Solve by dividing mentally. (Lesson 47)*

35. $12 \div \frac{1}{3}$ **36.** $9 \div \frac{1}{5}$ **37.** $7 \div \frac{1}{11}$ **38.** $8 \div \frac{1}{12}$

K. Solve these fraction problems. *(Lessons 42–48)*

39.
$$\begin{aligned}&\tfrac{1}{4}\\ &+\tfrac{1}{5}\end{aligned}$$

40.
$$\begin{aligned}&\tfrac{1}{6}\\ &+\tfrac{1}{4}\end{aligned}$$

41.
$$\begin{aligned}&1\tfrac{3}{4}\\ &+2\tfrac{1}{6}\end{aligned}$$

42.
$$\begin{aligned}&3\tfrac{7}{8}\\ &+4\tfrac{2}{3}\end{aligned}$$

43.
$$\begin{aligned}&\tfrac{3}{5}\\ &-\tfrac{1}{3}\end{aligned}$$

44.
$$\begin{aligned}&\tfrac{5}{6}\\ &-\tfrac{1}{8}\end{aligned}$$

45.
$$\begin{aligned}&6\\ &-1\tfrac{2}{5}\end{aligned}$$

46.
$$\begin{aligned}&9\tfrac{1}{4}\\ &-5\tfrac{2}{3}\end{aligned}$$

47. $5 \times \frac{2}{7}$

48. $7 \times \frac{5}{7}$

49. $\frac{2}{5} \times \frac{5}{8}$

50. $\frac{7}{9} \times \frac{3}{8}$

51. $2\frac{2}{5} \times 5$

52. $3\frac{2}{3} \times 7$

53. $3\frac{3}{4} \times 1\frac{1}{3}$

54. $3\frac{1}{2} \times 5\frac{2}{3}$

55. $\frac{4}{7} \div \frac{4}{9}$

56. $\frac{5}{8} \div \frac{7}{8}$

57. $3\frac{1}{4} \div \frac{2}{3}$

58. $4\frac{1}{5} \div \frac{5}{6}$

59. $4\frac{2}{3} \div 1\frac{2}{5}$

60. $4\frac{1}{5} \div 1\frac{2}{7}$

L. Copy and solve these problems by the vertical method. *(Lesson 46)*

61.
$$\begin{aligned}&8\\ &\times 2\tfrac{1}{4}\end{aligned}$$

62.
$$\begin{aligned}&15\\ &\times 3\tfrac{3}{5}\end{aligned}$$

M. Use the bar graph to answer the following questions. *(Lesson 51)*

63. What is the height of the tallest known coast redwood tree?

64. What is the height of the tallest known giant sequoia?

65. How much taller is the tallest known coast redwood tree than the tallest known western hemlock?

66. How much taller is the tallest known coast Douglas fir than the tallest known grand fir?

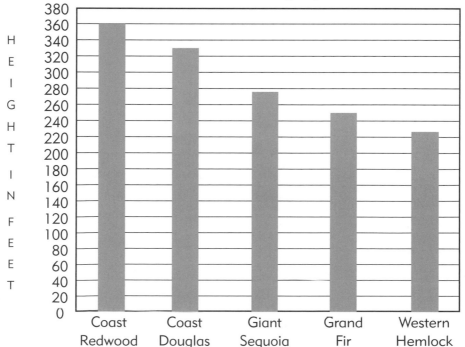

Tallest Known Trees of Several Large Species in the United States

Source: *World Almanac, 1994*

N. *Find the unknown numbers.* *(Lesson 49)*

67. 7 is $\frac{1}{4}$ of ____

68. 6 is $\frac{2}{3}$ of ____

69. 9 is $\frac{3}{7}$ of ____

70. 15 is $\frac{5}{9}$ of ____

O. *Solve these reading problems, using only the information needed.* *(Lesson 50)*

71. God's greatness is evident in the large living things He created. The world's largest known living thing (not the tallest) is the General Sherman giant sequoia in California. A 4-ton elephant weighs $\frac{1}{1,500}$ as much as this huge tree. What is the weight of the tree?

72. God's greatness is also seen in the exceedingly small things He created. A single bacterium, one of the smallest things, is sometimes as small as $\frac{1}{25,000}$ inch long. How many times longer is a 5-inch earthworm than a $\frac{1}{25,000}$-inch bacteria?

73. Brother David raises produce in a $15\frac{1}{2}$-acre field. One year he planted $\frac{1}{4}$ of the field in cabbage and $\frac{1}{3}$ of it in sweet corn. How many acres of cabbage did he plant?

74. Brother David's family planted about 10,000 celery plants and 12,000 cauliflower plants that summer. During their busiest week, they cut 1,500 cauliflower plants. What fraction of their total number of cauliflower plants did they cut that week? Reduce your answer to lowest terms.

75. Janet has a piece of elastic that is 1 inch wide and $\frac{8}{9}$ yard long. How many $\frac{1}{6}$-yard pieces will she be able to cut from the elastic? Drop any fraction in your answer.

76. Grandfather had a 10-pound package of bean seeds. His married children used $2\frac{1}{2}$ pounds, $\frac{3}{4}$ pound, and $4\frac{1}{4}$ pounds of the seeds. Grandfather planted the rest of the seeds in his garden. How many pounds of seeds did Grandfather plant?

And God said, Let the earth bring forth grass, the herb yielding seed,

and the fruit tree yielding fruit after his kind, whose seed is in itself, upon the earth:

and it was so. . . . And the evening and the morning were the third day.

Genesis 1:11, 13

**165. Review of Chapters 5 and 6:
Decimals, Ratios, and Proportions**

A. Express these decimals as common fractions. *(Lesson 54)*

1. 0.49　　　　2. 0.307　　　　3. 0.0039　　　　4. 0.00709

B. Write these decimals, using words. *(Lesson 54)*

5. 0.06　　　　6. 0.032　　　　7. 0.00109　　　　8. 0.000111

C. Express these common fractions as decimals. *(Lesson 54)*

9. $\frac{48}{100}$　　　　10. $\frac{7}{100}$　　　　11. $\frac{9}{1,000}$　　　　12. $\frac{91}{100,000}$

D. Copy each set of decimals, compare them, and write > or < between them. *(Lesson 55)*

13. 0.0777 ____ 0.77　　　　　　14. 5.505 ____ 5.511

E. Round these numbers as indicated. *(Lesson 55)*

15. 2.717 *(tenth)*　　　　　　16. 6.4517 *(hundredth)*

17. 5.3099 *(thousandth)*　　　　18. $5.515 *(cent)*

F. Express these money amounts as decimal parts of a dollar. *(Lesson 55)*

19. 2.09\frac{3}{10}$　　　　　　20. 0.70\frac{6}{10}$

G. Change these common fractions to decimals. These all divide evenly by the ten-thousandths place. *(Lesson 56)*

21. $\frac{13}{40}$　　　　22. $\frac{11}{16}$　　　　23. $\frac{1}{16}$　　　　24. $\frac{7}{80}$

H. Change these fractions to nonterminating decimals. Follow the instructions in working with the remainder. *(Lesson 57)*

Divide to the hundredths' place, and express the remainder as a fraction.

25. $\frac{2}{17}$　　　　　　26. $\frac{3}{19}$

Round to the nearest thousandth.

27. $\frac{13}{15}$　　　　　　28. $\frac{11}{13}$

Identify the repeating digits by drawing a bar above them.

29. $\frac{5}{11}$　　　　　　30. $\frac{7}{12}$

I. Solve these multiplication and division problems mentally. *(Lesson 59)*

31. 4.2 × 100

32. 0.112 × 10

33. 4.0121 × 1,000

34. 241.078 ÷ 100

35. 3.114 ÷ 1,000

36. 0.0012 ÷ 10

J. Solve these problems involving decimals. If the divisions do not come out evenly by the ten-thousandths' place, round to the thousandths' place. *(Lessons 58–63)*

37. 3.1 + 2.7786

38. 0.1512 + 2.16

39. 12.01 – 2.145

40. 18 – 15.717

41. 2.6 – 1.3556

42. 7.08 – 5.0067

43. 3.455 + 45.1 + 9 + 1.0083

44. 2.15 + 1.001 + 9 + 0.454

45.
$$\begin{array}{r} 2.3 \\ \times\,0.008 \\ \hline \end{array}$$

46.
$$\begin{array}{r} 2.303 \\ \times\,0.28 \\ \hline \end{array}$$

47. $5\overline{)\$68.30}$

48. $7\overline{)0.4158}$

49. 3.15 × 0.77

50. 1.35 × 0.007

51. 5.15 ÷ 0.06

52. 3.88 ÷ 7.3

K. Solve each problem by first changing the decimal fraction to a common fraction. Do all the work mentally if you can. *(Lesson 61)*

53. 0.5 of 26

54. 0.25 of 48

55. 0.125 of 72

56. 0.75 of $44

57. 0.6 of $45

58. 0.875 of 48

59. $0.33\frac{1}{3}$ of 21

60. $0.66\frac{2}{3}$ of 18

L. Write a ratio in lowest terms for each statement. *(Lesson 67)*

61. Esther had 19 math problems correct for every problem she had incorrect.

62. Marlin had 1 math problem incorrect for every 16 problems he had correct.

63. Twenty-seven of the 66 books in the Bible are in the New Testament.

64. Six of the 39 books in the Old Testament are before the Book of Judges.

65. In the Book of Genesis, six chapters deal with history from the Creation to the Flood, and forty-four chapters with history from the Flood to the death of Joseph. Write a ratio showing the number of chapters dealing with history before the Flood, compared to the number of chapters in the entire book.

66. In the Book of Joshua, the first twelve chapters tell how Israel crossed the Jordan and conquered the land of Canaan. The remaining twelve chapters relate the history of God's people until the death of Joshua. Write a ratio showing the number of chapters describing the crossing of Jordan and the conquest of Canaan, compared to the number of chapters in the entire book.

M. Check each proportion by cross multiplication, and write the two products that you obtain. Then write *true* **if the proportion is true and** *false* **if it is false.** *(Lesson 68)*

67. $\frac{4}{6} = \frac{34}{51}$

68. $\frac{7}{11} = \frac{39}{62}$

69. $\frac{30}{21} = \frac{60}{45}$

70. $\frac{15}{18} = \frac{45}{54}$

N. Find the missing parts of these proportions. Express any remainders as fractions. *(Lesson 68)*

71. $\frac{3}{7} = \frac{n}{40}$

72. $\frac{8}{18} = \frac{n}{45}$

73. $\frac{24}{9} = \frac{88}{n}$

74. $\frac{27}{15} = \frac{45}{n}$

O. Use proportions to solve these reading problems. *(Lessons 68–70)*

75. One day Matthew and David decided to measure the height of their silo by measuring its shadow. They found that a 7-foot clothesline post cast a 5-foot shadow. If the silo casts a 40-foot shadow, how high is it?

76. After supper that evening, the boys decided to measure the height of their barn in the same way. By that time the 7-foot clothesline post cast a 12-foot shadow. If the barn cast a 40-foot shadow, how high was it?

77. Marvin correctly completed 18 out of every 19 math problems. How many problems did he have correct out of every 100 problems? Round your answer to the nearest whole number.

78. Judith correctly completed a certain number of math problems out of a total of 24. Her score was 92%. (She had 92 out of every 100 problems correct.) How many problems did she do correctly? Round your answer to the nearest whole number.

79. The seventh- and eighth-grade classroom has 3 seventh graders for every 2 eighth graders. There are 25 students in the classroom. How many seventh graders are there?

80. Father milked 6 cows for every 4 cows that Stanley milked. Father milked 36 cows. How many cows did they milk in all?

166. Review of Chapters 6–8: Percents, Money, and Banking

A. Finish these statements, using the terms *base, rate,* **or** *percentage.* *(Lesson 73)*

1. In the problem *7 is 14% of 50,* 50 is the _____.

2. In the problem *6 is 80% of 7.5,* 80% is the _____.

3. In the problem *8 is 50% of 16,* 50% is the _____.

4. In the problem *16% of 70 = 11.2,* 11.2 is the _____.

B. Solve mentally. *(Lesson 91)*

5. 50% of 40 = _____

6. $33\frac{1}{3}$% of 21 = _____

7. 9 is 25% of _____

8. 8 is $12\frac{1}{2}$% of _____

9. 8 is _____% of 16

10. 15 is _____% of 25

C. Solve these percent problems. *(Lessons 73, 83–88)*

11. 23% of 53

12. 7% of 56

13. 315% of 277

14. 462% of 71

15. $\frac{3}{4}$% of 80

16. $\frac{3}{5}$% of 277

17. $3\frac{1}{5}$% of 770

18. $2\frac{1}{4}$% of 620

19. 8 = _____% of 40

20. 24 = _____% of 32

21. 33 = 55% of _____

22. 26 is 65% of _____

23. 57 = 76% of _____

24. 45 = _____% of 75

25. 18 = _____% of 150

26. 27% of 49 = _____

D. Find the new price, showing both the increase or decrease and the new price as your answer. Round to the nearest cent. *(Lesson 74)*

27. $14.56 decreased by 6%

28. $17.57 increased by 9%

29. $43.60 decreased by 4%

30. $25.40 increased by 7%

E. Find the new price after each increase or decrease. Round to the nearest cent. *(Lesson 84)*

31. $23.00 decreased by 8%

32. $67.00 increased by 12%

33. $22.80 increased by 23%

34. $44.50 decreased by 18%

F. Find the missing numbers in these commission problems. *(Lesson 89)*

35. $s = \$227$
$r = 9\%$
$c =$ _____

36. $s = \$495$
$r = 14\%$
$c =$ _____

37. $r = 7\%$
$c = \$50.47$
$s =$ ___

38. $s = \$550$
$c = \$27.50$
$r =$ _____

G. Find the rate of increase or decrease, to the nearest whole percent. Label your answers. *(Lesson 90)*

	Original Price	New Price
39.	$12.00	$17.00
40.	$35.00	$31.15

H. Find the rate each profit or loss is of the sales, to the nearest whole percent. *(Lesson 97)*

	Sales	Profit or Loss	Rate			Sales	Profit or Loss	Rate
41.	$650	$67	_____		**42.**	$255	$28	_____

I. Find the simple interest on these amounts. *(Lessons 99, 100)*

	p	r	t			p	r	t
43.	$2,300	6%	3 years		**44.**	$750	7%	9 months
45.	$1,600	5%	80 days		**46.**	$2,200	9%	120 days

J. Find the ending balance and the total interest if the interest is compounded annually. *(Lesson 101)*

	Principal	Rate	Time	Ending Balance	Total Interest
47.	$100	8%	2 years	_____	_____
48.	$300	6%	2 years	_____	_____
49.	$200	7%	3 years	_____	_____
50.	$400	5%	3 years	_____	_____

K. Do these exercises. *(Lessons 71–102)*

51. Express $\frac{13}{20}$ as a percent. (Lesson 71)

52. Express 62% as a fraction in lowest terms. (Lesson 71)

53. Express $\frac{13}{15}$ as a percent. (Lesson 72)

54. Change $\frac{12}{17}$ to a percent. (Lesson 72)

55. If the scale of miles on a map is $\frac{3}{8}$ inch = 12 miles, what is the distance represented by $1\frac{7}{8}$ inches on the map? (Lesson 75)

56. If the scale of miles on a map is $\frac{1}{2}$ inch = 4 miles, how much distance on the map is needed to show 15 miles? (Lesson 75)

57. If the scale on a blueprint is $\frac{5}{8}$ inch = 1 foot, what is the distance represented by $3\frac{3}{4}$ inches on the blueprint? (Lesson 76)

58. If the scale of a blueprint is $\frac{3}{4}$ inch = 1 foot, how much distance on the blueprint is needed to show 20 feet? (Lesson 76)

59. Estimate: $7\frac{5}{8} \times 6\frac{1}{2} = [32\frac{9}{16},\ 41\frac{9}{16},\ 49\frac{9}{16},\ 57\frac{9}{16}]$ (Lesson 77)

60. Estimate: $11.2 \times 9.7 = [95.64,\ 108.64,\ 121.64,\ 134.64]$ (Lesson 77)

61. Change 175% to a whole or mixed number. (Lesson 83)

62. Change 700% to a whole or mixed number. (Lesson 83)

63. Change $7\frac{1}{2}$% to a decimal. (Lesson 85)

64. Change $72\frac{1}{4}$% to a decimal. (Lesson 85)

65. If the income is $275 and the expenses are $315, the profit or loss is _____. Write *profit* or *loss* with your answer. (Lesson 96)

66. If the income is $495 and the expenses are $335, the profit or loss is _____. Write *profit* or *loss* with your answer. (Lesson 96)

67. Find the sales tax on $8.75 if the rate is 5%. (Lesson 98)

68. Find the total cost of an item priced at $14.75 if it is subject to $8\frac{1}{4}$% sales tax. (Lesson 98)

69. If a principal of $3,750 earns $300 simple interest in one year, what is the rate of interest? (Lesson 99)

70. If a rate of 4% earns $500 interest in one year, what is the principal? (Lesson 99)

71. If 12 pens cost $7.19, what is the unit price? Round your answer to the nearest tenth of a cent. (Lesson 102)

72. If 500 sheets of typing paper cost $12.99, what is the unit price? Round your answer to the nearest tenth of a cent. (Lesson 102)

L. Refer to the histogram on page 493 to answer these questions. *(Lesson 93)*

73. Which range of production includes the most cows?

74. How many cows are represented on the histogram?

75. Does the histogram show how many cows produced 19,500 pounds of milk?

76. How many cows are in the highest range of production?

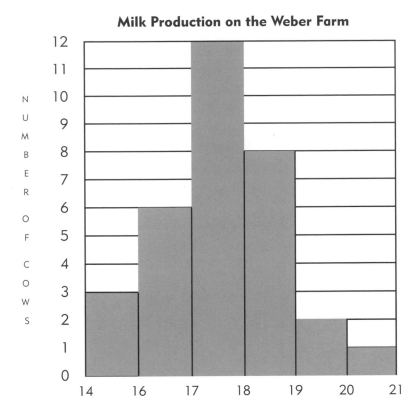

Milk Production on the Weber Farm

NUMBER OF COWS

THOUSANDS OF POUNDS OF MILK PER YEAR

M. Solve these reading problems.

77. Martha's father bought the book *At the Little White Cabin* for $5.90 plus 7% sales tax. How much did Father pay in all?

78. The book *At the Little White Cabin*, which normally sells for $5.90, was put on sale at 10% off the regular price. What was the sale price of the book?

79. A & K Lumber Company received a shipment of lumber for which the bill was $795.50. A 2% discount is allowed if the bill is paid within ten days. What is the bill if the discount is applied?

80. In 1900, the population of Alaska was 63,592. In 1990, its population was about 865% of its 1900 population. To the nearest thousand, what was the population of Alaska in 1990?

81. To buy some steers, Father borrowed $25,000 for 100 days at 6% simple interest. What was the interest?

82. What is the interest on $4,000 at 7% compounded annually for 2 years?

167. Review of Chapters 9 and 10: Geometry

A. *Match the following items.*

1. Figure with length, width, and height
2. 3.14 or $\frac{22}{7}$
3. Distance from the center of a circle to its edge
4. Perimeter of a rectangle: $p =$
5. Area of a circle: $a =$
6. Any four-sided polygon
7. Surface area of a cube: $a_s =$
8. Five-sided polygon
9. Volume of a cylinder: $v =$
10. Area of a square: $a =$
11. Four-sided polygon with one set of parallel sides
12. Volume of a rectangular solid: $v =$

a. s^2
b. πr^2
c. quadrilateral
d. rectangular solid
e. $6e^2$
f. $\pi r^2 h$
g. radius
h. trapezoid
i. $\frac{1}{2}h(b_1 + b_2)$
j. hexagon
k. pentagon
l. $2(l + w)$
m. lwh
n. π

B. *Draw these geometric figures.* (Lesson 107)

13. line segment JK
14. perpendicular lines GH and IJ
15. parallel lines MN and OP
16. right angle MNO

C. *Measure these angles. All answers are multiples of 5 degrees.* (Lesson 108)

17.

18.

D. Write whether each pair is congruent or similar. *(Lesson 109)*

19.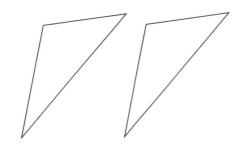

20.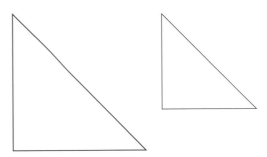

E. Find the areas of the following plane figures. *(Lessons 113–117)*

21. rectangle
    $l = 33''$
    $w = 27''$

22. square
    $s = 63$ cm

23. parallelogram
    $b = 68$ in.
    $h = 52$ in.

24. triangle
    $b = 24$ in.
    $h = 19$ in.

25. triangle
    $b = 35$ cm
    $h = 28$ cm

26. trapezoid
    $h = 28$ cm
    $b_1 = 40$ cm
    $b_2 = 32$ cm

27. circle
    $r = 31''$

28. circle
    $r = 28''$

F. Find the surface areas of these geometric solids. *(Lessons 123, 124)*

29. rectangular solid
    $l = 9''$
    $w = 7''$
    $h = 5''$

30. rectangular solid
    $l = 19$ cm
    $w = 17$ cm
    $h = 14$ cm

31. cube
    $e = 13$ cm

32. cube
    $e = 21''$

33. cylinder
    $r = 4$ cm
    $h = 7$ cm

34. cylinder
    $r = 6$ cm
    $h = 15$ cm

G. Find the volumes of these geometric figures. *(Lessons 125–128)*

Rectangular solids

35. $l = 7$ in.
    $w = 4$ in.
    $h = 6$ in.

36. $l = 8$ in.
    $w = 5$ in.
    $h = 4$ in.

37. $l = 19$ cm
    $w = 16$ cm
    $h = 14$ cm

38. $l = 32$ m
    $w = 28$ m
    $h = 24$ m

Cubes

39. $e = 7$ in.

40. $e = 9$ ft.

41. $e = 14$ cm

42. $e = 19$ m

Cylinders

43. $r = 4''$
$h = 8''$

44. $r = 7''$
$h = 18''$

45. $r = 8$ cm
$h = 15$ cm

46. $r = 9$ cm
$h = 25$ cm

Cones

47. $r = 2$ cm
$h = 6$ cm

48. $r = 3$ m
$h = 9$ m

49. $r = 6'$
$h = 12'$

50. $r = 9'$
$h = 18'$

H. Write the answers.

51. A 50° angle is a/an _____ angle. (Lesson 108)

52. A 170° angle is a/an _____ angle. (Lesson 108)

53. A 90° angle is a/an _____ angle. (Lesson 108)

54. A triangle with angles of 90°, 35°, and 55° is a/an _____ triangle. (Lesson 109)

55. A triangle with angles of 55°, 45°, and 80° is a/an _____ triangle. (Lesson 109)

56. A triangle with sides of 15", 14", and 15" is a/an _____ triangle. (Lesson 109)

57. What is the size of the third angle in a triangle if the other two angles are 26° and 38°? (Lesson 109)

58. What is the size of the third angle in a triangle if the other two angles are 48° and 108°? (Lesson 109)

59. What is the perimeter of a rectangle that has a length of 15" and a width of 11"? (Lesson 111)

60. What is the circumference of a circle with a diameter of 8 centimeters? (Lesson 112)

I. Calculate the missing degrees on this table for preparing a circle graph.
(Lesson 118)

Sources of Energy Produced in the United States - 1992			
Source	*Quadrillion Btu's*	*Decimal*	*Degrees*
Coal	21.59	0.323	**61.**
Natural Gas	18.38	0.275	**62.**
Crude Oil	15.22	0.228	**63.**
Natural Gas Plant Liquids	2.36	0.035	**64.**
Nuclear Electric Power	6.61	0.099	**65.**
Hydroelectric Power	2.50	0.037	**66.**
Other	0.19	0.003	**67.**
Totals	66.85	1.000	**68.**

J. Solve these reading problems. Draw sketches to help you solve 69 and 70. Exercises 71–74 are two sets of parallel reading problems.

69. Bricks and boards are used to make a bookshelf. At each end there are first 2 bricks, one on top of the other, and then a board. Next there are 5 bricks and another board, 4 more bricks and a third board, and finally 1 brick on top. How many bricks are used for the bookshelf?

70. If you start from Wilson, pass through Lincoln, and come to Douglas, you travel 12 miles. The distance from Wilson to Lincoln is 3 times as far as from Lincoln to Douglas. How far is it from Lincoln to Douglas? Your sketch should be a scale drawing.

71. Daryl walked 2 miles in $\frac{3}{4}$ hour. What was his rate in miles per hour?

72. A train traveled 325 miles in $4\frac{1}{2}$ hours. What was its rate in miles per hour?

73. Sarah purchased $\frac{3}{4}$ yard of material for $2.55. What was the cost per yard?

74. Mother purchased 5 yards of material for $16.25. What was the cost per yard?

168. Review of Chapter 12: Algebra

A. *Do these exercises.*

1. Write all the literal numbers in the equation $n = 4z - 3k$. (Lesson 145)

2. Write all the literal numbers in the equation $z = \dfrac{4d}{jkl}$. (Lesson 145)

3. Write this algebraic expression in words: $3k - 5$. (Lesson 145)

4. Write this algebraic expression in words: $5(d - 3)$. (Lesson 145)

5. Write "16 times the sum of 3 and a" as an algebraic expression, using the appropriate form for showing multiplication. (Lesson 145)

6. Write "$14 \times b$" as an algebraic expression, using the appropriate form for showing multiplication. (Lesson 145)

7. Write the number of the rule that determines that $3 \cdot 4$ is solved first in the equation $n = 7 + 3 \cdot 4$. (See Lesson 146.)

8. Write the number of the rule that determines that $6 + 5$ is solved first in the expression $7(6 + 5) - 8$. (See Lesson 146.)

9. Write "4 more than the product of 4 and d" in algebraic form. (Lesson 145)

10. Write "6 times the sum of 7 and d" in algebraic form. (Lesson 145)

11. Find the sum of negative 12 and positive 9. (Lesson 157)

12. Find the product of positive four and negative six. (Lesson 159)

B. *Write these sentences as equations.* (Lesson 150)

13. Six less than a certain number is equal to the difference between 22 and 12.

14. The sum of 4 and a certain number is equal to 45 divided by 5.

15. A certain number divided by 7 is equal to the sum of 28 and 7.

16. Twelve less than a certain number is equal to the product of 6 and 8.

C. *Simplify these expressions, using the correct order of operations.* (Lesson 146)

17. $15 - 2 \cdot 4$

18. $7 + 8 \cdot 2$

19. $7 + \frac{15}{3} - 2 \cdot 5$

20. $4(\frac{20}{5} - 4)$

21. $8(12 - 6)$

22. $25 + 3 \cdot 4 - 5$

D. Evaluate these algebraic expressions by substituting the numerical values given for the literal numbers. *(Lesson 147)*

23. $\frac{(14+z)}{4}$, if $z = 6$ **24.** $15y$, if $y = 4$

25. $x - 8$, if $x = 15$ **26.** $\frac{w-10}{8}$, if $w = 16$

E. Evaluate these algebraic expressions by using the following substitutions: $k = 6; l = 7; m = 8$. *(Lesson 147)*

27. $21 - l$ **28.** $\frac{lm}{m-k}$

29. $(k + l)(k + l)$ **30.** $(k + l)(m - l)$

F. Solve by using the correct axiom to get the literal number by itself on one side. *(Lessons 148, 149)*

31. $n - 8 = 35$ **32.** $5p = 35$

33. $q + 15 = 6 \cdot 7$ **34.** $r - 8 = \frac{56}{7}$

35. $3 \cdot 5 = s - 13$ **36.** $\frac{45}{9} = t + 2$

37. $u - 8 = 4 \cdot 9$ **38.** $\frac{v}{5} = 12 \cdot 3$

39. $9w = 6 \cdot 12$ **40.** $x - 6 = 14 + 9$

41. $\frac{y}{4} = 5 \cdot 6 - 5$ **42.** $8z = 91 - 11$

G. Simplify the following expressions with exponents. *(Lesson 152)*

43. 16^2 **44.** 7^3 **45.** 6^4 **46.** 3^6

H. Find these square roots. *(Lesson 153)*

47. $\sqrt{1{,}296}$ **48.** $\sqrt{6{,}084}$ **49.** $\sqrt{6{,}561}$ **50.** $\sqrt{8{,}464}$

I. Copy and complete the following tables. *(Lesson 154)*

51. $a = s^2$ **52.** $v = e^3$

s	1	2	3	4	5
a					

e	1	2	3	4	5
v					

J. Draw graphs as indicated. *(Lesson 155)*

53. Make a line graph based on the table you prepared for number 51.

54. Make a line graph based on the table you prepared for number 52.

K. Solve these problems with signed numbers. *(Lessons 156–159)*

55. -14 **56.** $+18$ **57.** -12 **58.** $+15$
         $+(+12)$ $+(+13)$ $+(-6)$ $+(-8)$

59. $\begin{array}{r} -12 \\ -(+5) \\ \hline \end{array}$ **60.** $\begin{array}{r} +2 \\ -(+11) \\ \hline \end{array}$ **61.** $\begin{array}{r} -2 \\ -(-5) \\ \hline \end{array}$ **62.** $\begin{array}{r} +17 \\ -(-18) \\ \hline \end{array}$

63. $\begin{array}{r} -8 \\ \times(+7) \\ \hline \end{array}$ **64.** $\begin{array}{r} -11 \\ \times(-9) \\ \hline \end{array}$ **65.** $\begin{array}{r} +7 \\ \times(-5) \\ \hline \end{array}$ **66.** $\begin{array}{r} +5 \\ \times(+9) \\ \hline \end{array}$

67. $-8\overline{)64}$ **68.** $-9\overline{)-63}$ **69.** $+2\overline{)+28}$ **70.** $+4\overline{)-64}$

L. Use equations to solve these reading problems.

71. The Hillcrest Mennonite Church has 2 rows of 16 benches. Each bench has racks holding 9 songbooks. How many songbooks are in the racks?

72. The Hillcrest Church recently bought a certain number of songbooks for $1,643.75 at a unit price of $13.15. How many songbooks were purchased?

*Enter into his gates with thanksgiving,
and into his courts with praise: be thankful unto him, and bless his name.*
Psalm 100:4

73. Grandmother had 35 cookies. After she gave 2 cookies to each of her grandchildren, she had 3 cookies left. How many grandchildren does she have?

74. The Miller family's van has three seats that hold three people each, and two more people can sit in the front seats. When all the Millers are in the van, there is room for 2 more people. How many persons are in the Miller family?

75. Uncle Nathan's had 72 old hens to send to market for butchering. Uncle Nathan told the children to place the hens in a certain number of crates, with 8 hens in each crate. How many crates did the children need?

76. Robert hauled 3 equal-sized wagon loads holding a certain number of straw bales from the field. He stacked 30 of the bales on a truck to take to the neighbor and 420 bales in the barn. How many bales of straw were on each wagon load?

169. Final Review

A. Copy and solve these problems.

1. $16,189.32
    29,433.87
    + 16,765.23

2. 3,765,734
    − 2,165,814

3. 4,832
    × 9,361

4. $82\overline{)76,488}$

5. $4,100\overline{)780,000}$

6. $\frac{4}{5}$
    $+ \frac{2}{3}$

7. $\frac{3}{4} \times \frac{2}{7}$

8. $4\frac{2}{3} \times 3\frac{1}{4}$

9. $6\frac{3}{4} \div 1\frac{4}{5}$

10. $0.0558 + 3.76$

11. $7 - 2.7326$

12. 2.37×0.98

13. $4.45 \div 0.05$

14. $\frac{18}{12} = \frac{n}{22}$

15. $\frac{9}{24} = \frac{n}{56}$

16. 48% of 79

17. 278% of 168

18. $\frac{3}{5}$% of 95

19. 9 is _____% of 20

20. 15 is _____% of 125

21. 21 is 35% of _____

22. − 16
     + (+ 9)

23. − 8
     − (− 9)

24. + 14
     − (− 27)

25. − 7
     × (− 7)

26. $-6\overline{)-36}$

B. Solve these problems mentally.

27. $2 + 7 + 8 + 4 + 6 + 1 + 9$

28. $91 - 47$

29. 44×25

30. $900 \div 25$

31. $48 \times \frac{5}{8}$

32. 0.125 of 96

33. 0.875 of 64

34. $0.66\frac{2}{3}$ of 27

35. 9 is $12\frac{1}{2}$% of _____

36. 12 is _____% of 80

C. *Change these measures. Round all degrees to the nearest whole number.*

37. 192 oz. = _____ lb.

38. 1.21 MT = _____ kg

39. 4,275 mg = _____ g

40. 360 sq. mi. = _____ km²

41. 28°C = _____ °F

42.   7 lb. 13 oz.
    + 4 lb. 12 oz.

43.   8 ft.
    − 2 ft. 6 in.

44.   2 hr. 40 min.
    ×   8

45. 5)‾15 lb. 10 oz.

46. 5)‾12 ft. 7 in.

47. 7 × 12 kg 20 g = _____ kg

48. 24 *l* 36 ml ÷ 12 = _____ ml

D. *Find the areas of polygons with these dimensions.* (Lessons 113–117)

49. *rectangle*
  l = 71″
  w = 42″

50. *triangle*
  b = 24 in.
  h = 19 in.

51. *trapezoid*
  h = 24 cm
  b_1 = 31 cm
  b_2 = 25 cm

52. *square*
  s = 63 cm

53. *circle*
  r = 38″

E. *Find the surface areas of these geometric solids.* (Lessons 123, 124)

54. *cylinder*
  r = 9 cm
  h = 12 cm

55. *rectangular solid*
  l = 12″
  w = 10″
  h = 8″

F. *Find the volumes of these geometric solids.* (Lessons 125–128)

56. *rectangular solid*
  l = 18 cm
  w = 16 cm
  h = 12 cm

57. *cylinder*
  r = 8 cm
  h = 22 cm

58. *cone*
  r = 6′
  h = 15′

G. *Write the answers.*

59. Round 879,300 to the nearest hundred thousand.

60. Write 48,000 as a Roman numeral.

61. In the problem 48 × 26 = 1,248, what is the multiplier?

62. Estimate the product of 2,301 × 598.

63. If the distance is 286 kilometers and the time is 5.2 hours, what is the rate?

64. Use division by primes to find the prime factors of 72.

65. Find the lowest common multiple of 14 and 18.

66. Reduce $\frac{18}{30}$ to lowest terms.

67. Write the reciprocal of 12.

68. 35 is $\frac{5}{6}$ of what number?

69. Round 2.05158 to the nearest thousandth.

70. Change $\frac{17}{18}$ to a decimal fraction. Place a bar above the repeating digit(s).

71. Dwight had 5 rabbits and 9 guinea pigs. Write a ratio comparing the number of rabbits to the total number of animals.

72. An $18.00 item increased 8% in price. Find both the increase and the new price.

73. What is the simple interest on $9,000 at 8% for 200 days?

74. If $500 earns 6% interest compounded annually for 2 years, what is the amount of interest?

75. If the scale of miles on a map is $\frac{3}{8}$ inch = 12 miles, what is the distance represented by $1\frac{7}{8}$ inches on a map?

76. Write the formula for finding the area of a circle.

77. Draw a geometric figure to show "perpendicular lines BC and DE."

78. An 80° angle is an example of a/an _____ angle.

79. A triangle with sides of 12", 12", and 12" is a/an _____ triangle.

80. What is the perimeter of a rectangle that has a length of 22" and a width of 14"?

81. Write an equation for this sentence: Six less than a certain number is equal to the difference between 22 and 12.

82. Solve the equation $n = 4^4$.

H. Solve these equations. *(Lesson 146)*

83. $a - 5 = 6 \cdot 4$

84. $\frac{b}{4} = 11 \cdot 5$

85. $4c = 9 \cdot 8$

86. $d - 7 = 12 + 15$

87. $\frac{e}{6} = 7 \cdot 8 + 4$

88. $7f = 72 + 5$

I. Solve these reading problems.

89. The Witmers traveled to another province to visit their cousins. They left their home at 5:00 A.M. E.S.T. and arrived at their cousins' home at 10:00 A.M. M.S.T. the next day. How many hours did they travel?

90. The blue whale is the largest of all whales. The largest blue whale observed weighed about 392,000 pounds. How many tons is that?

91. A circular rug has a radius of 2 meters. What is its area?

92. The Roseville Congregation distributed the *Star of Hope* to 1,224 homes in their community. If there is an average of 3.23 persons in each home, how many people received the *Star of Hope*? Round your answer to the nearest whole number.

93. Simeon traveled 625 miles in $12\frac{1}{2}$ hours. If his average speed was constant, how long did it take him to travel the first 100 miles? Write a proportion in solving this problem.

94. A storage bin has a diameter of 35 feet. What is its circumference?

170. Final Test

INDEX

SYMBOLS

>	greater than	7 > 3	"7 is greater than 3"
<	less than	2 < 5	"2 is less than 5"
·	multiplication	6 · 8	"6 times 8"
$\sqrt{}$	radical	$\sqrt{9}$	"the square root of 9"
∧	caret	2.05∧	insertion of decimal point
↔	line	$\overset{\leftrightarrow}{AB}$	"line AB"
—	line segment	$\overline{CD}$	"line segment CD"
→	ray	$\overset{\rightarrow}{EF}$	"ray EF"
∠	angle	∠G	"angle G"
⌐	right angle	⌐	indication that an angle is a right angle
⊥	perpendicular	ST ⊥ UV	"line ST is perpendicular to line UV"
‖	parallel	WX ‖ YZ	"line WX is parallel to line YZ"
π	pi		relation of circumference to diameter of a circle; value near 3.14 or $3\frac{1}{7}$

FORMULAS

distance, rate, time	percent	interest
$d = rt$	$P = BR$	$i = prt$
$r = \frac{d}{t}$	$R = \frac{P}{B}$	$r = \frac{i}{p}$
$t = \frac{d}{r}$	$B = \frac{P}{R}$	$p = \frac{i}{r}$

PLANE GEOMETRY

	perimeter	area
square	$p = 4s$	$a = s^2$
rectangle	$p = 2(l + w)$	$a = lw$
parallelogram		$a = bh$
triangle	$p = a + b + c$	$a = \frac{1}{2}bh$
circle	$c = \pi d$	$a = \pi r^2$

SOLID GEOMETRY

	surface area	volume
cube	$a_s = 6e^2$	$v = e^3$
rectangular solid	$a_s = 2lw + 2wh + 2lh$	$v = lwh$
cylinder	$a_s = 2\pi r^2 + 2\pi rh$	$v = \pi r^2 h$ or $v = Bh$
cone		$v = \frac{1}{3}\pi r^2 h$ or $v = \frac{1}{3}Bh$

Also see the conversion formulas with metric tables of measure.

Tables of Measure

Bible Measure

	Approximate English Equivalent	Approximate Metric Equivalent

Length

1 finger . . . .$\frac{3}{4}$ inch . . . . .1.9 centimeters

1 handbreadth = 4 fingers . . . .3 inches . . . . .7.6 centimeters

1 span = 3 handbreadths . . . . .9 inches . . . . .23 centimeters

1 cubit = 2 spans . . . . .18 in. or 1$\frac{1}{2}$ feet . . . .46 centimeters or 0.46 meters

1 fathom = 4 cubits . . . . .6 feet . . . . .1.8 meters

1 furlong . . . . .606 feet or $\frac{1}{9}$ mile . . .184.7 meters or 0.18 kilometers

Weight

1 gerah . . . .$\frac{1}{50}$ ounce . . . . .0.6 gram

1 bekah = 10 gerahs . . . .$\frac{1}{5}$ ounce . . . . .5$\frac{2}{3}$ grams

1 shekel = 2 bekahs . . . .$\frac{2}{5}$ ounce . . . . .11.3 grams

1 maneh = 50 shekels . . . . . . .20 ounces . . . . .566 grams

1 talent = 60 manehs . . . . . . .75 pounds . . . . . . .34 kilograms

Liquid Measure

1 log .almost 1 pint . . . . . .$\frac{1}{3}$ liter

1 hin = 12 logs . . . . .5$\frac{1}{3}$ quarts . . . . . . .5 liters

1 bath = 6 hins . . . . .8 gallons . . . . .30.3 liters

1 firkin . . . . .9 gallons . . . . .34 liters

1 homer = 10 baths . . . . .80 gallons . . . . . . .303 liters

Dry Measure

1 cab .2$\frac{3}{4}$ pints . . . . .1.5 liters

1 omer = almost 2 cabs . . . . . . .5 pints . . . . .2.8 liters

1 seah = 6 cabs or 3$\frac{1}{3}$ omers . . .1 peck . . . . .9.3 liters

1 ephah = 3 seahs or 10 omers . .3$\frac{1}{4}$ pecks . . . . .28.2 liters

1 homer = 10 ephahs . . . . .8 bushels . . . . .282 liters

Tables of Measure

Metric Measure

Length

   basic unit: **meter**

   1 millimeter = 0.001 meter
   1 centimeter = 0.01 meter
   1 decimeter = 0.1 meter
   1 dekameter = 10 meters
   1 hectometer = 100 meters
   1 kilometer = 1,000 meters

Area

   1 hectare = 10,000 square meters

Capacity

   basic unit: **liter**

   1 milliliter = 0.001 liter
   1 centiliter = 0.01 liter
   1 deciliter = 0.1 liter
   1 dekaliter = 10 liters
   1 hectoliter = 100 liters
   1 kiloliter = 1,000 liters

Weight

   basic unit: **gram**

   1 milligram = 0.001 gram
   1 centigram = 0.01 gram
   1 decigram = 0.1 gram
   1 dekagram = 10 grams
   1 hectogram = 100 grams
   1 kilogram = 1,000 grams
   1 metric ton = 1,000 kilograms

Temperature, Celsius scale

   0° = freezing point
   100° = boiling point

Metric-to-English Conversion

Linear Measure
   1 centimeter = 0.39 inch
   1 meter = 39.4 inches
   1 meter = 3.28 feet
   1 kilometer = 0.62 mile

Weight
   1 gram = 0.035 ounce
   1 kilogram = 2.2 pounds

Capacity
   1 liter = 1.06 quarts (liquid)

Area
   1 hectare = 2.5 acres
   1 square kilometer = 0.39 square mile

Temperature
   $\frac{9}{5}$ degrees Celsius + 32 = degrees F

English-to-Metric Conversion

Linear Measure
   1 inch = 2.54 centimeters
   1 foot = 0.3 meter
   1 mile = 1.61 kilometers

Weight
   1 ounce = 28.3 grams
   1 pound = 0.45 kilogram

Capacity
   1 quart (liquid) = 0.95 liter
   1 tablespoon = 15 milliliters

Area
   1 acre = 0.4 hectare
   1 square mile = 2.59 square kilometers

Temperature
   $\frac{5}{9}$ (degrees Fahrenheit − 32) = degrees C